THE BURNING OF THE SHIPS

'Good, then we'll . . .' Bishop never finished the sentence. The words died in his mouth as a wave of cataclysmic sound rent the air. The ship beneath their feet seemed to lift and fall in a sickening movement as further cascades of booming thunder eddied at them in ear-splitting waves. The temperature in the day-cabin seemed to leap thirty degrees as the ports and metal fitments shook, a book-case was shaken from the wall, the light fittings rattled, and the air was filled with an acrid stench.

'Good God!' breathed Bishop. All three men rushed for the door. Clifford was first the reach the bridge-deck, but only seconds ahead of the other two.

The first thing they saw was a pillar of smoke and flame. It was high, and still rising like an opening umbrella over the harbor. It completely blotted out the sun. Its base was less than half a mile away along the quay.

Almost with puzzlement, Rennie became aware of rapid, patternless crashing sounds. It took Rennie a moment to associate the sound with what he could see with his eyes. Even then, he could not quite believe it . . .

Also in Arrow by Douglas Scott

THE ALBATROSS RUN
CHAINS
DIE FOR THE QUEEN
EAGLES BLOOD
THE GIFTS OF ARTEMIS
THE HANGED MAN
IN THE FACE OF THE ENEMY
SHADOWS
THE SPOILS OF WAR

THE BURNING OF THE SHIPS

Douglas Scott

ARROW BOOKS

Arrow Books Limited
62-65 Chandos Place, London WC2N 4NW

An imprint of Century Hutchinson Limited

London Melbourne Sydney Auckland
Johannesburg and agencies throughout
the world

First published in Great Britain
by Martin Secker & Warburg Ltd 1980
Fontana edition 1981
Arrow edition 1989

Printed and bound in Great Britain by
Anchor Press Limited, Tiptree, Essex

ISBN 0 09 958740 8

To *mon ami, mon frère*—a certain Sergeant in the Cinquième Chasseurs d'Afrique—whom I last saw on 15 August, 1944, on the beaches of St. Tropez. By then, the twin bayonet scars on each of his thighs had healed.

Foreword

ALTHOUGH thirty-five years have passed since the end of World War Two, many of the things that happened in that war are still veiled by secrecy. One could particpate in and witness events of a cataclysmic nature during wartime without ever learning why they occurred or what human agency was responsible. They remained mysteries, with the power to haunt and puzzle the people touched by them.

As more and more secret documents are declassified, it is possible to piece together the facts of some wartime mysteries. But some vital records have a nasty habit of disappearing or being destroyed. Some are never released. Gaps remain which prevent the full story ever being known.

Consequently, the novelist who wants to build his story on a solid foundation of fact and actual events may find himself short of essential building materials. He has to use intelligent guesswork to cement between the most tantalizing gaps.

For the purposes of this story, Kim Philby—the Russian spy who penetrated the British Secret Service—has been allotted a role. The activities attributed to him are based on fact. The principal characters are products of my imagination—but many of the events in which I have involved them are not. They happened.

I should like to express my thanks to the Ministry of Defense and the Public Records Office for help received in my research. I am indebted, too, to David Farrer for his much valued editorial guidance.

Last but not least, I must express my gratitude to Bernard Karsenty, an active member of the French Resistance who, over the years, has become my very good friend. By providing me with authentic documentation of events which took place in Algiers between 1940 and 1944, he not only rendered me valuable assistance but forced me to restore my neglected French to something like working efficiency.

Douglas Scott

Chapter One

RENNIE's watch told him that only twelve hours had passed since the *Blairmount Castle* had disappeared below the surface of the Atlantic. The liner's great stern had risen almost to the vertical, then she had dived amid a bubbling turbulence of ocean and disappeared from sight.

Twelve hours! It already seemed a lifetime.

From the stern-sheets of the lifeboat, Rennie tried once again to count heads. In the moonless dark, his count reached fifty before he gave up. It was no use. He would have to wait for daylight.

One thing was certain: the boat was dangerously overloaded. It had been built to accommodate forty persons. Rennie reckoned there must be at least seventy Italians in the boat in addition to the only British personnel: himself and the two Navy gunners up in the bows.

He had half expected the Italians on the *Blairmount Castle* to have panicked when the two torpedoes had struck. Many of their number had been killed or trapped when the explosions had torn two great holes in the liner's hull but, with only one or two exceptions, the prisoners of war had behaved with commendable discipline. Certainly, they had made a lot of noise, shouting and gesticulating like *contadine* in a Calabrian market as they had argued and elbowed their way to their boat stations, but there had been no stampede.

"Are we all going to die, Signore?"

The question was directed at Rennie by a man crouched uncomfortably in front of him in the stern well. His face was pressed against Rennie's right knee because of the crush of humanity in the boat.

"We're not in any danger," replied Rennie, keeping what misgivings he had to himself. "But it will not be pleasant when the sun gets up."

"It is not very pleasant now," said the man. "I feel like a fish in a barrel!"

Rennie moved his leg to make more space on the stern-sheet.

"Get up here beside me. You speak good English and I'll need someone to translate for me when we have enough light to get things organized."

The Italian struggled out of the well and squeezed into the space beside Rennie.

"Grazie," he murmured. "Are we far from land, Signore?"

"It's a long way to swim," said Rennie. "I reckon we are about six or seven hundred miles west of Sierra Leone."

"The British have a naval base there, no?"

"At Freetown."

"They will be sending ships?"

"I hope so. This is a lonely ocean."

The boat was drifting in a long, lazy swell. Since the last rain squall had passed, soaking the occupants of the boat to the skin, there had been not a breath of wind. The surface of the sea was oily calm in spite of the ceaselessly heaving canyons of swell. In an hour, that glassy mirror of ocean would be reflecting the glare of a merciless sun.

As the final hour before dawn passed, the low overcast began to disperse and permit a flicker of starlight here and there. Daylight came with a rush: a spreading of gray-green to the east, then shafts of red and yellow light preceded the first fiery arc of sun as it thrust from the ocean.

As his boat rode the long swell, momentarily high as it sat on a crest and in the next instant sliding like a slow-motion toboggan along the thirty-foot ride to the base of the trough, Rennie glimpsed other boats from the *Blairmount Castle* scattered about the empty expanse of ocean. He counted six, but guessed that there were more hidden here and there in the lazy rolling valleys created by the swell. Rennie's boat was so heavily loaded that the midships gunwales were barely clear of the water. Even at the stern, where he sat, there were but a few meager niches of freeboard. The boat rode so low in the water that his visible horizon was severely curtailed except in those moments when it crested the tops of the swell.

The shock, therefore, of the submarine's sudden appearance was breath-taking. It surfaced less than a cable's length away, seeming to materialize from the side of a long, sloping roller.

The appearance of the submarine triggered a babble of excitement amongst the Italian prisoners in Rennie's boat. As some moved position to get a better view of the unexpected manifestation from the ocean depths, the boat lurched violently to starboard and threatened to capsize. Rennie bawled at the top of his voice, demanding that everyone keep to his place, but the movement of the boat exerted more caution among the Italians than his shouted words. Bodies subsided to former positions, encouraged in no uncertain fashion by a score of voluble tongues making it plain that their owners had no desire to be plunged into the Atlantic. The boat settled but a hubbub of sound persisted as the submarine maneuvered and kept way close by, its 2-shaft diesels throbbing at low power.

Rennie could feel a nervous fluttering of apprehension in his stomach at the sight of the Merchant Navyman's most dreaded foe. A chill prickle of fear ran over his skin, making him shiver involuntarily in the heat of the equatorial morning. There were no "U" markings or number on the conning tower of the underwater monster, but Rennie guessed correctly that this was a VIIC type of U-boat, recognizable by the round-front conning tower with its turned-up lip at the top and by the single 3.5-inch gun mounted immediately before the conning tower.

Sunk for a moment in deep thought as a succession of possible eventualities and consequences raced through his mind, Rennie roused himself when he realized that a voice booming out across the water was addressed at him.

"Ahoy, officer in charge. I am going to take you in tow. Be ready to take my line."

The voice was accented, but its owner undoubtedly had a good command of English. He was speaking through a hand-hailer from the submarine's bridge. He wore a gray shirt and gold-encrusted epaulettes. A battered naval cap with tropical white cover was jammed carelessly on the back of his head. Rennie could make out the man's untidy ginger-colored beard and the spread eagle which topped the gold-leaf cluster of his cap badge.

Cupping his mouth in his hands, Rennie shouted back across the short expanse of water:

"You can't take us in tow. We have far too many people on board. If you try to tow us, the boat will swamp."

There was a silence as the U-boat's commander appeared to discuss the situation with another officer. Then the voice came again.

"I can take a maximum of twenty-six aboard my ship. Italian personnel only and precedence according to rank. Officers first. How many Italian personnel do you have?"

How the hell did he know about the Italians, wondered Rennie, but he held back his reply only momentarily.

"There are more than seventy Italians on this boat."

"Do you have any wounded?"

"One or two who were in the water swallowed some oil, but they aren't too bad. A bit sick—but they'll get over it."

"What rank did you hold on the *Blairmount Castle?*"

Rennie allowed himself a brief smile. The U-boat captain *was* well-informed if he knew the name of the ship.

"None," he answered the question. "I was only a passenger." There was no need to tell the German that his own ship, the *Oakville,* had been sunk off the Cape six weeks before and that he had been making passage back to UK as a survivor. Now, he was a survivor again. It was becoming a habit.

The voice came again.

"Why are you in charge of a lifeboat if you were only a passenger on the ship we sank?"

"I'm a seaman and I know about boats. I volunteered to man one of the boats allocated to the prisoners of war."

All the time the two men had been shouting across to each other, the submarine had been maneuvering closer and closer to the boat. Now, the two vessels drifted in the swell, almost side by side. The U-boat captain no longer had need of the megaphone in his hand. He was close enough for Rennie to make out the detail of his face, the bright blue eyes which somehow contrived to show a twinkle of humor and yet, too, were underhung by lined skin suggestive of strain and fatigue. The flesh above the wispy red beard was not tanned, as Rennie's face was tanned, but had the pallor of the submariner; that pinched whiteness which is the penalty of days locked away from the sunlight.

Rennie looked up boldly toward the conning tower of the submarine.

"You killed several hundred of your Italian allies with

your torpedoes, Captain. The men in this boat may not be over-anxious to come aboard your submarine."

The face peering down from the conning tower became stern.

"They will obey orders," said Kapitänleutnant Rudolf Olberg. "I am here to give such assistance as I can. You may tell them that I deeply regret the deaths of their comrades . . . The fortunes of war . . . My concern now is the safety of all survivors. I shall take in tow as many boats as I can and I shall stay with you until a rescue ship arrives. Have you enough food and water to see you through the day?"

Mention of a rescue ship surprised Rennie, and puzzled him. The SOS transmitted by the *Blairmount Castle* had almost certainly been picked up by Freetown, and if a ship were on its way the odds were heavily in favor of it being a British warship. Rennie didn't think that, in that eventuality, the warship or the submarine would give much thought to survivors of the *Blairmount Castle* until one or the other had been blasted off the face of the ocean. Indeed, in the lonely shipping lanes where merchantmen plied without escort, wasn't it a favorite U-boat ploy to sink a ship, listen for its SOS, and then lie in wait for anything that came along to pick up survivors?

Via his interpreter, Rennie passed on to the Italians the gist of the U-boat commander's message. It transpired that there were no fewer than eighteen officers in the boat, including two Italian Air Force pilots. Contary to Rennie's expectations, they showed not the slightest reluctance about transferring to the submarine, and one arrogantly grinned his triumph at Rennie, mouthing something at him in Italian that was plainly not meant to be complimentary.

German sailors on the deck of the submarine helped twenty-six of the Italians to climb aboard from Rennie's boat. Then a line was passed to the boat to act as a towline.

Olberg shouted out final instructions to Rennie.

"I'll keep our speed down to four knots—but be ready to slip the tow if one of your navy's ships appears. I may have to dive in a hurry."

"What about this mythical rescue ship?" Rennie shouted back.

Olberg seemed to ponder for a moment over the word mythical. Then a grin creased his face.

"She is no myth," he shouted. "We should be up with her by tonight. She is French and very beautiful—the destroyer *Marande*. Your war is over, Herr Volunteer. You will spend the rest of it in a camp in Dakar."

The sun was burning its way to its noon-day zenith as Olberg's rescue mission neared completion. By then, ten lifeboats from the *Blairmount Castle* had been taken in tow by the U-boats and were strung out in three processions of three, four and three astern of the submarine. The U-boat altered course and, like a mother-duck with a flotilla of tiny ducklings, headed slowly north-east.

Rennie's boat was still overloaded but, compared with what they had been throughout the night, conditions were now tolerable. From his place in the stern, he was studying his enemies: the olive-skinned Italian soldiers who had been taken prisoner in East Africa and had been destined for farm labor camps in Wales, and the German submarine crew who were taking spells on deck as relief from the interior of their tomb-like metal home.

The Germans, in particular, seemed to be in good spirits. Rennie noted how alike they were to the British sailors with whom he had sailed the seas these past dozen years. He hated U-boats and the killing work they did—preying on lightly armed merchant ships in what seemed a one-sided contest—but he grudgingly respected the men who manned the U-boats. The conditions in which they had to live and fight were grim and Rennie would not have changed places with a submariner, no matter what odds favored the U-boat, for all the tea in China. No, he liked the smell of the open air and he preferred to take his chances on top of the ocean.

The navigating officer of the submarine was busy at a task which Rennie had done often enough. Sextant in hand, the German was taking noon sights as the sun reached the meridian, calling out to a colleague below so that the chronometer time could be noted.

Kapitänleutnant Olberg hovered unobtrusively in the background until his navigating officer had completed his sights and calculations thirty-five minutes later, and had marked the noon position on the chart. The officer pencilled the position on a pad of scrap paper, tore off the top sheet, and handed it to Olberg.

Olberg studied the figures.

"So we should rendezvous on time?" he said.

"At twenty-one hundred hours, sir. She's making thirty-five knots and we're making just under four—three point eight to be precise. That means the *Marande* is covering as much ocean in one hour as we are likely to travel in the next nine. We should meet up here . . . Almost on the tenth parallel. Approximately ten degrees north by eighteen and a half west."

"Good," grunted Olberg. "I'll get a message off to base saying that we have ten boats of survivors in tow."

The navigator was thoughtful.

"Sir? The British must have picked up that troop-ship's distress signals. She was transmitting for more than an hour before she went down . . . Won't the British be sending ships to look for survivors?"

"I would have thought so but there's no indication that they have. My old friend Heinrich Schell is sitting off Freetown in anticipation of a north-bound convoy coming out, but he has reported that nothing has left or entered the harbor in the last twenty-four hours. As far as I know, we have the ocean to ourselves."

But, in this assumption, Olberg was wrong.

Steaming on almost a reciprocal course to his own, and less then 170 miles away, was a thirty-three-year-old converted steam-yacht. HMS *Wyvis* fell some way short of being the pride of the Royal Navy. Built in the Kaiser's Germany five years before the First World War, she had started life as the sea-going palace of a German colonial who had made a fortune from diamonds in South-West Africa. She had fallen on leaner times, however, before being seized as a prize by the Royal Navy in 1939.

The dilapidated once-proud yacht had spent nearly a year in Simonstown before emerging with a new name and a new flag as HM escort and patrol vessel, *Wyvis*. She had operated from Freetown ever since and, although still graceful in line, had achieved an infamy for bad luck which was legend far beyond the West African station.

The principal reason for *Wyvis'* notoriety was the unreliability of her engines, which broke down with monotonous and frequently embarrassing regularity. She was known far and wide as "Fred Carno's Sewing Machine."

Contributing, too, to the *Wyvis'* unhappy reputation

was the disposition and style of the ship's commanding officer since her re-commissioning. Lieutenant-Commander Matthew Bishop was known behind his back as Captain Bligh, and not because of any connection with his famous predecessor's achievements as a navigator. The story of Bishop's court-martial in Malta in 1938 for striking a rating was common knowledge. Most acknowledged that, but for this fall from grace, he would probably now be commanding a cruiser and not a converted 1909 relic.

Bishop, since 1938, had been a career officer without a career. Stripped of his seniority and deprived of his Commander's stripe, he had been relegated to a port security job in Devonport. For a year after the country had gone to war, the Admiralty had paid no attention to his repeated requests for sea duty—but the acute shortage of trained officers had finally overcome official misgivings over Bishop's fitness for a command. Bishop's consolation prize had been HMS *Wyvis.*

Wyvis was making fifteen knots. Hunched against the open wheelhouse window, trying to get the gentle fanning of air afforded by the forward movement of the ship, Bishop scowled at the shimmering ocean. For five days, until they had picked up that SOS from the *Blairmount Castle,* a black cloud of misery had hung over him. It irrigated and fed the roots of bitter anger in his mind at the injustice of his fate.

Most men would have resigned the service rather than live with the humiliation and indignity that had been his lot ever since Malta. But not Bishop. He had made one mistake, one easily forgivable and understandable mistake as far as he was concerned, and they had bloody well crucified him for it. Well, he was determined to show my Lords of the Admiralty that they had made a far bigger mistake by failing to recognize his true worth.

The bloody fools had expected him to be overflowing with gratitude when he had been given the *Wyvis.* He had *pretended* to be grateful. It did allow him to get back to sea, and to *command.* But Bishop felt no gratitude to the Lords of Admiralty. They were inferior men, devoid of talent and imagination, and their award of the *Wyvis* to him was at best a gratuitous insult. He had been trained to take command of bigger ships. His entire career, until Malta, had been a testament to his capacity to do great things and reach the very top. They had no right to deprive him of the advancement he had been promised because of one trivial error of judgment.

It had been bitter enough gall to swallow that his first command had turned out to be a museum-piece with a miserable twelve-pounder gun as its main armament but, on top of that indignity, had come the growing realization that the *Wyvis* was a mechanical freak which drove engine-room artificers to nervous breakdowns and her commander to apoplexy. Then, too, there was the frustration of having to serve—forever, it seemed—in a malarial backwater like Freetown. Other officers seemed to come and go with great frequency from the oppressive heat of the West Africa station, but Bishop, it appeared, was destined to serve there for the duration.

Five days ago, Bishop's latest humiliation had overtaken him. *Wyvis* had been one of six escorts taking a convoy north to a rendezvous near the Canaries, where escorts from Gib would take over, but the worst had happened. *Wyvis* had broken down yet again. The escort leader had ordered her to make such repairs as she could and return to Freetown.

The former yacht had wallowed helplessly in solitude for the best part of a day while the engineers had sweated in the vessel's bowels trying to remedy her boiler failure. The cause was mysterious. Equally mysterious was the outcome of the now routine procedure which the *Wyvis'* engineers followed when their temperamental change decided not to function. Although they failed to diagnose any obvious reason for the malfunction, the *Wyvis'* motive power returned to baffling normality when the engineers had completed their standard repair routine.

Bishop had sulked in his room until the *Wyvis* once more had a full head of steam. Then he had ordered course to be set for Freetown, conscious that his ship was once more returning to base in the manner of a naughty dog with tail between its legs.

The black mood which settled on him did not lift until, with the Senegal coast some miles over the eastern horizon, the radio watch on the *Wyvis* picked up the *Blairmount Castle's* distress signals. Bishop did some calculations on the chart and ordered an alteration of course away from the south-easterly track which would have taken *Wyvis* within thirty miles of Bathurst.

"Steer two-two-oh," he had instructed the helmsman, unaware that the track to the south-west was as near identical as didn't matter to that which the Vichy French destroyer, *Marande,* would be following within a matter of hours.

Before the French destroyer could sail, however, there would be a quadrangular flurry of signals passing to and fro, between Olberg's U-boat, Admiral Dönitz's U-boat headquarters, the French Government in Vichy and Naval Headquarters in Dakar. Intelligence sources would identify the ship sunk by Olberg as the *Blairmount Castle,* known to be carrying several hundred Italian prisoners of war. Out of consideration for their Italian allies, the German Command deemed it necessary that every effort should be made to rescue survivors from the torpedoed troop-ship. The assistance of the Vichy French Navy was sought and readily obtained.

Thus it was, on the afternoon following the sinking of the *Blairmount Castle,* while Olberg's submarine made painfully slow progress with its string of lifeboats in tow, two vessels raced towards it. The *Wyvis* had had a head start, but the *Marande* was overhauling the former yacht by a distance of twenty sea miles in every hour.

By six in the evening, a distance of only forty-eight miles separated the *Wyvis* and the U-boat. The *Marande,* cleaving through the water at thirty-five knots, was sixty-seven miles dead astern of the *Wyvis.*

Bishop, his binoculars slung round his neck, had taken up position alone on the highest point of the *Wyvis'* bridge. A nervous excitement had gripped him from the moment, only twenty-four hours before, when Freetown had confirmed his response to the *Blairmount Castle*'s distress signal. As the *Wyvis* drew nearer and nearer to the area where the liner had gone down, Bishop's excitement had increased—but he was anxious to conceal from his officers how intoxicated he was with the sudden smell of glory.

He could have saved himself the effort. Used as they were to his moods, everyone in the ward-room had noticed the change in his behavior that the distress signal had caused. Gone was the thunderous blackness which had enwrapped him since the *Wyvis'* breakdown. It had been replaced by a kind of furtive self-satisfaction.

"The Old Man's running around like an alcoholic

who's found gin coming from his bath-tap," observed Crawford, Bishop's long-suffering First Lieutenant. All the same, Bishop's new ploy of hiding himself away, like Greta Garbo wanting to be alone, puzzled him.

Crawford plotted the six-hour run from noon on the chart and walked through the wheelhouse to the flying-bridge.

"Seen the Captain?" he asked the Leading Signaller on lookout duty.

"He went topside half an hour ago," said the Signaller.

Crawford made a face and climbed the wooden ladder leading to the small decked monkey-island above the wheelhouse. Bishop was in the mounted binnacle-box, scanning the ocean with binoculars.

"What do you want, Number One?" he asked brusquely when he became aware of Crawford's presence.

"We should be up with that SOS position about midnight, sir."

"I'm fully aware of that," snapped Bishop.

"The U-boat's still in the area, too. The latest Admiralty positions put one just to the north of the spot where the ship went down."

"Good!" exclaimed Bishop, his eyes gleaming, realizing too late that he had momentarily dropped his mask. He had allowed his feelings to show.

"We'll have to be careful," said Crawford.

"Are you trying to tell me my job, Number One?"

"No, sir. I meant that if we sight any survivors from that ship, we'll need to be on our guard. That U-boat may be lying in wait for the first ship to come looking for survivors."

"Do you think I don't know that, Crawford? Do you take me for a complete bloody fool?"

"I was only making an observation, sir," said Crawford.

Bishop glowered at him.

"You reservists are all the bloody same. Ten minutes at sea and you're telling the Captain how to run his ship. I don't want any advice from you, Crawford."

The First Lieutenant remained silent, biting down on the anger he felt at being lectured like an errant schoolboy.

"I'll tell you something, Crawford," Bishop went on in

only a slightly less aggressive tone, "I've been banking on that submarine still being there! We are going to bloody well sink it! We are going to let those bastards in Freetown and London see that this glorified ferry-boat can behave like a real ship of war when there's a professional running it!"

He spoke softly, but the glint in his eyes was almost maniacal. That's all we need, thought Crawford. Now he thinks he's Lord Bloody Nelson. Crawford was by no means displeased at the prospect of a duel with a U-boat. A kill would work wonders for the morale of the ship's company. But Crawford believed in keeping things in proportion. A tussle with a solitary sub didn't exactly constitute a second Battle of Trafalgar.

There was no doubt, though, that Bishop saw it differently. That's why he had been acting so strangely ever since they'd heard that SOS. He had been quietly working himself up, measuring the glory that would be his if the *Wyvis* could claim a U-boat captain's scalp. Bishop didn't give a damn about finding survivors from that ship. All he had on his mind was the U-boat. Well, maybe it was understandable. There had been damned little glory in Bishop's career so far.

At sunset, Bishop closed the crew to Action Stations. He stood, gazing out of the wheelhouse window, with Crawford at his shoulder. The whirring metallic voice of the telephone shattered the silence on the bridge.

Crawford answered it.

"Radar contact timed twenty eighteen hours," he repeated for Bishop's benefit. "Unidentified vessel bearing two-two-seven degrees. Small vessel. Could be submarine on the surface."

"Hah!" There was triumph in the monosyllabic sound which exploded from Bishop's throat. He turned to the helmsman.

"Starboard the wheel. Steer two-two-seven degrees."

He snatched up the ship's address microphone from its cradle and flicked the switch "On."

"Forward gun crew, stand by. Target bearing dead ahead. I'll give you distance in a moment. Depth charge crew, stand by. Target on surface dead ahead. Radar room, I want a minute-by-minute check on that contact. Put your bridge communication set to 'On' and I'll keep the receiver at this end open. Understood?"

A voice from the Radar room croaked unemotionally from the deckhead speaker above Bishop.

"Contact range now six thousand yards and closing, sir. Early yet to say how fast contact is moving but closing speed seems to be less than twenty knots. Contact bearing two-two-five degrees."

"Steer two-two-five degrees," Bishop ordered the helmsman.

At about the same time as the flurry of activity on the *Wyvis,* a message had been relayed from the control-room of the submarine to Olberg on the conning tower.

"Surface vessel had altered course. Her speed is fifteen

Olberg glanced at his watch. The luminous dial showed nearly twenty after eight.

"The *Marande?*" breathed the First Lieutenant, standing beside him. "One of us must have been making better time than we thought."

"Well, it isn't us, Mannfried," said Olberg. He fingered his beard thoughtfully. "It has to be the Frenchman."

"Do we dive?"

"That would be the prudent thing to do, just in case by some long shot that isn't the Frenchman up ahead. But it has to be the Frenchman. These 'Mogador' class destroyers can do thirty-eight knots and she has probably been pulling out all the stops. No, we stay on the surface."

Further messages were relayed to the conning tower bridge.

"Surface vessel had altered course. Her speed is fifteen knots."

"She must have us on radar," said Olberg. "She has reduced speed already. It must be the *Marande.*"

He glanced aft towards the dim shapes of the lifeboats fanned out astern of the U-boat.

"Get everybody below," he ordered the First Lieutenant, "except for two hands to stand by those towing painters. Tell them to be ready to cast off the moment I give the order. And get below yourself, Mannfried. I'll look after things here until we're a hundred per cent sure it's the Frenchman."

Crewmen, who had been enjoying their rota on deck, moved one at a time through the hatch into the dank stiffness of the submarine. Olberg, scanning the horizon ahead with his night-glasses, picked up the slim dark tower of the *Wyvis'* superstructure.

An enemy destroyer would have opened fire by now, reasoned Olberg. We've been within four-inch range for some time.

The vessels were close enough for Olberg to see the white foaming crest of water at the *Wyvis'* bow when an orange flash lit up the light gray bridgework of the approaching ship. The flash was followed seconds later by a clipped booming sound like a single thump on a bass drum.

Olberg heard the whirred flight of the shell as it passed close overhead. It sailed beyond the stern of the submarine and exploded in the middle of its retinue of lifeboats. In one astonished glance, Olberg saw two of the boats lifted out of the water. They seemed to stand on end, pouring out their human contents, before falling again behind a curtain of water.

"Cast off the boats and get below!" Olberg roared to the ratings on the after-deck. A second shell exploded forty feet off the starboard bow as he bellowed orders below to stand by to flood the main ballast tanks.

Olberg waited, calm-faced, his fingers clenched round the guard-rail in a pinion grip, as the two men on the after-deck went through the process of casting off the tow ropes. Their deliberate movements seemed to take an eon of time. Throughout every second, Olberg could feel the coursing of his blood. It seemed to rush through his arterial system with the streaming intensity of a mill-race in flood. But not by as much as the twitching of a muscle nor the flickering of an eyelid was his seething inner turmoil betrayed. It did not matter that there was no one to observe his iron control. Long experience as a submarine commander had schooled into him a self-discipline that allowed his exterior appearance to give no inkling of the rushing fears and anxieties which crowded through his intelligent brain as inexorably and as vividly as through the minds of other mortals.

In a submarine, it was on the Commander that every eye focused. His every expression was read like a barometer for any sign of storm or doubt. Olberg had long ago recognized that mastery of himself was the prime prerequisite to mastery of a submarine and its crew. Now, he practiced it as second nature.

He realized he had made a serious error of judgment in assuming that the approaching vessel was the French destroyer, but the situation was very far from lost if he made the correct judgments now. With nerve and with the coolness to bring the lessons of his long experience into play, he could still turn the tables on an adversary who had so far gained only initial surprise.

Olberg was deeply conscious that his vessel was classified in Navy jargon as an "attack" submarine, and it was in this role that he excelled. He did not neglect the tactics of defense, but his nature was to attack. To him, there was a negativeness about any philosophy in which defense was the uppermost consideration. His instincts demanded that he must always carry the battle to the enemy, especially if that enemy caught you at a disadvantage and believed he held the initiative.

Two more shells exploded in the water before the last lifeboat had been set adrift. Olberg waited, his face like granite, as first one seaman and then the next scrambled through the deck hatch and the water-tight door was pulled down. Then he was giving the order to dive and scrambling himself through the conning tower hatch.

By the time he reached the control-room, sea-water was already pouring into the main ballast tanks and the hydroplanes were set at the angles which would control the initial depth of the dive. In this, the forward hydroplanes would be inclined at the slightly steeper angle. For the first moments of the dive, the after hydroplanes had to be angled only slightly below the horizontal. Otherwise, the submarine's stern would lift from the water and, with the propellers thrashing air, the motive power for the dive would be lost.

Below the surface, the U-boat's electric motors immediately took over from the diesel engines. Then the inclination of the hydroplanes was increased to steepen the submarine's angle of descent.

In the eerie blue light of the control-room, Olberg tried to put himself in the shoes of his opponent on the surface. What would he do? Would he risk a depth-charge attack with the water full of men from the upturned lifeboats? Would he expect the submarine to dive deep and then lie doggo? Or simply try to get the hell out of it?

Olberg, in calculating the possibilities, added together those items of information which he knew or could deduce about his enemy. The ship on the surface was almost certainly an escort vessel of some description: single-screw, so not a destroyer. Not even a corvette, because these shells had been fired from something lighter than a four-inch—probably a twelve-pounder. What was it, then? Bigger than an armed trawler and fast enough to do fifteen knots. Olberg reckoned he was dealing with a converted coastal liner.

If that were the case, he could probably outgun it on the surface and beat it for speed, too. But what if that ship up there had company not too far away? He would back the crew of his three-point-five in single combat any time, but against any more than one similarly armed ship he would be pushing his luck. Still, it would mean saving precious torpedoes.

Watching Olberg's face as he calmly gave orders the men in the narrow confines of the control-room were given no sign of the myriad thoughts flashing through their commander's brain. If they had, it would not have surprised them to learn that at no time did it occur to him that instant flight was the answer.

The enemy had engaged him. There was only one response. And that was to fight back.

Chapter Two

On the bridge of HMS *Wyvis*, Biship had been hard put to contain his delight and surprise when he had realized that the U-boat dead ahead was taking no evasive action whatsoever, but was remaining on the surface and plodding nearer and nearer at less than four knots.

It occurred to him that the submarine must be damaged: unable to dive and unable to increase speed. That made her a sitting duck. Well, that made no damned difference. This was war.

"Maybe it's a fishing-boat?" said Crawford.

"Fishing-boat be damned!" said Bishop. "It's a sub—and we're going to get the bastard!"

"I can't understand why she doesn't dive. Are you going to open fire, sir?"

"You bet your boots I am, Number One. But not until we're close enough to be sure we can't miss. My guess is that Fritz can't dive, perhaps because of damage. Well, it's going to be his funeral."

When the range had narrowed to fifteen hundred yards, Bishop ordered the twelve-pounder in the bows to commence firing. He and Crawford watched the result through their glasses.

"A hit!" exclaimed Bishop, after the first shell.

"I think we overshot," said Crawford.

"We got a hit!" Bishop persisted. "I saw a bloody great lump of submarine flying in the air! And bodies falling!"

He watched more shells send up pillars of water in the vicinity of the submarine and his delight of a moment before turned to anger.

"What are they bloody playing at?" he snarled, referring to his own gun's crew. "Christ almighty, they only have to fire the way they're looking to hit the bloody thing—and they're popping off all over the bloody ocean!"

"Good God!" Crawford, his glasses still fixed on the

scene ahead, seemed frozen with awe. "She's gone—dived. But there's still something there . . . Boats! About half a dozen boats!"

Bishop had inadvertently turned the eye-pieces of his glasses and was having difficulty refocusing them.

"I can't see a damned thing," he complained. "What are you blithering about boats?"

The gun's crew had ceased firing and, almost immediately, the wheelhouse telephone jangled.

Crawford picked it up to hear his report of boats confirmed by an agitated Sub-Lieutenant Groves, the ship's gunnery officer. He could see eight boats with lots of men in them and what appeared to be another floating upside down.

Crawford's stomach turned over as the truth began to dawn on him. Now he knew why the submarine was making only three and a half knots. Now he knew why she had made no attempt to get out of the way. Now he knew what it was that the Old Man had seen as a result of the first shell-burst.

"The U-boat had survivors in tow," he said weakly to Bishop. Then a new thought struck him. "Christ! We're going to run right through them!"

This last agonized exclamation had to compete with the voice which crackled out from the overhead speaker.

"Asdic room to bridge. Asdic room to bridge. We have a contact dead ahead. Range eight hundred yards. Very positive."

Bishop pushed Crawford aside and unhooked the telephone. His eyes seemed to burn in the dark of the wheelhouse.

"Bridge to after-deck. This is the Captain speaking. Prepare for depth charge attack. Be ready to roll off three pairs. Five seconds interval between each pair. First pair setting, two hundred feet. Second setting two-five-oh feet. Third setting deepest."

The rating, whose job it was to stand by the after-deck telephone, sang out Bishop's orders word for word to the officer in charge of the depth charge crew. He in turn repeated them to the waiting crew.

The square-handled primers were set and inserted into the heavy cylinders of explosive and twisted home. When dropped in the sea, these regulated the intake of water into the detonating chamber, so that the charges would explode according to the quantity of water admitted. The deeper the charge setting, the smaller the apertures in the primer for allowing water into the chamber. The shallower the charge setting, the bigger the water-admission apertures.

"Depth charges ready to fire, sir," the after-deck telephonist reported to the bridge.

Above Bishop's head, the speaker from the Asdic room crackled yet again: "Almost instantaneous echo. Distance under three hundred yards."

Bishop waited. Crawford, tight-lipped beside him, still had his glasses trained on the lifeboats ahead. They could be seen quite clearly now. They seemed to be strung out in a line at right-angles to the *Wyvis'* course.

"We're going to mow these boats down, sir," Crawford warned hoarsely.

"Instantaneous echo! We've got Doppler effect!" came an excited voice from the Asdic room.

"Fire two!" he shouted again into the telephone.

"Fire two!" echoed the rating on the after-deck.

Two depth charges were rolled down the twin sets of rails, port and starboard, at the *Wyvis'* stern.

Bishop, on the bridge, counted the seconds.

"Fire two!" he shouted again into the telephone.

"For Christ's sake, alter course!" screamed Crawford. "We're going to hit these lifeboats!"

Bishop ignored him. He continued to count seconds.

"Fire God's sake, hold your tongue, Number One. And take a grip of yourself!"

He directed his gaze at the sea ahead.

"Hard a-starboard the wheel," he called out.

The sound of voices raised in shouting carried up from below the *Wyvis'* bows to the bridge. Then the ship's curved stem carved through one boat and the bow plates carried another briefly forward before tossing it aside like snow before a plough. The second boat stood on end and then seemed to cartwheel.

The *Wyvis'* alteration of course had come just too late to avoid the two lifeboats on the westerly end of the string. Rennie, in the stern of the boat that was seized in the *Wyvis'* bow wave and tossed end over end by the bow plates of the ship, found himself propelled in the same churning bow wave like a man in a barrel going over Niagara Falls. For an instant, the boat was suspended above him. Then, as it began to fall at a crazy angle, bodies falling everywhere, he felt himself sucked down and carried away from the advancing ship in the great wall of water it was pushing away from her bows.

Lungs bursting, he clawed and thrashed with his arms to assist his passage through the tumbling cataract in which he was caught. Even when his head burst clear into fresh air, he continued the frantic swimming motions. One thought was uppermost in his mind—and that was escape from the *Wyvis'* threshing screw which, even in that turmoil of crashing water and splintering boat timber, he could hear like an approaching rhythmic thunder.

His fear and the swing to starboard of the *Wyvis* saved him. He was still windmilling his arms in relatively quiet water, aware that the great dark wall which was the ship's hull seemed to be advancing on him as a large mass and that, at its far end, was the booming turbulence thrown up by the whirling propeller. But the white churning water passed him by a good thirty feet away and he was drifting in the bubbling wake of the fading ship.

Half a mile away along that glistening phosphorescent wake, tall geysers of white water pillared from the sea. Before there was any sound, Rennie could feel the ocean tremble. Waves of shock charged through his body. It was as if his intestines had been squeezed by an invisible hand and instantly released. Then again and again in rapid sucession.

Then came the sound as the exploding depth charges erupted from the ocean.

In the first moments of the U-boat's dive, Olberg was computing the various options open to him. He considered, then rejected, the temptation of fighting his attacker on the surface. One, there could be other ships about—which would quickly change the odds. Two, the warship thundering down on him could have much heavier armament on her after-deck and stern than the pop-gun which had let off those first shells. The fact that the vessel had been coming at him head-on may have simply prevented the heavier stuff being brought to bear.

Olberg decided on tactics which had paid off for him once before when he had encountered a long corvette south of Iceland. It was a bold maneuver, but Olberg believed that fortune favored the bold.

The submarine was already at a depth of a hundred and fifty feet. Olberg glanced at the men controlling the hydroplane rudders. Their faces were tight with concentration. He forced a cheerful expression on to his own face.

"What glum faces we all have!" he announced to the control-room at large. "Let's see how good that Tommy captain up there is, eh? Let's start bringing her up again. Gently now. Not too fast."

The deep rhythmic thud of the *Wyvis'* screw could be plainly heard. And there was a more unnerving sound. The steady "ping" caused by the surface ship's Asdic sending impulses against the submarine's hull and echoing back to its source. The impulses were transmitted in a circular sweep, reaching out in the ocean like a cone, with the "ping" occurring whenever the signals encountered an undersea object of great enough solidity to bounce them back.

From the length of time it took these electronic impulses to travel out from the parent ship and echo back, the Asdic operator cold tell how far away the undersea object was and in what direction it lay. The nearer the submarine-hunter was to its prey, the more rapid the "ping." In the event of the surface ship passing over its contact, the out-going impulses would echo back almost in the same instant as they were transmitted—so that the "pings" ran together in a continuous wave of sound, known as the "Doppler effect" or instantaneous echo.

The "pinging" noise was coming at very short intervals as Olberg conned his submarine on to what—if the ships had both been on the surface—would have been a collision course. There was a lot of ocean underneath him and he reckoned that the hunter on the surface would expect him to dive deep as the best means of escape. His depth charges would, therefore, be set deep.

For this reason, Olberg opted not to do the obvious thing. Bringing his U-boat gently out of her dive, he brought her up again to eighty feet and headed her straight towards the throbbing sound of the enemy ship's screw. He calculated that from the moment of diving to what was technically collision point with the surface ship, he would have less than four minutes to complete his maneuvering and get the trim of his ship right. Any error could result in his adversary slicing the top off the submarine like a can of peas.

His radio operator, right beside him in the control-room, eyed him anxiously, as the "pinging" noise accelerated in frequency until there seemed to be little length of interval between the sounds. The commander seemed icy calm, not a sign of emotion, although there were little globules of sweat on his forehead. But there wasn't a man in the control-room who wasn't sweating visibly.

The submarine was now steady at eighty-five feet and the electric motors, on full power, were pushing her through the water at eight knots.

The "pings" became a continuous wave of sound.

"Full starboard rudder!" ordered Olberg.

The noise of the ship's propeller right above them seemed deafening in the enclosed space of the control-room. Eyes looked up, as if expecting to see the hammering screw rip through the shell of the submarine.

The sound above them began to recede perceptibly.

"She's turning away from us," said the hydrophone operator.

Olberg was counting off seconds mentally. He broke off briefly to say:

"Brace yourself for a few big bangs, my lads."

He continued his silent counting, permitting himself a small smile of satisfaction when he realized that any depth charges dropped had most certainly sunk now below the hundred-feet level. Every second of escape time was vital in putting distance between the submarine and the point where the depth charges would explode. Every extra foot of depth for which the charges had been fused provided Olberg with vital seconds to get farther away from the point of detonation.

The first shock tremor of exploding depth charges came at them from behind and below, lifting the submarine's stern and shaking the entire craft, so that for a moment its even trim was lost. The U-boat rocked violently, as disturbed, agitated water hit its outer shell with a noise like breaking glass. Inside, there *was* breaking glass—as light fittings were shaken from their sockets.

More explosions followed, deeper and farther away but still close enough to send trembling water surging against the submarine's hull.

Olberg had steadied the course at right-angles to that

when he had swung to starboard. Now, he came forty-five degrees to port and ordered surfacing procedure. Compressed air was pumped into the main ballast tanks. The U-boat came up until her decks were awash. Sitting low in the water, she had just the faint chance of presenting minimal register on the enemy's radar.

Olberg scanned the ocean to the south through the periscope. A moon like a half cheese was lighting the ocean from low in the south-east. Better if it had been setting, thought Olberg, but realized that in a situation where the moonlight gave—as it did now—a fifty-fifty advantage, he had the better chance of seeing without being seen.

He gave a cluck of admiration for the lines of the *Wyvis* when he sighted her angled silhouette as she turned away to the south-west.

Keep turning, my lovely, keep turning—he breathed to himself. Using engines to assist a full lock of rudder, he put the U-boat into a tight turn, steadying with the *Wyvis* still clearly visible on the port bow. Asdic contact had been broken since immediately after the U-boat's alteration of course beneath the *Wyvis* and the explosion of the depth charges. Olberg did not delude himself that his escape from detection would have been of any duration but for his gamble in staying shallow and then resurfacing.

Now, if the enemy picked him up on their radar, it would be interesting to know what they made of it. Olberg was not to know it but the gods were already dealing a card which was to mislead his enemy and present the *Wyvis* to him on a plate.

Presented with the fact that Asdic contact with the submarine had been lost, Bishop's immediate reaction had been one of elation. He was convinced the submarine must have sunk. Completing a wide turn, he reduced to half speed and steered east by north, calculating that if the submarine had escaped the first attack, it would continue in a north-easterly direction as fast as it could. If that were the case, he would "creep" up in roughly the same direction until Asdic contact was re-established.

Ideally, of course, Bishop would have liked a companion vessel to have aided the search in case the submarine had taken off to the south and east, where a half-moon was rising, but the *Wyvis* could not cover every eventuality. Bishop had to gamble on the U-boat running deep and along the route which put distance between it and the position of the first attack.

He reckoned without Olberg's cunning and the unheralded approach of what constituted the "X" factor in the war of wits. Although she played no part in the action directly, the presence of the French destroyer *Marande* was to be of vital consequence in the ultimate outcome.

As the *Wyvis* crept north by east, her Asdic probing through a 360-degree sweep of the ocean, two contacts appeared on her radar screen. One—a very faint signal—was less than two thousand yards away on the starboard beam. The other—a much more positive signal—was straight ahead and well to the north. Rage clouded Bishop's immediate assessment of this double development. Rage, because his first conclusion was that the submarine had indeed escaped the depth charges and had covered a remarkable distance northwards in the time available. He ordered an immediate alteration of course towards the more positive of the two radar contacts.

The nearer contact he dismissed as possibly one of the lifeboats from the *Blairmount Castle*. This reminder of what had happened to two of the ship's lifeboats brought the taste of gall to his mouth. He found no joy in massacring British seamen, even in the line of duty first. His anger transmitted itself in his furious jangling of the engine-room telegraph to indicate he wanted full speed. He did not know in that moment that he had already made the decisive error which was to cost the lives of most of his ship's company.

Less than two miles away, Olberg could not believe his luck at the realization that the enemy ship was maintaining a course, broadside on, right across his bows. The four bow torpedo tubes had been loaded. The crews awaited his order to fire.

Olberg ordered a rudder correction to starboard and waited for the submarine to steady on its course. He could see the full graceful lines of the *Wyvis* now and a pang of regret rose in him unbidden that he should destroy such beauty. She was built like a yacht and did not have the stubby ugliness of the corvette.

"Fire number one."

The long sleek cylinder swam away from the bows of the U-boat in a swirl of foam as the main switch to the motor circuit was triggered and the twin propellers, in series, went into rapid rotation. The depth control gear, housed near the tail of the torpedo, switched into operation and immediately began to regulate the running depth.

Forward of the humming torpedo motor, the electric generator, which fed power to the homing gear supply, jumped into action. Its brain sat right in the tip of the blunt nose; an acoustic receiver tuned to detect the hammering big ends and rotating shaft noises of the target ahead. Housed in the same nose section was the thermal relay device which prevented the torpedo being triggered by sounds from its vessel of launch or by the near-silent running of its own mechanisms.

Shark-like, the missile homed towards the sleek throbbing shape that was the *Wyvis*. The narrow curved bow leapt from the crest of a long swell and the former yacht surfed—high in the water—as the torpedo passed underneath her engine room and exploded some ten feet below her keel. A giant force tore upwards, breaking the *Wyvis* in two. A plummet of smoke, water and twisted steel pinnacled two hundred feet in the air. A secondary explosion caused the rising stern and after section of the ship to disintegrate into the atmosphere.

The *Wyvis*' raked funnel was blasted into the after end of the bridge, slicing through the timbers of the Asdic and radar cabins. Bishop, who had left the wheelhouse for the bridge-wing to search the sea to starboard for the lesser of the two radar contacts, was caught in a roaring blast of fiery air. It hurtled him against the grey-painted woodwork of the outer wing. The woodwork, in turn, gave way like papier-mâché and he found himself catapulted amid splintering wood and shreds of canvas dodger far into the sea. His clothes were whipped from his back and his skin blackened by the scorching wall of air.

Then he was sinking deep, deep, in black water. He was beyond conscious thought, senseless of what was happening to him, even when the water closed around him. The first spark of survival instinct and the awareness that he must battle to escape the blackness which had enveloped him came with a monstrous pressing on his lungs and a beating behind his eyes of such intensity that it seemed they would pop from his head.

He struggled to the surface of the ocean, shooting free into fresh air with such force that he emerged almost waist-high from the water. Then he was going down again. He resurfaced a second time, vomiting sea-water and paddling instinctively to keep afloat.

He felt no pain, only a scorching of his skin alike to severe sun-burning. Shock prevented him from orienting his mind and working out what it was had happened to him. Time and place had lost meaning. He knew he must keep swimming but, beyond that necessity, his surroundings had no reality.

Some distance away, the fore section of the *Wyvis* was subsiding into the ocean in a great hissing, bubbling mass. Oil burned on the ocean; a billowing, flickering ghostly orange with a serrated fringe of black smoke.

Rennie watched the end of the *Wyvis* in stupefied wonder. He, too, was lost in a burdening unreality; aware that he still lived but shocked into a numbness of not fully comprehending where or why. One moment, he had been alone in an ocean quaking with gut-kicking tremors. The next, he had been aware of a boat—another from the *Blairmount Castle*—looming out of nowhere. Strong arms had pulled him clear of the water and he lay, as he lay now, his head on his arms across the gunwale, the visible world rising and falling with the movement of the boat.

Chapter Three

Lieutenant Jean-Paul Mercier stood stiffly to attention, looking neither to left nor right. His eyes were fixed unblinkingly on the cream-enamelled bulkhead beyond the Captain's desk.

From his seat at the desk, Captain Roget regarded the young officer with a sideways tilt of his head. He wore an expression which he believed to be paternal.

"Now, Mercier, what is all this nonsense about? You have had several hours to consider your folly. I trust you are now regretting our little contretemps on the bridge."

"I have thought about it, sir. My views remain the same." Mercier remained rigidly at attention as he spoke.

"You have not had a change of heart?" Captain Roget's question was softly spoken but his eyes were like gimlets. Sweat oozed from his forehead, spoiling the scrubbed and polished appearance he liked to present to the world. In spite of his spotless white uniform, Roget looked more like a civil servant—or the popular conception of one—than the commander of a sleek ocean greyhound like the *Marande.* His short, greying hair shone with Brilliantine and was plastered flat against his scalp. This and a pious rectitude of manner conspired to make him appear more *chef des fonctionnaires* than dashing sea captain. He sighed.

"You are a fool, Mercier," he said wearily. "I had you brought here to my cabin so that we could have a little talk alone, before I took your . . . your indiscretion . . . any further. Now you leave me no leeway. You force my hand."

"You must do what you think is right, sir," said Mercier. Roget glared at him.

"Damn you, Mercier, I'm throwing you a life-line. How can I help you if you don't help yourself?"

Mercier kept looking straight at the bulkhead beyond the Captain.

"You must do your duty according to your conscience, sir—and allow me the privilege of doing my duty according to mine."

"Dammit, man, you refused to carry out the lawful orders of your ship's captain when the ship was at battle stations. That is an offense punishable by *death!*"

"I did not disobey a direct order, sir. I merely advised you that in the event of you giving the order to fire on the British ship, I would not transmit that order to the gun crews."

"You're playing with words, and you know it!" flamed Roget. "A court-martial will interpret your conduct as mutinous."

Mercier did not answer. From far away below the deck on which he stood, the heavy throbbing rhythm of the *Marande's* engines maintained a relentless tattoo.

Roget struggled to contain the anger he felt. He had hoped that Mercier would have been penitent in the sobering light of morning and bitterly regretting his stupid quixotic stand of the night before. The whole incident could have been smoothed over and handled by him personally. The last thing Roget wanted was a full-blown inquiry in Dakar. These things had a way of rebounding on ship commanders and blighting their promotion prospects, no matter how innocent *they* might be.

He had a mental picture of a staff board considering his elevation to the ranks of admiralty and some old fool saying: "Roget? Roget? Wasn't he the fellow who had that trouble in Dakar with one of his officers? Must be something wrong with him if he can't keep discipline in his own ward-room, eh?"

The nightmare of marring his own promotion weighed much more heavily on Roget's mind than any concern for Mercier or any desire to help the young man. He was sensitive, too, to the fact that Mercier was well connected. The boy had married old Bousquet's daughter, and Bousquet still had a lot of influence, even if he was retired.

Roget made one last attempt to make Mercier see sense.

"Look, Mercier, your attitude is not making things easy for me. It's not as if we actually fired on the British ship. I simply took the precaution of preparing for action in case the Englishman tried to interfere with our rescue of the Italians. My orders were very explicit on that point. I was obeying my orders in the way that you, as a French officer, should have obeyed yours."

"With respect, sir, you were itching to blow that Englishman out of the water. I saw your disappointment when the U-boat beat you to it. You had every intention of firing on that ship."

Roget pushed his chair baçk and leapt to his feet. His expression was thunderous.

"Why! You insolent whipper-snapper! You dare to speak to me like that! Well, you've gone too far. You've stretched my patience just too far. I'm going to break you, Mercier. The fact that your father-in-law is one of the most powerful men in the empire cuts no ice with me. I am going to break you like a piece of straw!"

Anger—the first sign of any emotional reaction from him—flashed in Mercier's eyes.

"You need have no fear of my father-in-law on my account." He stared Roget straight in the eye. "He will not lift a finger to interfere. He's a bigger Vichy arse-licker than you and I want no favors from him."

Roget blanched with fury.

"You dishonor his name," he snapped. "You are not content to dishonor me and dishonor your ship, you drag in the mud the name of one of the great families of France!" He strode to the cabin door and wrenched it open. "Duty officer!" he bellowed.

A cherub-faced ensign, some years Mercier's junior, arrived breathlessly from the far end of the alleyway. He saluted smartly.

"Lieutenant Mercier is to be kept under close arrest until further notice," Roget. "Take the prisoner away and lock him up."

"In his quarters, mon Capitaine?" asked the ensign.

"No, you dolt. In the brig!"

The ensign looked perplexedly at Mercier with a question in his eyes.

"Lieutenant?"

"It's all right. I know the way," said Mercier. He stepped into the alleyway and, with a brief nod of his head to the younger man, led the way.

"There will be no talking to the prisoner," Roget called

after them. "I forbid all officers from visiting or talking to the traitor. He is to be kept incommunicado."

A military band was playing on the quayside as the *Marande* docked at Dakar. A committee of high-ranking French officers, government officials, and German consular staff waited patiently in the shade of a cargo shed to greet the Italians who had survived the sinking of the *Blairmount Castle*. The welcome was formal rather than warm. Polite handshakes and mumbled platitudes—rather than smiles and embraces—were the order of the day.

Rennie watched from the after-deck of the destroyer, where he and the other survivors of Olberg's torpedoes had been herded.

"There won't be any red carpet for us," he observed to the tall lean man at his shoulder.

Bishop, who had been hauled naked from the water, felt faintly ridiculous in the canvas trousers and matelot's work-shirt in which he had been kitted out.

"I just hope that there's someone ashore with the authority and breeding to show some respect for a British officer. I've had none so far."

Rennie looked at his neighbor with a mixture of wonder and amusement.

"The French Navy people haven't exactly been matey. But they've been polite and not unkind," he said.

Bishop glared at his compatriot.

"Do you call this ridiculous garb they've given me to wear a kindness? I tell you it was a deliberate insult."

Rennie looked down at his own clothes, which were identical.

"Yours are the same as the rest of us. Nobody else is complaining."

"I'm not a Merchant Navy deck-hand!" snapped Bishop.

"Neither am I," said Rennie evenly, "but it wouldn't make me froth at the mouth to be mistaken for one. Where did you spring from anyway? I don't remember seeing you around this morning."

Bishop looked down his nose at Rennie.

"If you must know, I spent the night in the sick bay with some bloody Eye-ties. I am . . ." Bishop began aggressively, but changed his mind ". . . I was the Captain of HMS *Wyvis*."

"That obviously makes you a second cousin of God Almighty," said Rennie drily. "Well, I wouldn't advertise it too much, if I were you."

Bishop was taken aback.

"What the hell do you mean?"

"I mean that there are one or two people around here who would take a lot of pleasure in kicking your teeth through the back of your head after what happened the other night."

"What are you talking about?"

"I'm talking about the small matter of blowing a couple of lifeboats out of the water and then ramming another two. You may not know it, chum, but one of these boats had women and kids in it. *And* the Captain of the *Blairmount Castle.* They were all lost. Believe me, Captain whatever-your-name-is, you're no pin-up boy around here. Last night, they were trying to work out who had killed the most people—you or the U-boat."

Bishop's face had crumpled. He was looking at Rennie as if beseeching him to keep his voice down. Some of the others already appeared to be taking an interest in the conversation.

Bishop need not have worried. Although there was contempt in the glances of his fellow-Britons, there was no trace of intended violence. All, at that moment, were more occupied with the unanswered questions concerning their immediate future in the hands of the French. Nor, if the truth be known, did the survivors entertain strong feelings for revenge on Bishop. If any animosity was harbored against him, it was more of a nauseous disdain than anything else. Most had seen enough of the war at sea, and it's horrors, to realize that the naval ship's first priority had been the destruction of the enemy. What they found hard to forgive was the fact that, having recklessly squandered the lives of so many, Biship had failed miserably to achieve his objective.

Not until long after the Italians, the band and the reception committee had departed were the British survivors herded down on to the quay from the *Marande.*

There, guarded by half a dozen Senegalese soldiers, they had to stand in a line and wait while each was taken individually for interview in an office inside the cargo shed. Rennie and Bishop were at the tail of this queue and were, therefore, interested spectators in a little drama which took place.

A closed truck drew up at the foot of the *Marande*'s gangway and, down from the ship, a French naval officer was led under armed guard. He was ushered into the back of the truck, followed by the guard. And then the truck was driven away.

It was all over in minutes but it gave the survivors on the quay something to talk about while they awaited interrogation by the French authorities.

Rennie was the last to be taken. He was conducted into a glass-fronted, airless office. A big three-blade fan hung from the ceiling but was not working. Three men sat behind a long table. They were perspiring freely and their shirts were wet with sweat in the areas spreading out from their arm-pits. None of them looked particularly happy in his work.

The central of the three characters eyed Rennie sourly. He spoke in English:

"Name?"

"Rennie. John Laidlaw Rennie."

"You were on the *Blairmount Castle?*"

"Yes."

"What was your status?"

"I was a passenger."

"Ah, you are in the English Armed Forces then?"

"No."

The interrogator looked at Rennie with interest.

"You are a civilian?"

"Yes."

"What is your occupation and nationality?"

"I am a navigating officer in the Merchant Navy, temporarily unemployed. My nationality is British. My discharge number is R-two-seven-seven-four . . ."

The interrogator cut him off.

"Never mind that. What were you doing in South Africa and why were you going to England?"

"I am not obliged to answer these questions. I am obliged only to give you my name and my discharge number."

Rennie was acutely aware that to give details of the *Oakville* and its sinking off the Cape by a U-boat was to give direct military intelligence. Consequently, he had no intention of providing these facts to the Vichy French.

The interrogator forced the pretense of a smile.

"Come now, you are talking as if you had been made a prisoner of war by an enemy power."

"If I'm not a prisoner of war, perhaps you'll tell me what I am?" said Rennie.

"At the moment, you are a Distressed British Subject—a person without means and without permission to be in this country. We simply wish to assess what status you should be given in this country. To do so, we must ask questions in order to establish whether, as an alien, you should be given limited liberty, interned according to International Law, or repatriated on humane grounds."

Rennie grinned.

"How about deporting me to Sierra Leone as an undesirable alien?"

The three officials were not amused. Their spokesman warned Rennie that any more flippancy would earn him an indefinite period in the local jail, where he would have ample time to consider the merits of a more serious frame of mind.

"What rank do you hold in the British Merchant Navy?" snapped the spokesman.

"I hold a Master's Certificate, Foreign-Going. But I have no ship, so I have no rank."

"What were you doing in South Africa? And how did you get there?"

Rennie did not answer.

The question was repeated. Rennie remained silent.

The three officials conversed rapidly between themselves in French. Rennie had a good knowledge of the language but could not follow them, other than to gather that he was highly unpopular with them.

The man in the middle was again their mouth-piece.

"You are not being very co-operative, Monsieur Rennie, but we are patient people. How can I persuade you that we bear no ill-will? All the other survivors were most co-operative with us. They realized that there is a lot of, what you call, red tape. Indeed, all but one were quite happy to sign documents like this."

He handed Rennie a four-page form with a fold in the middle.

A quick glance showed Rennie that it had spaces for name, age, physical description and other details. At the end was a declaration of some length with space below for a signature. Rennie handed the form back.

"You want me to sign this?"

"Yes. A formality. You understand?"

"I don't understand," said Rennie. "Especially the small print at the end. It's a surrender of rights, isn't it? A promise to be a good boy and not to try to escape?"

"That is your phrasing. I would put it another way. It signifies that, under the terms of the Armistice Commission, you voluntarily accept certain restrictions."

"I think I get the picture," said Rennie. "What if I don't sign?"

The official shrugged his shoulders.

"Refusal to sign would be tantamount to declaring yourself an enemy alien. I would warn you strongly against such folly. It would leave us no alternative but to place you in the closest custody, without status or privilege, and to keep you there indefinitely."

"That's what it will have to be then," said Rennie. "I have no intention of signing your piece of paper."

"You are a fool," said the man.

"So I've been told," said Rennie, "but if I'm going to lose my freedom, somebody has to take it away from me. A bigger fool in my book is someone who signs his freedom away."

He began to wonder what he had let himself in for when he was manhandled out of the cargo shed by two far-from-gentle Senegalese soldiers and thrown unceremoniously into the back of a closed truck. The vehicle looked like a Black Maria, only it was painted a dull khaki-green. It had a door at the back with a small barred grille for a window. This opening admitted the only light.

Rennie looked up from the floor of the truck to make out another figure in the dim interior. He recognized the Captain of the *Wyvis*. Bishop was dabbing at a cut on his forehead with the sleeve of his shirt.

"Hello, there," said Rennie, rubbing a grazed nose. "You must be the other one who refused to sign on the dotted line."

"Good God, man, I'm a naval officer. I intend to tell them nothing and I'm going to sign nothing. They're hand in glove with the Nazis."

Even in the stifling interior of that van, his face bloody

and dirt-smeared, Bishop managed to sound pompous. He scowled at Rennie.

"Didn't you sign their damned paper? The rest of your chaps seem to have signed it readily enough."

"They probably thought it was just a port formality," said Rennie.

"Why didn't you sign?"

"Perhaps I didn't like signing away my freedom."

Presently, the van rumbled off. It was dark, and a heavy equatorial rain-storm was beginning when the van reached its destination more than an hour later. They were in the court-yard of what appeared to be a medieval castle but which was, in fact, a coastal fort built by the French a century before.

Rennie and Bishop were marched down a stone stairway into a dank, smelly, subterranean chamber hacked from solid rock. Along one wall was a row of grilled doorways, each so low that a man of average height could not enter without stooping.

A Senegalese corporal unlocked one of the iron-barred doors and motioned to Rennie and Bishop that they should enter.

"This must be our hotel," said Rennie. "I wonder what the room-service is like."

Bishop, casting off his previous aloofness and wanting to present a united front to their captors, made a show of bowing and inviting Rennie to precede him.

"After you, my dear chap." He turned, before entering himself, and gave an imperious wave of his hand to the Sengalese jailer. "You, my good man. I would like two boiled eggs for breakfast. Lightly boiled—just two minutes. Not a second more and not a second less."

The African looked at Bishop without comprehension. His look managed to convey both his mystification and the suspicion that Bishop had been touched by the sun.

Rennie appreciated Bishop's unexpected show of bravado in silence. It gave him hope that, behind the plummy accent and pompous manner, there was perhaps a gritty individual. There was a strange comfort, too, in the knowledge there was one other person mad enough to thumb his nose at the Vichy French. There was no doubt in Rennie's mind that, in registering their non-co-operation, he and Bishop were probably in for a rough ride. But better that than tamely accepting internment.

Rennie did not consider himself a saint but he did regard his word as his bond. There were no circumstances in which he would make a promise without every intention of keeping it. He might laughingly have admitted that the result was some personal parsimony in making promises but, in this, he would have been belittling himself.

He made no show of his honesty, nor how he prized it, but it ran deep. He set little store on money or material possessions. His earthly treasure was his independence to act and think honorably. Self interest never came into it. Self respect had everything to do with it.

For this reason, there was never even a remote possibility that he might have signed a slip of paper acquiescing to his own loss of liberty. He was grateful to the French Navy for having snatched him from the ocean, but he had no intention of enduring the enforced hospitality of the Dakar authorities for one minute longer than was absolutely necessary.

There was to be no immediate opportunity for escape, however, for Rennie or Bishop. They soon discovered that the hell-hole to which they had been taken had a name, Fort Cap des Tigres. They were to spend a week there, most of it in the dark stinking cell below ground.

Twice a day, they were brought food: bowls of rice mixed with high-tasting boiled fish, plus a lump of coarse bread. Three times a day, they received mugs of muddy unsweetened coffee.

The only occasions they were allowed out of the cell were when they were taken daily to be asked the same dreary questions by small groups of faceless men from this Bureau or another: the Bureau of Immigration, the Bureau of Colonial Administration, the Bureau of Internal Security, the Bureau of Colonial Affairs.

The questions seldom varied as far as Rennie was concerned. Why had he gone to South Africa? How did he get there? Why was he returning to England? What ships had he served on? Was he not, in fact, concealing his true identity? Did he not realize how difficult he was making things for himself by refusing to answer simple questions?

Bishop faced the same kind of interrogation although, in his case, the questions were more blatantly military. They knew all about HMS *Wyvis*. But what was the frequency of her anti-submarine patrols? What sea areas were covered? What naval vessels were maintained on the

Freetown base? What kind of radar and Asdic gear did *Wyvis* have? What were the new convoy procedures?

Both men maintained a resolute silence throughout all their questioning. Their interrogators reacted with varying degrees of anger, impatience and threat, but at no time was actual physical violence used. At the end of the week, the pair was given shaving gear and a change of clothing, taken to an ablutions compound off the main court and parade-ground, and told to clean themselves up.

They luxuriated in the plentiful supply of water and the feel of fresh clothes against their bodies. Then they were escorted up three flights of stone stairs inside a tower overlooking the sea. They could hear the wash of the Atlantic rollers against the narrow strip of sandy beach at the base of the promontory on which the fort was built. The sound of the surf had been muted in their subterranean cell but, here, it funnelled up the stairway well of the outer tower with a hissing echo.

Reaching a broad gallery, the Senegalese guards prodded Rennie and Bishop with their rifles along a passageway. A Senegalese stood on guard outside the furthest door.

This door opened from the inside and a short dapper man in a white Panama suit emerged. He had a shiny bald forehead, and what sparse hair he had was gleaming with oil and brushed flat across the crown of his head.

"Ah, les Anglais!" he said with a sparrow-like brightness. "Colonel Boudin is waiting. You may go in."

He ushered Rennie and Bishop into a high-ceilinged room. It was partially panelled with dark timber but the outside wall was dressed stone and, through one deeply recessed window, Rennie caught a glimpse of ocean. The floor was covered in heavy-duty green lino and the room meagerly furnished except for an ornate table desk, behind which sat a man.

The huge desk would have dwarfed most people, but not this man. Even sitting down, he dominated his surroundings. He was huge without being fat. His massive shoulders were slightly rounded, giving him almost a hunched-back appearance. His grey hair was cropped to a uniform shortness, covering his oval-shaped head like the stubby spikes of a wire brush. He wore a white shirt, open at the neck.

"Ah, les Anglais!" he said, parroting his assistant's

words of a moment before. "Get a couple of chairs for the gentlemen, Marchant. There is no reason why they should have to stand up while I tell them of their fate."

The man in the white suit took two straight wooden chairs from against a wall and placed them in front of the big desk.

"Asseyez-vous, Messieurs," he invited. Bishop and Rennie sat down.

Rennie could not take his eyes away from Colonel Boudin. There was a fascinating ugliness about the man. It was as if his maker had chiselled his face out of granite and abandoned the job half-way through. The nose was twisted and flattened, suggesting that at some time in his life Boudin had had a head-on collision with a double-decker bus. The thought conjured up in Rennie's mind the mental picture of a wrecked bus. Boudin gave the impression of being unbreakable.

Boudin smiled. That is, he extended the corners of his mouth in a manner which revealed a row of teeth. One canine had a glistening gold cap.

"Well, gentlemen," he said, "you seem to have proved an unwanted irritation to several Government departments. Your lives were saved by our Navy but you have shown no sign of gratitude and no desire to co-operate with the Authorities. What do you have to say for yourselves?"

It was Bishop who replied.

"We did not ask to be rescued by a French ship but, since we were, we believe we at least have the right to be treated as well as prisoners of war and according to the standards laid down by the Geneva Convention. Instead, we have been treated like common criminals . . ."

Boudin held up a huge hand and waved it slackly.

"You have no rights," he said. "You forfeited these the moment you refused to comply with the standard immigration regulations for foreigners. So say no more about rights."

Bishop pushed his chair back and stood up. The sudden movement drew a reaction from the two Senegalese soldiers, who had remained just inside the door. Boudin waved them away.

"Sir," said Bishop icily, "as a Colonel, I believe . . . As a military man, you must know that Mr. Rennie and I are honor-bound to withhold any information concerning ourselves, our ships and our activities which is likely to be of use to an enemy. That is the reason why we have not co-operated with your people and that is why we will not be bullied into co-operating now."

"Bravo," said Boudin. "I applaud your sense of duty." There was, however, a lack of conviction in his words. His demeanor suggested that Bishop bored him.

"Have you anything to add?" he asked Rennie languidly. "Do you honestly think that, between the pair of you, you can supply the smallest snippet of information which could be of military value to us or anybody else?"

"I'm sure that we don't know anything that you don't already know yourselves," said Rennie affably, "but I'm in complete agreement with Lieutenant-Commander Bishop. We don't mind you asking questions, we just regret that you find it necessary to do so and to expect answers."

A semblance of a smile crossed Boudin's face.

"Your case was well judged by the others," he said. "You are a pair of irritants. Minor irritants, perhaps, but irritants nonetheless. I can't think why they passed the buck to me to get rid of you."

"Get rid of us?" said Bishop. His tone was one of shock.

Boudin grinned.

"Oh, not in a permanent sense, Commander Bishop. We have not yet reached the stage of liquidating undesirables, although the temptation is always there. No, we follow a good old Civil Service dictum when we are presented with a disagreeable problem for which no solution is apparent. We file it in an obscure place and hope it will remain lost until it becomes someone else's problem."

He lifted two documents from the desk and waved them at Bishop.

"These papers should take care of you two for the foreseeable future," he said. "All they need is my signature. They are papers of authority ordering that you be placed in the custody of the Commandant of Fort Raphael on L'Ile de Voleurs until such time as your credentials for entry into the country can be satsifactorily established by the Bureau of Colonial Affairs. That could take a very long time."

With a flourish, he signed the two documents in turn. Then he handed the papers to the man in the white suit.

"Take care of the transport arrangements, Marchant." He raised his great bulk from behind the desk and gave a slight bow towards Bishop and Rennie. "Good afternoon, gentlemen. With luck, we shall never meet again."

Chapter Four

WHEN Portuguese navigators first made explorative forays along the coast of West Africa, they searched for the openings of great inland waterways such as the Congo and the Niger, the Senegal and the Gambia Rivers. The great rivers were the key to trade with the great unknown hinterland and the highways along which the riches of the vast continent could be borne.

Pedro Cuintahiljas believed, when he dropped anchor off L'Ile de Voleurs in 1453, that he had discovered a great new estuary. He had, in fact, discovered a heavily silted bay where two small and quite unnavigable rivers discharged their waters through a filter of tangled swamps into the sea.

In spite of the island's unimportance, commerically or strategically, L'Ile de Voleurs remained a Portuguese possession until the late seventeenth century, when it was seized by the Dutch. Thereafter, it was occupied by French and British in turn, finally reverting to the French in the Napoleonic Wars.

The island was little more than a mile-long sandspit, shaped like a boomerang. A carbuncle of a hill dominated the middle, with two legs dropping away to sand flats at the extreme ends. A small protected harbor had been built under the hill within the elbow-like crook of the boomerang.

The place had been used as a way-station for slaves being shipped to the Americas. The island's harbor and the naval fortifications on the seaward side of the hill had, however, been constructed by convict labor, and it was because of the convicts that it had become known as the Island of Thieves.

The somber prison building and the two-hundred-year-old Slave House had been allowed to fall derelict but, after the defeat of France in 1940, a camp had been built under the shadow of the prison walls to house political internees, ostensibly to await trial. But no one had ever been brought to face trial from L'Ile de Voleurs. Once transported there, the prisoners were conveniently forgotten, like so many embarrassing skeletons locked in an out-of-the-way closet.

Rennie's first sight of the island was from the deck of the supply tender which made the once-weekly trip from Dakar. He and Bishop had been brought up on deck by their guards after the tender had berthed in the small harbor.

They were marched past the small Customs House and Harbor Master's office, past a small Roman Catholic chapel and a mosque standing side by side, a huddle of yellow ochre houses, and past the crumbling Slave House, where tiny doors at ground level led to windowless cellars. Inside here, slaves had been chained to the walls and supporting pillars while they awaited transport. Two curved stone stairways led to the second storey, where a balcony terrace ran the whole length of the building. In former days, the wide-windowed rooms of the top floor had housed the slave masters in rather more comfort than their unfortunate charges.

The path continued past a straggling military barracks terraced against the hillside and then descended towards the ocean side of the island. Naval batteries had been built into the highest reaches of the hill, facing the Atlantic. To the south, the land dropped dramatically and was dominated by a long low building built hard against the sea. This was the old prison. It had been heavily eroded by the constant sweep of Atlantic rollers and part of the outer wall had collapsed and fallen into the sea. Like the Slave House it was now derelict, but on the sandy spit of land towards the southern tip of the island were four orderly rows of sectional huts. They were fenced off from the rest of the island but open to the sea.

The small encampment was journey's end for Rennie and Bishop. They arrived at the path's end through a natural avenue of palm trees to find further progress barred by an eight-foot-high wire gate. An elderly French corporal, who looked as if he hadn't shaved for two days and who spoke no English, kept them standing in the guard-room hut for more than an hour while he filled in countless forms. The man was sweating freely and blobs of perspiration kept running down his nose from his forehead, making ink-runs and staining the documents over which he labored.

Finally, he handed one set of papers to the British pair's Senegalese escort and dismissed them. They went off laughing with each other like children who had been let out early from school.

The Corporal issued Rennie and Bishop each with a tatty towel, a bar of coarse soap, a tin plate, a mug, a spoon, and a blanket. Each item had to be signed for separately. Then he led the way to one of the sectioned huts. He pointed to a door and signalled with a thumb that they should enter.

Rennie climbed the four wooden steps and opened the door. The section was about fourteen feet long by eight feet wide. It contained four wood and rattan beds and very little else. A man was stretched out on his back in the furthest of these beds. He looked up in surprise as the door opened.

Bishop followed Rennie into the room. The Corporal climbed the steps and pushed the door shut after him.

"Qui êtes vous?" asked the man on the bed.

"Nous sommes Anglais," said Rennie. "Et vous?"

The man leapt from the bed and, beaming, held out a hand to Rennie.

"English? Well, what do you know? Welcome to the Club. I'm Richard Hobart." He had an American accent.

"I'm John Rennie. This is Lieutenant-Commander Bishop, Royal Navy."

"Pleased to meet you, Commander," said Hobart shaking hands with Bishop. "Gosh, you don't know how good it is to be able to speak in English again! Jean-Paul speaks it pretty good but my French is no sweat, so we speak in French most of the time."

"Jean-Paul?" queried Rennie.

"Our room-mate. Jean-Paul Mercier. He's French Navy. The bastard, Junot, has him in the sweat-tank again. They've really got it in for him."

"Sweat-tank?" said Bishop with puzzlement.

"Sure," said Hobart, "sweat-tank! You never seen any of them old Devil's Island movies, Commander? Well this is straight out of one. They got a corrugated box out there in the yard—there's barely room for a man to get inside it—and that's where they've got Jean-Paul. It's his own fault. I keep telling him not to rub Junot the wrong way, but he calls him names straight out to his face, like Vichy arse-licker and Hitler-lover . . . And Junot just has him thrown in the sweat-tank and keeps him there till sundown."

"Who is Junot?" asked Rennie.

"You ain't met him?" said Hobart with surprise. "Well, you sure as hell will. This is Major Junot's island. He is the commandant of the military at Fort Raphael. He runs this place. He runs everything."

Hobart, who was over six feet tall, nodded towards the two beds nearest the door.

"You'd better help yourself to a bed and make yourselves at home. And you can tell me how come a coupla Englishmen wound up in this Alcatraz with palm trees. Except for me, all the other inmates are Frenchies."

Bishop frowned at the American.

"I hope you appreciate, Mr.—er—Hobart, that we can't tell you a great deal more than we have told the French. If we'd been prepared to blab about ourselves, we wouldn't be in this bloody place, would we?"

Hobart's open friendly face registered surprise at Bishop's reproachful tone of voice. Rennie grinned to himself.

"We're ship survivors," he explained to Hobart, his eyes and expression telling the American not to be upset by Bishop's manner. "A U-boat got the ship I was on. And the Commander's. A French destroyer picked us out of the Atlantic and put us ashore at Dakar. There's not much more to tell."

"But why bring you here? The people in this camp are mainly politicos—French military who tried to get out and join the Free French, or civilians who advocated secession from Vichy and throwing in with the Allies."

"How about you?" answered Rennie. "When did Vichy start getting nasty with Americans?"

"We stayed on talking terms with Vichy—but don't let that fool you that we approve of what they are doing. It has just suited Uncle Sam to know what was going on, that's all."

"It doesn't explain where you fit in," said Bishop. "Surely, there's an American consulate in Dakar. Why haven't they got you out of here?"

"Because they don't know I'm here," said Hobart. "I was on my way upcountry to Tambacounda when they arrested me. That was three months ago. They've kept me under wraps ever since. I was accused of being a spy."

"Are you?" asked Rennie quietly.

Hobart returned Rennie's firm stare.

"I'm a geologist," he said, challenging Rennie to disbelieve it if he liked. Rennie smiled, as if a great deal more had been communicated by the unwavering stare than Hobart's simple statement. Rennie's eyes flashed back an unspoken message of his own. It was a signal of understanding, an agreement to suspend the whole truth for the time being.

"What made the French think you were a spy?" he asked.

Hobart smiled.

"They seemed to think that most of the people I had been seeing in Dakar were not wholly loyal to Vichy and that I was stirring up some kind of mischief for the Authorities."

"Which, of course, was nonsense. You're not the least bit interested in politics. The only people you saw were those that you had to see in the course of your work as a geologist?"

"You're a very sharp man, John Rennie," said Hobart, his smile getting even wider. "That's exactly the way it was. Unfortunately, the French weren't exactly convinced. They wouldn't let me go. On the other hand, they couldn't prove anything. I was obviously a great embarrassment to them. The head of the Vichy version of their Gestapo told me so himself—Colonel Boudin . . ."

"Colonel Boudin?" said Bishop.

"Yes, you know him?" asked Hobart.

"He signed the papers sending us here," said Rennie. "He said we were irritants—minor irritants but irritants nonetheless."

"*You* are irritants. *I* was an embarrassment," said Hobart. "Boudin said that there were two courses open to him as far as I was concerned. He said it would be a simple matter to arrange an 'accident' for me. Geologists were always getting lost in deserts, murdered by bandits, bitten by snakes, or falling off cliffs. He said that an 'accident' would be no trouble at all but that it was rather a drastic solution to the problem. Better, he said, to follow the old bureaucratic procedure of losing me in the files. The accusations against me would remain until proof was found one way or the other which established my guilt or my innocence. He said it would take a hell of a long time, either way."

"More or less what he told us," said Bishop. "Well, I suppose we'll just have to make the best of it."

Rennie threw him a questioning look. He said nothing for the moment, but squeezed past Bishop and went to the window. It looked out over a strip of vegetable allotment where a dozen or so men were working with wooden hoes. Beyond a clump of palm trees was a wisp of sandy beach and blue sea.

"A better view than from our last dungeon," he said, "but I would rather have London on a foggy day." He turned and faced Hobart. "What chance do we have of getting off this island?"

The American looked at Rennie with interest.

"Well now," he said. "They say a good swimmer has a fifty-fifty chance of making it to the shore but that, once he gets there, he only has one chance in a thousand of making it alive through the swamps that lie all round the bay. That's why they hardly bother to guard you here. That and fear of what Junot says he'll do to any man caught trying to escape."

"What would he do?"

"Well, he hasn't spelled it out to me. Just hinted that anybody trying to escape will be punished like Foreign Legion deserters. He was never in the Legion himself but he spent a lot of time up in Morocco and Algeria with the Army. I gather that the Legion used to do something nasty with bayonets to deserters. Nobody here has so far had the courage to make a run and find out what."

"Well, we'd better plan not to get caught," said Rennie.

"You mean you're really set on getting out?" asked Hobart.

"Why not? If I'm only a minor irritation, surely they're not going to miss me all that much. I didn't ask to be picked up by the French destroyer. I'd just as soon have taken my chances with the ocean."

"If you want to get clear of this damned island, you may have to take your chances with the ocean," said Hobart, "but you can count on one thing."

"What?"

The American grinned.

"You can count on me being there right alongside of you. I don't plan to stick around here any longer than I have to. And you can bank on Jean-Paul, too. We thought about stealing a perogue and trying to make it to the Gambia River, but these overgrown canoes need a lot of paddling."

He turned to face Bishop.

"How about you, Commander? Are you with us?"

Bishop looked from one to the other with a face like the wrath of God. There was no doubt in his mind that he was the only person of any consequence in the room, and the other two were pre-supposing that he would just fit in with any hare-brained scheme they concocted.

"Your determination to escape does you credit, gentlemen," he said icily, "but if you think that I'm going to risk my life on a stupid piece of bravado, you'd better think again. You're talking like a couple of overgrown schoolboys. Good heavens, I haven't been in the place ten minutes and you're rabbiting on as if there weren't a moment to lose. I really know nothing about either of you and you expect me to fall in line with the first idiotic scheme that comes into your heads."

Rennie groaned.

"For crying out loud! Nothing's been decided!"

"If you don't want any part of it, all you've got to do is say so," said Hobart. Bishop looked him squarely in the eye.

"You are a civilian, Mr. Hobart, and probably know a great deal about geology—but you have no qualifications that I know of which entitle you to exercise leadership over a commissioned officer in the Royal Navy. The same goes for Mr. Rennie. If an escape enterprise is to be planned—and I am certainly in favor of the idea—then it should be planned and led by someone with the competence and authority to make sure it is successful."

"That person, of course, is you," said Hobart.

"If there is an officer senior to me in the camp, then naturally I would defer to his wishes. But if we are to confine the—er—enterprise to the occupants of this room, then I would have to insist that I be given sole charge of the operation."

Hobart was staring at Bishop in disbelief.

"Bullshit!" he said.

Bishop drew back as if he had been slapped in the face.

"I beg your pardon."

"Bullshit!" repeated Hobart. "That is what is coming out of your mouth, Admiral. Bullshit! You don't want to play unless you can be leader of the band. Well, let me tell you something, the stripes on your arm don't count for a goddamned thing around here. If anybody breaks outa here, it'll be a few guys who play it all-for-one and one-for-all. There ain't gonna be any place for prima donnas wanting to call all the shots."

Bishop's mouth was working angrily.

"Well, damn you!" he snarled. "Do what you bloody well like. I won't try to stop you but don't count on me to lift my little finger to help!"

Pushing angrily past Rennie, he went over to the bed nearest the door and sat down with his back to the other two. Rennie gave a despairing shake of his head. There was a megalomaniac streak in Bishop which was beyond his comprehension.

"Does he speak for you?" Hobart asked Rennie.

"I speak for me," said Rennie. "And I'm with you."

"That just leaves Jean-Paul," said Hobart.

At that moment, Jean-Paul Mercier was undergoing more than the hundred-degree torment of the heat in the sweat-tank. He was mentally punishing himself with the agony of self-recrimination and doubt. All his sufferings he had brought on himself because of romantic ideals. Why, when it would have been so much easier to abandon these ideals, had he clung to them and expected them to sustain him through all manner of pain and humiliation?

Why didn't he just give up? Why didn't he just conform, as so many others like him conformed and kept their misgivings to themselves? You're a fool, Jean-Paul Mercier, he told himself over and over again. One man on his own can achieve nothing. They'll let you rot, perhaps even kill you, and at the end of it all you will have achieved precisely nothing.

It seemed to him now that if he had wanted to make an effective protest against the Government which was collaborating so wholeheartedly with the Nazi conquerors of France, he should have proceeded by stealth. He should have kept his feelings of outrage to himself and planned ways and means of reaching Allied territory and offering his services to de Gaulle.

It was too late now. Arlette had warned him that it would end up like this. She insisted she felt the same way as he did about Vichy's Nazification of France and the African territories, but she was vehemently opposed to public action of any kind. Open confrontation was not the way.

"You don't charge a wild elephant head-on," she had argued. "You don't even let him know you are there. Then you strike when he's least expecting it. You are so naïve, Jean-Paul. An innocent! For you, everything is black or it is white. It's right or it's wrong. You can never be subtle in anything you do. Even when you make love to me, it is all fire and straight up the front. There is no surprise, no finesse. You are hungry and so you must gorge yourself. It's as simple as that."

He had to admit the truth of this. He knew that to his wife he was as transparent as plain glass. He could keep no secret thought from her. She knew precisely how he would react to any given situation. He was like a book which she knew by heart. Arlette, on the other hand, was a constant mystery to him. He seemed unable to tell in advance whether she would be pleased or displeased by anything he did. Her moods were mercurial, so that he did not know from one moment to the next whether he would be in favor or otherwise. And he knew he would do anything for her rather than experience the *otherwise*. She had the power to enslave him totally—and he wanted nothing more than to be totally enslaved by her.

The three years of marriage to Arlette had been tinged, as far as Jean-Paul was concerned, with a constant feeling of surprise that this lovely creature was his wife. She could have had any one of two dozen admirers of exalted rank and better prospects, but she had chosen him; then a mere ensign in the Naval Cyphers and Communications Department in Algiers. Her father, Admiral Bousquet, had made it plain from the start that he thought she could have done better for herself—but she had stood up to her father and got her way, as she usually did. Jean-Paul had not questioned his luck too closely. Arlette was his and that was all that mattered.

Only occasionally did Jean-Paul have qualms that he

and Arlette were intellectually from quite different molds. He oversimplified the reason for their minds working on separate tracks by putting it down to differences between male and female psyches. In any case, he believed so firmly in the attraction of opposites as a fact of life that a lack of common ground for a meeting of their minds gave him no cause for concern.

From the very start, he had been attracted by her looks and her body. The magnetism which she exercised over him was intensely physical. It precluded the need for spoken communication or any other distraction from the compulsion to possess and be possessed.

By allowing Jean-Paul to possess her body, Arlette had become the possessor of Jean-Paul's mind and soul. It was an arrangement which seemed to suit them both. He enjoyed his enslavement because of the intimate pleasures which were rationed out to him exclusively as a reward. She drew pleasure from her power.

But it had gone sour on that last leave in Algiers. Was it only six weeks ago? There had been a succession of stormy scenes—over politics, for God's sake! What the hell had politics to do with the fire in their bodies?

She had warned him repeatedly that he must not let his hatred for the Vichy gang drive him to some spontaneous act of indiscretion. He in turn had criticized both her and her father for the way they not only fraternized with the worst Vichy Nazis but the way their cloying subservience bordered on adulation.

Jean-Paul had been sickened to the point of revulsion when old man Bousquet had accepted the job on the Directorate of Port Administration from which a one-time friend had been ham-handedly removed. Letroux had dared to question the latest piece of political gangsterism perpetrated by Vichy and had been arrested and badly treated. He must have been hurt to the core when old Bousquet took over his job with an alacrity that was breath-taking, and proceeded to effect the politically motivated appointments against which he had rebelled.

Jean-Paul tried to re-arrange his stiff and aching body within the cruelly limited confines of the sweat-tank. His lips were puffed and dry and his dehydrated tongue was swollen and raw in his mouth. Oh, God, was this day never going to end?

He recalled now Roget's threat on the *Marande* that he

would break him. Well, I'm nearly broken now, thought Jean-Paul. This is my body broken for what?

The only satisfaction afforded to Jean-Paul after his arrest and temporary imprisonment in barracks in Dakar had been the reaction of the naval brass to the whole affair. They had left Roget in no doubt at all that, as far as they were concerned, he was the villian of the piece. He could kiss his promotion hopes good-bye. He was immediately relieved of his command and hints were thrown that he would be lucky if he ever aspired to command anything bigger than a sand-dredger in what was left of his career.

Roget's crime was in not treating Jean-Paul's breach of his authority as a matter of ship-board discipline. Most certainly it was a very serious breach of discipline by Mercier, but was Captain Roget aware that Mercier was the son-in-law of Admiral Bousquet, who had friends in the highest places? No one on the Naval Command staff had the slightest intention of aiding and abetting Roget's desire to commit professional suicide by making a martyr of Mercier. They had consequently chosen a course of action of which Pontius Pilate would surely have approved.

They had relieved Roget of his command, as insurance against Bousquet arranging earthquakes from above, and they had sent Mercier to the Department of Internal Security for screening and security assessment. Colonel Boudin, who ran the Department of Internal Security, was known to be a close friend of Bousquet's. So Mercier's fate was left to Boudin's discretion. The young lieutenant's commission as an officer in the French Navy had been temporarily suspended, pending the outcome of Boudin's investigation.

The Navy Command had confidently assumed that Mercier would be returned to them within a fortnight with a clean bill of health. It had come as a shock to them when Boudin had furnished them with a personal report, which stated that Mercier had been found to be a self-declared security risk and unwilling to conform to naval discipline. He had, therefore, been detained under Colony Emergency Regulations and would be the subject of medical and psychological inquiries of an exhaustive nature.

As he crouched uncomfortably in the sweat-tank, Jean-Paul reflected grimly on the extent of his father-in-law's influence. How was it that an old man, long ago retired from the Navy, and living hundreds of miles away in Algiers, could still carry such weight on his name that high-ranking officers trembled at the possibility of causing him offense? "Old Incorruptible" they called him, but how much of it was true? He had reached the corridors of power by the patronage of others, and he had maintained his power by practicing patronage in every corner of the empire.

Bousquet may well have been a hero of France, but he was no hero to Jean-Paul. He was a God-player, and Jean-Paul had the most profound suspicions of any man who justified his every act by saying it was for his country. Bousquet spoke much about the honor of France, but seldom had made a decision that was not in the interests of Bousquet. He, of course, identified his own interests so closely with that of France that he saw the two as indivisible. To Jean-Paul, this was self-delusion on a grand scale.

What Jean-Paul could neither understand nor forgive was his father-in-law's acceptance of defeat by Germany. His name was such that he could have rallied the whole of North Africa behind him in rejection of the surrender. Army, Navy and Air Force leaders in the colonies had looked to him to say the word which would have kept substantial military forces still fighting for the Free World —but Bousquet had spurned the opportunity.

"Marshal Pétain has spoken for France," he said. "We must honor the pledges he has given to Germany in the name of France."

This wasn't how Jean-Paul saw the situation at all. He saw Pétain as a man with a German pistol at his head trying to get the best deal he could for Metropolitan France. He could hardly urge the colonies to continue the war alone, but the old warhorse was probably hoping like hell they would ignore his words and do just that.

Bousquet had continued to give Vichy moral support as the regime in North Africa became more and more repressive, even sending cables of congratulation to his old pals in Dakar when they had beaten off de Gaulle's abortive attempt to take the port. Jean-Paul had been involved in that and had been sick to his heart. Frenchmen fighting Frenchmen, and he had no doubts that he was on the wrong side. He had vowed then that he would never again fire on a friend, even if it meant finishing up in front of a firing-squad.

Well, thanks to the unholy respect for the name of Bousquet, it hadn't come to a firing-squad. Arrows of pain shot through his back muscles and spine as Jean-Paul once again tried to redistribute his body and legs in the cramped space. Despair filled him. Maybe a firing-squad would have been preferable to this torture.

He recoiled against the metal of the sweat-tank as he heard the outside bolt suddenly moved. The door above him was removed and a flood of blinding sunlight dazzled down on him, forcing him to shield his eyes.

"Get him out!" clipped a voice.

Two pairs of ebony hands lifted Jean-Paul by legs and shoulders and deposited him roughly on the baked earth beside the tank. The two Senegalese soldiers stepped aside and Jean-Paul, still dazzled by the light, saw through the mists swimming in front of his eyes the immaculately uniformed figure of Major Junot. He stood, feet apart and hands on hips, riding whip protruding from one fist at an angle to his body. His riding breeches looked, as they usually did, as if they had just been steamed and pressed. His brown knee-length boots were burnished to a glassy polish.

"Stand up, Mercier."

Jean-Paul struggled to his feet, but waves of giddiness hit him. He fell to his hands and knees. Gritting his teeth, he made a second attempt. This time he managed to stay on his feet but he swayed like a drunken man.

"I've got news for you, Mercier," said Junot. "You're going to have a visitor."

Jean-Paul said nothing. He stared at Junot trying to keep him in focus.

"Well, aren't you pleased, Mercier? I said a visitor."

Junot prodded Jean-Paul with the handle of his riding whip. He promptly fell over. Junot laughed.

"What's wrong, Mercier? Feeling weak at the knees? Can't you stand up like a man when I'm talking to you?"

Jean-Paul scrambled to his feet and made a lurching step to keep his balance. He continued to sway unsteadily.

"We'll have to get you cleaned up," said Junot. "What would your wife say if she saw you like this?"

"My wife?" mumbled Jean-Paul.

"She's in Dakar. Must have a bit of pull, too. The

Navy are laying on a boat to bring her down specially. The name Bousquet obviously carries a lot more weight in Dakar than it does on this island."

Jean-Paul attempted a smile of derision.

"Don't you shake in your boots at the name of Bousquet, Major? The old octopus has tentacles everywhere."

Junot's eyes gleamed.

"I'm Army, Mercier. No Navy has-been puts the wind up me. Certainly not a senile bag of crap like Bousquet. He may have been the darling of France in nineteen hundred and eight, but as far as I am concerned he's a museum piece, a fossil. I'm the boss on this island."

"You will permit my wife to see me?"

"But of course. I'm told she's very pretty. She will make an interesting dinner companion for me tomorrow evening. I have been told to give her every co-operation and, who knows, she may have favors to ask of me. How far do you think she will go Mercier, to win my good graces?"

"You're a bastard, Junot." cried Jean-Paul.

Junot was unruffled.

"Of course I am, Mercier. Ask anyone who has ever served under me, from Morocco to Saigon. They'll tell you what a bastard I am. It means I have a reputation to uphold—and I'm certainly not going to spoil it on account of your wife or her high and mighty friends."

He turned to the two Senegalese.

"Bring this betrayer of his flag to his hut," he ordered.

The soldiers assisted Jean-Paul towards the hut by half-dragging him over the baked ground of the square.

Junot mounted the few steps, pushed open the door and strode in, his riding whip under his arm. Three pairs of eyes turned to stare at him.

"You will stand when a French officer enters the room!" Junot snapped.

Rennie, Bishop and Hobart got sheepishly to their feet.

"Sorry," said Rennie with an insolent smile. "I didn't hear you knock." Junot glared at him.

"I am Major Junot, Commandent of Fort Raphael."

"Well, what Junot!" said Rennie.

The pun brought Rennie a warning glance from Hobart and no reaction at all from Junot. He took two more steps into the room and then turned and looked Rennie up and down.

"Your name?" he asked.

"Rennie."

"Rennie," repeated Junot. "I shall remember it."

Without warning, his arm went up and he brought the riding whip down in a flashing arc. The single cut drew blood in a line from Rennie's temple to his chin. He staggered backwards, hand raised to fend off another blow.

"I say . . ." began Bishop, but fell silent before the venomous glare flung at him by Junot.

"That will help you to remember my name and speak it only with respect," said Junot to Rennie. He turned to the door. "What's keeping you out there with Mercier?" he bawled.

The Senegalese brought Jean-Paul in and dumped him on his bed. He lay there, looking up at the others. Junot prodded him with his whip.

"You have company, Mercier. Wasn't it kind of me to put them in here with you? Look, two Englishmen. You love the English, don't you? That's why you're here, isn't it? Because you didn't want to fire at them. Well, get them to clean you up. We want you all spruced up for your wife tomorrow, don't we?"

He turned and marched out of the room. The two Senegalese followed and closed the door.

Hobart made a sighing sound, as if he had been holding his breath for five minutes and had just been given the OK to exhale.

"*That* was Major Junot," he declared.

Rennie was dabbing at his face with a towel. He looked thoughtfully at Hobart.

"Nice sort of chap, isn't he?" he said. He looked across at Jean-Paul, who seemed weak and dazed. The other's condition made Rennie forget the weal of fire on his own face. He moved to Jean-Paul's side.

"Hey, you don't look in too good shape. Are you hurt?"

"Je ne suis pas blessé," murmured Jean-Paul. He hunched round on to his left elbow and stuck out his right hand. It trembled slightly.

"Glad to know you, Englishman." He gripped Rennie's hand and held on to it. "I am Jean-Paul Mercier. That pig has wounded your face . . . Does it not give much pain?"

"It's not too bad," said Rennie. "I've done worse shaving."

Jean-Paul did not at first understand what Rennie meant because the other's idiomatic English had to be pieced together mentally. Then he realized the Englishman was making a jocular dismissal of his injury. He felt a warm glow of comradeship for the stranger before him.

Hobart appeared at Rennie's shoulder and smiled down at Jean-Paul.

"This is John Rennie, Jean-Paul. He's crazier than me and almost as crazy as you. Wasn't in here five minutes and he was talking about getting off the island."

Less than an hour before, Jean-Paul had considered himself a broken man and, even now, his aching body and limbs cried out to him to end his futile resistance and accept defeat. Now, he was no longer alone. He was no longer separated from Hobart's sure support and, in addition, a fresh ally had been presented out of the blue. His spirits soared. Then he glanced in Bishop's direction.

"And the other Englishman?" he asked.

It was Rennie who replied.

"Lieutenant-Commander Bishop had reservations that we mightn't give enough thought to how we could best get off the island . . . But I'm sure that if we discuss all the possibilities adequately and can all agree on a plan . . ."

Rennie had no wish to exclude Bishop, and it was for this reason that he was now offering the *Wyvis*' captain an olive branch. Bishop chose to ignore it.

Rennie could see from his face that Bishop was wrestling with his pride. He wanted back in the fold but some devil in him wanted it to be on his terms.

"I told you before that you could count me out," he said stiffly. "Any escape is ultimately the responsibility of the senior officer. If you choose not to acknowledge my seniority in this or any other matter, then I cannot be party to anything you undertake."

"Don't you think you're being just a bit touchy about protocol?" said Rennie. "This isn't the ward-room of a battleship. It's a godforsaken African hell-hole that nobody ever heard about. Hobart and the Frenchman here probably know a hell of a lot more but it than either of us, which makes us junior partners. Don't you think we should be talking about *how* we get out instead of arguing about whose responsibility it is?"

"He's right, Admiral," said Hobart. "The priority is *how* we get out. If we don't make it, we all carry the can."

Jean-Paul was looking from one to the other in bewilderment. Bishop remained sullenly obstinate.

"It's my duty to insist that you submit any escape plan to me for approaval. If I don't like it, I shall say so. In the event of you going ahead in opposition to my wishes, then I shall be absolved of any responsibility for the consequences."

Rennie stared at him in disgust.

"You can go and get stuffed, you self-righteous bastard! I don't need your approval for anything I do." He half turned away from Bishop, who had no intention of leaving it at that. He took two strides round Jean-Paul's bed and whirled Rennie round by the shoulder. He grabbed Rennie's shirt-front.

"Don't you dare use your gutter language on me," he snarled. He ground the words out through gritted teeth. He was white with fury.

With an air of infinite weariness, Rennie tried to brush the hand away but Bishop held firm. His grip was almost maniacal.

"Go away," Rennie said, his voice even and without threat. "Go away. I don't want to fight with you."

"You'll damned well apologize!" persisted Bishop. He was so charged with emotion that the words came out in a screech.

Rennie, who was shorter than Bishop but of far stronger muscular build, placed a brawny hand round Bishop's wrist and firmly removed it.

"Go away," he said, with a little more edge to his voice. With a look on his face that suggested he might burst into tears. Bishop retreated hesitantly. He sat down on his bed and remained there, his eyes fixed on the others in woebegone fashion.

Hobart and Jean-Paul had watched silently, their discomfort written on their faces. The incident had soured the atmosphere of the hut.

"I'm sorry," said Rennie, looking down at Jean-Paul. The Frenchman made a sympathetic grimace.

"Perhaps tomorrow it will be different. Eh?"

Hobart seized on Jean-Paul's remark.

"Hey, yes, Jean-Paul . . . Tomorrow. What was that that Junot said about your wife? About cleaning you up?"

Even Jean-Paul had momentarily forgotten Junot's surprise news, and he had been too befuddled to grasp what significance it might have.

"Maybe she's coming to bail you out," said Hobart, after Jean-Paul had imparted what little he knew about Arlette's imminent arrival.

Jean-Paul shook his head. No, it was more likely that Arlette had just heard he was in trouble and had used her father's influence to find a way of seeing him. Either that, or old Bousquet himself was at the back of it. The thought made Jean-Paul uneasy. The old man never did anything for anybody unless there were strings attached.

Chapter Five

THE afternoon sun was baking the dried patch of lawn in front of Junot's bungalow but the east-facing veranda was entirely in shade. The airs of a cooling north-easterly ruffled the corners of the papier-grass cover on the cane table, around which three people were seated. Junot was as immaculate as ever, not a button out of place. Jean-Paul sat on his left, eyes downcast, toying with the glass of iced lemon squash which had been poured from the large jug on the table in front of him. The drink was a luxury, a concession bestowed by Junot in the manner of a treat for a schoolboy being entertained in the headmaster's study.

Opposite Jean-Paul sat Arlette. She looked lovelier than ever. The breeze played at the wisps of her short blond hair. She had a natural, almost boyish beauty, rather than that achieved by careful grooming and subtle aids. She wore a simple white dress, cut low to reveal the firm swell of her breasts and providing an enticing contrast to the smooth bronze of her skin. It angered Jean-Paul the way Junot could not keep his eyes from the gap at the top of Arlette's dress. The man was almost slavering with lust.

Junot had over-ruled Arlette's request to talk with her husband alone. His compromise had been to chair the meeting on the veranda and order the lemon drinks as a token of his graciousness and his desire to conduct affairs in a civilized manner. It did not dismay him at all that Jean-Paul's obstinacy was destroying the object of his wife's visit.

"It seems that your long journey has been a waste of time, Madame," Junot said to Arlette. "Your husband has decided to behave like a mule. He seems deaf to reason and much more impervious to your charm than I could ever be."

Arlette smiled at Junot without any warmth in her eyes.

"I have until tomorrow. Perhaps with a day to think over my father's proposition, Jean-Paul will change his mind."

"I think that your father's terms are a great deal more generous than your husband deserves, Madame. Mercier is a lucky man to have the support of Admiral Bousquet at a time when the admiral must be tempted to disown him. I am touched also by your own loyalty. It does you credit."

"It shames her!" Jean-Paul interrupted fiercely. "Damnit, Arlette, why did you allow yourself to be talked into this? You must have known I couldn't agree. Is your father so insecure now that he feels he has to do a white-wash job on me in order to stay sweet with Darlan and the rest of his chums?"

Anger flashed in Arlette's eyes.

"My father said you should have been shot for what you did. He only agreed to help because I begged him to. He has gone to a great deal of trouble to get you a second chance. There will be no stain on your name."

"What about the stain on my conscience?" snapped Jean-Paul. "Do you honestly think that I could carry on in the Navy where I left off and convince people that what happened on the *Marande* was nothing, the ravings of a tropical fever?"

"People do strange things when they're ill with fever. No one will hold it against you that a fever made you be-have out of character. Especially if you have the courage to admit it in public."

"Oh, yes, the public confession!" scoffed Jean-Paul. "That's the ingenious touch—the radio interview with the young officer who nearly wrecked his career by for-getting to take his malaria pills! How I became delirious at the height of a great Franco-German operation to res-cue Italian prisoners of war from the Atlantic. There, was a British warship ramming the Italian's lifeboats and dropping depth charges on the men in the water, and there was I, going out of my head with fever and having a terrible misunderstanding with the Captain about open-ing fire on the British murderers. He thought I was re-fusing his orders to be ready to fire when, in fact, I was urging him to intervene and stop the slaughter of the Italians."

"It's near enough the truth, isn't it?" said Arlette.

Jean-Paul stared at her.

"It's near enough the truth to be faintly plausible and yet so far away from the truth that it makes my blood run cold thinking about the mind that thought it up. You don't know me at all, Arlette, if you think I would ever have anything to do with that kind of propaganda!"

The blond head went up with an angry tilt.

"I'm not asking you to enjoy it. It's the price of your freedom!"

"I don't buy it that cheaply," retorted Jean-Paul. He pushed his chair back and stood up. He tried not to read the pain in Arlette's eyes. She was staring at him with a look of agonized appeal. Then, she lowered her eyes. With head slightly bowed, she tried to stifle a sob. Quietly, she began to cry.

Junot got quickly to his feet and went round the table to comfort her. He flashed a reproachful look at Jean-Paul.

"You're a fool! It's time this nonsense was ended." He stooped over Arlette. "Do not waste your tears, my dear."

She looked up with tear-filled eyes.

"I'm sorry, Major," she murmured. "These last few days have been an immense strain. I can't do anything more. I'm defeated."

Junot patted her shoulder, then turned and walked to the end of the veranda.

"Guard! Come and take the prisoner away."

Two Senegalese appeared at a trot. Junot nodded his head towards Jean-Paul.

"Your wife will be staying here overnight. If she wishes to say good-bye to you in the morning before the boat sails, I shall arrange it. Now, I think you should get out of her sight."

Jean-Paul looked at him grimly.

"There's just one thing, Major. The Englishman whose face you cut with your whip . . . the wound is festering. He needs attention. The wound should be cleaned properly and treated with antiseptic."

Arlette looked up at the Major questioningly. Wondering just what kind of a brute I am, he thought.

"You know we have no doctor on the island," he said.

Arlette put a hand on his sleeve.

"If it's only simple first aid, perhaps I . . . ?"

Junot considered this. The liquid look in Arlette's eyes persuaded him.

"Very well, my dear. Good of you to offer. I'll have him brought up after I do my evening rounds. But don't waste too much time on him. We're having aperitifs at eight and dinner at eight-thirty sharp."

His long stare at Jean-Paul was full of meaning. And Jean-Paul got the meaning. Whatever else happened this evening, Arlette was going to have her hands full coping with Major Junot.

Junot's bungalow was built on a rise of ground a short distance from the arched stone gateway to the three terraces of buildings comprising the barracks and stores. A gate-house accommodated the guard-room, two small offices, a tiny kitchen, toilet, a small store and a narrow cement-walled extension known as "the medical office."

It was to the latter that Rennie was brought for treatment to the wound on his face.

The small extension to the gate-house was no more than a single room, eight feet wide by twelve feet long. One end was used as a dispensary and housed store cabinets for various medicines and drugs. There was a table and chair, used by the visiting medical officer who called once a week with the boat from Dakar. There was a wooden bench on which soldiers from Fort Raphael would sit awaiting their turn in the pill parade. It was equipped to handle only minor cases of illness or injury. Anything worse than abrasions or stomach upsets was shipped to the mainland.

The now inevitable escort of two Senegalese who had brought Rennie up from the detention camp indicated that he should sit on the bench in the medical office and wait. They squatted outside the door.

It was twenty minutes before Arlette came. Rennie heard her before he saw her. Her tinkling French was too rapid for him to follow but he heard and understood the words of the African houseboy, who had brought her down from Junot's house.

"Je vous attendrai ici, Madame . . . Le prisonier est dedans là . . . Oui, par cette porte."

The door opened and she came in. Rennie stared at

her. He couldn't help it. He was totally unprepared for such a vision of loveliness. She could have stepped straight out of a beauty advertisement for a product with a name like "Outdoor Girl." She had a haughty sensuality—an almost animal presence which invited touching and promised fire, if only you dared to touch. Rennie had to shake himself into response when he realized that this enchanting creature was actually talking to him.

"You are the Englishman?"

"Yes . . . I'm John Rennie."

"I am Arlette Mercier. You are a friend of Jean-Paul?"

"Yes."

"Will you help Jean-Paul?"

"If I can."

She was staring at his wound. She crossed to where he was sitting and ran cool fingers gently down the side of the raw, bloodied flesh. The action was one of spontaneous concern. Its effect on Rennie was almost sexual. He shivered involuntarily, but it was a sensation of exciting awareness and far from unpleasant.

"Major Junot did this to you?" she said.

"Yes."

"He is a pig. He thinks he is going to sleep with me tonight."

Rennie did not know how to answer this. He felt a flush of color rise to his face. Arlette sensed his embarrassment. She gave a tinkling laugh.

"You are shocked? Do not worry. I think I can handle the Major. I would gladly let him seduce me if I thought it would help Jean-Paul."

Her frankness made Rennie feel as worldly wise as a six-year-old boy. He felt slightly out of his depth with her.

"How can I help Jean-Paul?" he asked. "I got the impression that he thinks you have let him down badly."

"He told you about this afternoon?"

"Yes. He said he had been offered his freedom . . . But that there were strings attached."

She looked at him imploringly.

"Can I trust you?"

"I hope so."

"Then you must understand that what happened this afternoon was a pretense on my part. The only way I could get to see Jean-Paul was by using my father's influence, which is very considerable. A lot of people were prepared to go to a lot of trouble to hush up what really happened on Jean-Paul's ship and get him re-instated to the Navy—but only if he did the right thing by them."

"I gathered that Jean-Paul had to do some kind of political about-turn," said Rennie. "Having appeared to have been anti-Vichy and anti-German, he was going to have to retract in public and make out that it was all some terrible misunderstanding . . . That he really loved Vichy and that the Germans weren't the monsters they were made out to be . . . That it was all British propaganda . . ."

Arlette nodded her head.

"That is what I *had* to tell him. Do you understand that? The *only* way I could get to see him was by putting that monstrous proposition to him. Jean-Paul doesn't know it or seem to realize it but because of his connection with my father, he is important *politically*. The Government just can't afford to have anyone with his connections staging one-man rebellions. It could have repercussions all over North-West Africa if the story gets out. If Jean-Paul hadn't been the son-in-law of Admiral Bousquet, he wouldn't be on this island. He would have been shot."

"I think I understand," said Rennie, without being sure that he did. "But how can I help him?"

"By telling him all the things I couldn't say to him this afternoon because that peacock of a Major insisted on us never being alone together. Look, I'll have to do something with that face of yours. Major Junot could walk in here at any moment and it would look strange if I'm not doing what I'm supposed to be doing. I'll talk while I clean that wound."

She busied about finding disinfectant liquid and cotton wool, pausing only to dispatch the houseboy—who waited outside—for hot water. Once everything had been assembled, Rennie found it difficult to submit to her ministrations and keep his mind on all she was telling him.

She sat on one end of the wooden bench and made him stretch out on it with his head in her lap. She made him incline his face so that the long cut down one side could be bathed, with the result that his nose and half his face were pressed against her firm, flat belly, and his nostrils were filled with a perfumed sweetness that was totally feminine. Inches from one eye was a delicious protuberance of bosom. For someone who had not so much as seen a woman for several weeks, this intimate proximity to such an enticing bundle of female flesh was almost overpowering. Rennie had to force himself to listen to what Arlette was saying.

She began by impressing on him the risk she was running in making him accessary to the disclosures she was about to make. Her life depended on his absolute discretion. She was to trust him with a secret side of her life which was unknown even to Jean-Paul. She had been tempted to tell Jean-Paul all about it on his last leave—when they had had a bitter quarrel about politics—but she had refrained from doing so. Now, she had no choice. Jean-Paul had to know. And Rennie was her last chance of letting Jean-Paul know where her loyalties really lay.

"For some months now, I've been a member of a secret resistance organization in Algiers," she told Rennie, "but, as a cover for my work with them, I've had to appear to have pro-German sympathies. By keeping on good terms with the more extreme Vichyists, I've been able to pass on valuable information. Jean-Paul doesn't know it but the last time he was in Algiers, he nearly sabotaged my usefulness to the Resistance by being openly contemptuous of a politician I had been cultivating for some time. Jean-Paul thought I was buttering the man up because I approved of him. It was a relief to me when Jean-Paul went back to Dakar but it hurt, too, that I had to keep the truth from him."

Rennie remained silent as she continued to dab painfully at flesh below his eye which was beginning to suppurate. He almost sat bolt upright when Arlette declared in a soft low voice that she had arranged Jean-Paul's escape from L'Ile de Voleurs and that everything was fixed for nine days hence, on the first of October.

"What I want *you* to do," she said, "is pass on the details of what *he has to do.* It's essential he gets things absolutely right because there won't be a second chance."

The plan was simple, almost startlingly so, although it could not possibly have been conceived or executed from the camp on the point without outside help of the kind that Arlette had provided. It hinged entirely on the movements of a motor schooner named *L'Esperance,* which made regular runs between Safi, in Morocco, Dakar and Conakry, with scheduled calls at small places along the route. L'Ile de Voleurs was one of those small calling places.

On the first of October, *L'Esperance* was due into the Island's harbor to collect a consignment of ground-nuts farmed at the small plantation on the island's northerly tip. The schooner would load the ground-nuts in a day and sail for Conakry just after midnight. Although the ground-nuts cargo was destined for a refinery in Dakar, it would not be discharged until the schooner was returning northwards from Conakry.

Through contacts in Dakar, Arlette had met the schooner's master and paid him a substantial sum of money for his part in the rescue plan. Everything depended on Jean-Paul being able to fall in with that plan.

It meant that, after dark, he had to get through the wire and get to a small sandy beach on the south-east side of the island. There was a channel buoy about three hundred yards off the beach. He was to start swimming out to the buoy the moment he heard *L'Esperance* give a blast on her siren, signalling her imminent departure from the harbor. The schooner would pass close alongside the buoy and take Jean-Paul aboard. The following day, he would be put ashore near Bathurst, where he would be able to seek asylum from the British.

Nearly half an hour had passed since Arlette had arrived at the medical office and, now, she kept looking anxiously at her watch. She was anxious that Rennie had grasped and memorized the precise times and details with which she had trusted him.

"I've got it all," Rennie assured her, "and I'll not only see that Jean-Paul knows what to do, I'll be right there beside him swimming out to that buoy and right behind him when he jumps aboard the schooner."

"Non!"

The French style of the negative was uttered by Arlette like a cry of alarm. "The arrangement is for Jean-Paul only."

Rennie could not hide his disappointment.

"You could only afford one schooner ticket?" he said, with an attempt at a smile.

Her eyes were warm with sympathy. "I'm sorry. The possibility of others wanting to get off the island with Jean-Paul just didn't come into my thinking. It didn't occur to me at all. You understand, don't you? The schooner captain is expecting one man. If there's more than one, there's no saying what he will do. He might panic . . . Might not stop or keep his part of the bargain."

Rennie shrugged his shoulders philosophically.

"C'est la vie. Don't worry. We'll not spoil it for Jean-Paul—and we'll see he makes it."

Her smile was radiant. To Rennie's surprise, she cupped his face in her hands and kissed him warmly on the lips. It was a kiss of gratitude on her part: light enough not to be mistaken for one of passion, yet not so light that it wasn't memorable.

"Thank you, thank you," she said. "Now, I must put a cover on that wounded face of yours to keep the dirt out. Then I must fly before the Major begins to suspect something."

She cut a strip of gauze, smeared some ointment on it, and taped it over the worst of Rennie's cut.

"It does not look very pretty but it will do its work," she said, surveying the finished article. She kissed him lightly, chastely on the forehead this time.

"God be with you," she murmured, and with a soft rustle of skirt, she was gone.

Rennie could not credit the bereft feeling with which her departure left him. It was as if someone had stolen the sun on a summer's day.

The thought saddened him that he would probably never see her again. There was regret, too, that she was another man's wife. Rennie shrugged.

"C'est la vie," he murmured to himself.

Jean-Paul was astonished.

"You are trying to tell me that Arlette was play-acting this afternoon? She certainly fooled me."

"A good thing she did," said Rennie. "She obviously had to fool Junot. The fact that you swallowed the story made sure that Junot took it hook, line and sinker as well."

Jean-Paul raised his face heavenwards and rolled his eyes.

"Oh, mon Dieu!" he exclaimed with feeling. "I could have spoiled her game completely. At one time, I felt so much desire for her that I wanted to agree to the whole thing . . . Just to get my arms round her again."

Rennie smiled.

"Well, I wouldn't have blamed you if you had. You have a very lovely wife, Jean-Paul—and a brave one."

"There is only one thing I don't like about what you have told me," said the Frenchman. "It is wrong that I should be the only one to escape."

"She was very insistent about you going alone. She's afraid that the skipper of the schooner will welsh on the deal if he sees more than one man."

Hobart, who had been sitting quietly on the rattan bed opposite, nodded his head.

"It breaks my heart, but John's right," he said. "Your little lady has put her neck on the line to get you out of here. You can't afford to blow it by not playing it exactly as she says."

A stubborn look settled on Jean-Paul's face.

"You are my friends and this may be your only chance, too. I will not leave without you."

Hobart stood up and patted Jean-Paul on the shoulder.

"That's one terrific thing to say, Jean-Paul. John and I appreciate it. We'd probably feel the same way if it was one of us who had the chance. That right, John?"

"Yes," said Rennie. "I hope I'd feel that way about it anyway. It says a hell of a lot for you, Jean-Paul. It makes you very special in my book. But you've got to believe that the best turn you can do us is to get clean away. That will be the next best thing to getting away ourselves."

Jean-Paul smiled forlornly at the other two.

"Saving my own skin means nothing to me if it means leaving you behind."

"We've got to stay behind," said Rennie, "if only to see the look on Junot's face when he finds out you've gone."

There was a contemptuous snort from the far corner of the hut where Bishop, as usual, was keeping himself aloof.

"You disapprove of something, Admiral?" asked Hobart.

Bishop scowled across at them.

"Listening to the three of you makes me sick. You talk as though it's a foregone conclusion that Mercier will get off this island as easy as winking, as if there's no chance of anything going wrong. You could be in for some unpleasant surprises."

"Like what?" asked Hobart.

Bishop waved his arms aimlessly.

"Like all manner of things. I couldn't help hearing everything Rennie said and I can't say I liked any of it. For a start, whose plan is it? A woman's, for God's sake! Even supposing that she herself can be trusted, the same can hardly be said for the man with the schooner. What is there to stop him from just pocketing all the money Mercier's wife gave him and then just doing damn all about his side of the bargain?"

"Nobody's denying there are risks," said Rennie.

"And I would trust Arlette with my life," put in Jean-Paul.

"That's just what you *are* doing, aren't you?" said Bishop meaningfully. "Well, sooner you than me! I wouldn't trust a woman to post a letter for me . . . Any woman!"

"The Admiral must have had an unhappy love life," commented Hobart. The remark was wide of the truth. Bishop had never had any love life. A childhood dominated by a possessive mother had soured him against the opposite sex with the result that, in adult life, he had never been at ease with women. The Navy wives in places like Malta had done nothing to mellow his deep-rooted distrust of the female species.

Bishop ignored Hobart's remark.

"The only point I am making is that you are making a basic mistake in putting so much faith in this cock-and-bull scheme. You are not responsible for its origin. You have absolutely no control over the people on whose success it depends. Therefore, there is a high probability that it is doomed to failure."

"Thank you and good night," said Rennie. For some unknown reason, Bishop's words chilled him to the bone. The man was a born pessimist but, not only that, he seemed to have a genius for quenching hope where it flamed most brightly. Jean-Paul seemed stricken, and angry with it. Hobart, too, was angry.

"Why don't you shut your big mouth?" he growled at Bishop.

"Does reasoned analysis upset you, Mr. Hobart? Does the truth look more acceptable through rose-colored glasses?"

"So help me, Admiral, if you don't shut your goddamned mouth, I'll shut it for you. Why the hell did we have to be saddled with you?"

"Now, there's a sentiment that echoes mine, Mr. Hobart," replied Bishop. "I have to admit that I don't find your company any more desirable than you seem to find mine—but I intend to do something about it."

"Oh, yeah. What?"

Bishop waved a hand airily.

"If you must know, I intend to request a meeting with the Commandant tomorrow. For all that he seems a rather violent man, he is a professional soldier. I shall appeal to him as a fellow-officer to accommodate me in company more appropriate to my rank."

Hobart eyed him contemptuously.

"I hope he obliges. There's a wire run back of his bungalow where you ought to feel right at home—with the rest of the chickens."

It was ten the next morning when Junot made a surprise appearance at the camp. He was as meticulously turned out and groomed as always and in a bouncy, almost affable mood.

He stood outside Rennie's hut and told the scruffy corporal from the gate that he wanted the occupants paraded in front of him at once. They stood sheepishly in a line before him.

"Back to your duties, Corporal," he said to the slovenly one, and strutted up and down in front of the four men.

"Well, gentlemen," he began, "I trust that you did not find the night wearisome. I certainly did not."

He stopped beside Jean-Paul.

"Madame Mercier asked me to say good-bye to you on her behalf," he said, a teasng grin on his face. Rennie could almost feel Jean-Paul's anger. The Frenchman's fists were clenched in tight balls at his side and his lips were pursed so close together that they showed white.

Junot looked away from Jean-Paul and, holding up a hand, affected to study his finger-nails.

"I promised your wife, Mercier, that I would ask you if you had reconsidered the proposition which she delivered to you yesterday." He looked at the watch on his wrist. "Her boat sails at eleven. There is still time . . ."

"My answer remains the same," burst out Jean-Paul. "I want no part of it—or her!"

You sound as though you really mean that, thought

Rennie. He recalled Arlette's conversation with him the day before and felt slightly sick. Her and Junot. Surely she didn't? And yet Junot looked like the cat that had swallowed the canary. He was the hell pleased about something. And he was getting it across to Jean-Paul, making him jealous. No wonder Jean-Paul was standing there tighter than the spring of an overwound clock. Junot was at it again.

"It may be years before you see your wife again, Mercier—if you ever do. Just think of it—years. You could have been leaving with her, but no . . . You send her away—a lovely young woman like that. Do you expect her to spend the years in solitude?"

Jean-Paul could take it no more.

"Stop it, you evil bastard!"

Junot smiled.

"That is disrespect. Mercier. Will you never learn to curb your tongue? Must I always have to remind you whose word here is law?" He made a signal with his hand.

Two Senegalese came running from the gate.

Junot tapped Jean-Paul's chest with a podgy fist.

"Put him in the tank," he said to the Senegalese. They led Jean-Paul away. He allowed himself to be led, but the look he flung at Junot was one of unrepentant defiance.

Junot turned to the other three. He smiled, as a cobra might before it strikes.

"I apologize, gentlemen, that dicipline demands that I must make an example of Mercier. One must always be most severe on one's own, don't you think? Discipline, like charity, begins at home—and Mercier, although he has forfeited his rights to be called a Frenchman, is still one of ours."

He paused, stopping in front of Rennie and inspecting the protective strip on the whip wound.

"You must realize, of course, that your nationality gives you no protection from the way I enforce discipline. I demand respect from you, and instant obedience to my commands. If you remember that, you will be well treated. Forget it for one instant and you will discover that the price of forgetfulness is heavy. I will not shirk from punishing you as severely as I would a Frenchman. There is just one thing I would add for the benefit of our two newcomers. No one has ever escaped from L'Ile de Voleurs, although many have tried. I warn you not to try. If you are wise, you will settle down here and make the best of things. That is all. Good day."

He turned on his heel.

Major Junot?"

Junot stopped abruptly and stared at Bishop.

"Yes?"

"Sir, I request permission to speak with your on a personal matter."

"At this very moment?"

"Whenever it may be convenient, sir."

Junot was intrigued. He looked at Bishop, then he studied the faces of Rennie and Hobart. He could sense tension.

"You wish a private conversation?" he asked.

"I would be obliged, sir," said Bishop.

"Very well. At my bungalow in an hour's time. I shall make the instructions for an escort."

He strode off.

Hobart and Rennie stood a little distance away from Bishop, regarding him with distaste.

"Happy now?" said Rennie. "Looks like you've got your private audience with His Holiness the Gauleiter."

"Yeah," contributed Hobart. "Hope we didn't embarrass you from saying your piece right out."

Bishop stared at them grimly without answering. They could not even begin to understand. Their thinking was typically lower deck: all boys together. They knew nothing abut the loneliness of command or the ethics which divorced duty from a need to please the common herd. Anyone could court popularity by sacrificing certain standards, but that was not the way of the true officer. He had to stay apart, remain aloof. Only then could he make decisions objectively and distinguish what was right from what was popularly expedient. It was something which only another from a similar background could understand.

Just before eleven, two guards came to escort Bishop to Junot's bungalow. An hour later, the scruffy corporal came and removed Bishop's blanket, towel, and the other things with which he had been issued.

Hobart and Rennie did not see Bishop again that day. A week passed and his absence seemed complete. He was not returned to the encampment and none of their surreptitious querying of the guards elicited any clue to his whereabouts. Another day passed—and then the first day of October was upon them. It dawned cleared and bright and, with it, came the realization that there was more to think about than the eccentric naval officer, Bishop. This was the day the schooner *L'Esperance* was due.

Chapter Six

RENNIE and Jean-Paul crouched in readiness at the door of the hut. Their breathing was the only audible sound in the darkened section.

"How long has he been gone now?" whispered Jean-Paul.

"Fifteen minutes. He should be back soon."

"I am glad you both changed your minds. About coming."

"You may regret it yet," cautioned Rennie. "I'm still wondering how the hell you managed to talk us round."

"My persuasive Gallic tongue," suggested Jean-Paul with a grin.

"Your Gallic bloody-mindedness," corrected Rennie. "Would you really have sat tight here and not budged if we hadn't given in to you?"

"Yes."

"You're the craziest bastard I've ever met," said Rennie.

Jean-Paul smiled back at him in the darkness.

"Nothing will go wrong. You'll see. If the schooner captain tries any tricks, we'll take over his ship. What chance would he have against three desperate men?"

"We've still got to get aboard. We're not even out of the camp. Where the hell is Hobart? He should have been back."

"I'm right here, pal," said an American voice and Rennie nearly jumped out of his skin. The voice came from below the four front steps of the hut. Hobart's head appeared. He pulled his body clear from underneath the hut.

"For a geologist, you move around pretty well in the dark," said Rennie. "Did they teach you commando training as well as genning you up on rocks at the University of South California?"

"Let's just say I used to be a Boy Scout," said Hobart. "Are you guys ready?"

"My suitcase has been packed for three days," said Rennie. "For God's sake, let's get going."

Hobart could sense the tension in him.

"You scared, John?"

"The expression is scared witless," said Rennie. "I've never done this sort of thing before, remember?"

"You'll be OK. How about you, Jean-Paul?"

"This waiting is getting me down," replied Jean-Paul. "Cannot we move now?"

"Give it a couple of minutes," said Hobart, glancing at his watch. "The sentries are doing exactly the same tonight as we've timed 'em every night this past week. We've got to give the guy on the beach time to get to the south fence and then start on his way back."

They waited in silence. Hobart kept looking at his watch.

"Thirty more seconds," he murmured. "Remember now, no more talking once we move. We've been over the drill a dozen times. Best of luck, guys."

He stuck out a hand. Jean-Paul and Rennie took it in turn and shook it. Then Jean-Paul clasped Rennie's hand.

"Mes amis . . . Mes frères . . . Allons!"

One by one they slipped under the wooden steps and crawled under the hut to its rear. Hobart touched Jean-Paul's shoulder and pointed. The Frenchman nodded, got to his feet and set off at a crouching run down one side of the vegetable patch which the prisoners had to tend. He skirted a long row of straggly bean plants, and, reaching the end, waited.

Hobart tapped Rennie's shoulder. He, too, set off at a run past the line of beans. He reached the point where Jean-Paul was waiting and looked back. Beyond the huts, a light was burning in the office near the gate. The avenue of palms stood sentinel beyond, their fronds swaying in the humid southwesterly breeze. The sky was overcast and the oppressive atmosphere promised rain before morning.

Hobart loomed out of the gloom and crouched beside them. The air was alive with insects. Rennie brushed a mosquito from his ear, and with a pointing hand drew the others' attention towards the beach, from which came the constant swishing sigh of ocean upon sand. Walking on the sand at the far side of a tangled carpet of banana patch was a single figure. The African soldier was very tall. He stood in silhouette against the seaward horizon, rifle over one shoulder. The overcast seemed to stop just above the meeting place of sky and ocean, giving the soldier a distant backdrop of gray-blue light.

The man paused only briefly, then resumed his leisurely perambulation along the beach towards the north fence. Beyond the fence, the sinister shape of the abandoned prison was a ghostly black mass. Against it, the sea eddied and swirled with a dull monotonous booming and hissing.

Jean-Paul was first to his feet. Communicating by touch and sign, the three men moved swiftly through the banana patch and, reaching the beach, kept very low as they followed the curve of upper shore to the south. They were backtracking the path taken by the sentry moments before on his northward beat.

When the fence came in sight, across fifty yards of hard-baked ground devoid of grass or shrub, they dropped flat on their bellies. With an arm arched, Hobart pointed towards a glow of light. On the far side of the fence, a Senegalese soldier was squatting, his hands cupped round a cigarette. When he drew on the cigarette, the red glow fanned and then faded.

Hobart stared anxiously at his watch. Already, the guard who patrolled the beach would have started off on his southward leg.

After what seemed an age, the soldier beyond the fence got to his feet and stamped on the cigarette end. He contemplated the sea for a moment and then turned and walked slowly away from the shore, following the line of the fence as it stretched inland. He disappeared from sight near a cluster of palm trees.

Hobart began to edge forward on his belly. Rennie and Jean-Paul followed suit. The American was first to the fence. He skirted along it examining the lowest wire. Finding what he wanted, he made the briefest hissing sound to attract the others. Rennie and Jean-Paul crawled swiftly to his side.

Hobart indicated a depression in the ground below the bottom wire of the fence. The hollow was about two feet wide and left a clearance of about eighteen inches between ground and wire.

Rennie was first to go. Lying flat on his back, he wormed backwards under the wire while Hobart gently raised it upwards to take away the slack. Jean-Paul was second through the wire, then he held the wire tense as Hobart wriggled underneath.

They were now clear of the camp.

Using the shore-line as their guide, they crossed the south tip of the island and began to make their way north up the east-facing arm of the boomerang. The lower sand-spit gave way to rockier ground. They crested a rise which looked down on a strip of sand less than fifty yards long. Here, the sea only rippled against the shore, the cove being protected by the point from the long Atlantic rollers which pummelled against the island's western side.

Quite close to the shore, a light flashed every thirty seconds. It was the channel buoy. To the north, another light winked on the end of the harbor mole. The buildings around the harbor were just shadows, with only the square face of the mosque white against the hill.

Rennie pointed to the strip of sand and cautioned the others to wait. He explored the rocks where they dipped towards the beach. He disappeared from view for a moment as he investigated a crevice between two outcrops. Then the shadowy outline of his head and shoulders came back into view. He waved an arm and made a sound, a whistling of breath between his teeth which was only just audible to Hobart and Jean-Paul. They scampered across to the crevice. Rennie indicated the ledge on which he was standing. He squatted on it, then pushed himself out and dropped on to the soft sand of the beach six or seven feet below. Hobart and Jean-Paul dropped down after him.

They remained well back against the wall of rock, deep in shadow.

"So far, so good," Hobart dared to whisper. "It still needs fifteen minutes to midnight. All we've got to do now is wait."

"Maybe we should swim out to the buoy now," said Rennie. "Two of us will have to stay out of sight when the schooner comes, so it might be a good idea to see what it's like out there."

"Jean-Paul can get up on the buoy. We can stay in the

water and hang on to the side away from the schooner until the last minute. No point in going out there before we have to, though," said Hobart.

"It was just a thought," said Rennie. "I wouldn't mind the swim. I'm sweating like a pig."

Jean-Paul was flexing his hands nervously. He voiced a thought which had occurred to Rennie.

"The harbor looked very quiet from up above. I expected to see lots of lights. Could you see the schooner?"

"Nope," said Rennie. "I couldn't make out very much at all. But the hill at the back makes it hard . . . Throws everything into shadow."

Hobart was the least edgy of the three.

"Let's not worry about it, eh? I took it as a good sign. It probably means the schooner finished working cargo hours ago and is all ready to slip its lines."

They sat down in the sand to wait. Just after midnight a new sound disturbed the night air. It was the steady throb of a motor. The three men were instantly alert.

"Something coming out of the harbor?" breathed Hobart.

"No, it's the other direction . . . Near the point. It's coming from the sea." Rennie pointed towards the short stretch of water visible between the flashing buoy and the stubby promontory which obstructed their view to the south.

He had no sooner spoken when a squat dark shape became visible as it rounded the headland from seaward. It was moving quickly. It turned into the cove, passing between the buoy and the promontory, and seemed to be heading straight for the beach.

"It's coming straight in!" said Hobart. His voice was an alarmed croak. "Let's get out of here!"

They ran along the base of the rock wall, looking for a way up. But, whereas it had been an easy matter to drop six or seven feet down on to the beach, the sheer rock and the force of gravitiy conspired against as speedy a departure from it. The motor launch was now only twenty yards from the shore. Rennie's blood ran cold when he heard an order barked in French, followed by the unmistakable sound of the bolts on a dozen rifles being cocked simultaneously.

Suddenly the beach was as bright as day as a searchlight on the launch came flooding on. Rennie turned, as did Hobart and Jean-Paul, arms held over their eyes to shield against the brilliant dazzle of light in which they were bathed.

A voice rose from behind the light, sharp with urgency. "Ne tirez pas!"

Rennie recognized the voice. Junot's! It came again.

"Arrêtez-vous-là! Arrêtez! Levez les mains!"

Eyes turned away from the light, the three men froze on the beach, their hands held high. Rennie could feel himself trembling. He had never been more afraid in all his life. Junot's voice continued to rant.

Senegalese soldiers were splashing ashore from the launch. Junot followed them, shouting and cursing like a man possessed. Rennie was aware of a fleeting puzzlement at the man's demonic rage. He wondered what Junot was so mad at. After all, he had caught them, hadn't he? Rennie soon had other things to think about.

A grinning Senegalese loomed over him, blocking out the light from the launch. Rennie saw the rifle go up and turn with a movement of the man's wrist. Then the butt was coming straight for his face. He twisted away but a blow like the kick of a Clydesdale thudded into his shoulder and sent him sprawling face down in the sand. A red-hot lance of pain speared through his shoulder, making him cry out. A fresh seat of agony flamed as a heavy boot thudded into his ribs. The force of the kick turned him, it was followed by a second vicious kick which opened the side of his face. Blood spread into his nostrils and ran in the corner of his open mouth. The world became a whirling kaleidoscope of flashing lights. His body was on fire with pain as the rifle butt hit him again. He retched, choking up blood which had run from his mouth into his throat. The savage beating went on with no part of his anatomy escaping boot or rifle butt. He's going to pound me to death, thought Rennie. The thought flashed crazily into his brain that it never happened this way in Hollywood films or the tough detective books he liked to read. There was just one swift hard thump and the victim fell unconscious. He wasn't dropped into a sea of boiling pain like this, with every sense awake and registering every vicious blow as it found new flesh and bone to bruise.

At last, it ended. Rennie lay in the sand, sure that he would never rise again. There was no part of him that was not fiery with coursing pain: his head, his body, his arms his legs. One eye was swollen like a pomegranate. He could see nothing from it. There was sand in his puffed bloody nostrils and he moved his face so that he could blink through the other eye. He saw booted feet moving some distance away and realized they belonged to Junot's Senegalese soldiery. The beach was still flooded with light.

He moved his head half an inch more and opened the eye wide. Not far away, Jean-Paul was spread-eagled by four soldiers, each gripping a wrist or an ankle. Beyond him lay Hobart's body. He was very still. Unconscious? Or dead? There was no way to tell.

Junot was still screaming like a madman. His shiny brown boot came into view from the direction of the water's edge. Rennie moved his face a fraction more, blinked again, until he could see Junot in full focus. He was standing now over Jean-Paul. There was blood on Jean-Paul's face. Rennie tried to tune his mind to Junot's outpouring of words but only drifts of it made sense. He was going on about Jean-Paul's whore of a wife. Then he was telling Jean-Paul what he thought of traitor filth and traitor filth who tried to escape. Did he know that if it hadn't been for the Englishman and the American he would already be dead on the beach, full of bullets. Well, soon he would be wishing he was dead.

Rennie saw Junot seize the rifle of one of his soldiers. Then he barked a demand. The Senegalese pulled his bayonet into the rifle and took a step towards Jean-Paul. Rennie watched in fascinated horror as Junot fixed the bayonet into the rifle and took a step towards Jean-Paul. He raised the rifle and thrust down.

Rennie blinked his eye shut, unable to witness the sight of the bayonet being thrust into his friend's belly. But there was no way of shutting out the agonized scream that issued from Jean-Paul. Rennie dared to blink his eye open again. He sucked in his breath so sharply that he swallowed a mouthful of blood. Junot had not aimed for Jean-Paul's belly. He had plunged the bayonet through the fleshy part of his outstretched thigh with such force that Jean-Paul was pinned through his leg to the sand. Putting his boot on Jean-Paul's knee, Junot jerked the weapon out. Then he lunged it down a second time, this time pinning Jean-Paul to the ground with a thrust through the other leg.

"Now, let me see you run!" cried Junot. He threw the

rifle down on the beach and turned to stare over the water. Rennie could hear his great gasping breaths, as if he had just completed a five-mile run. The breathing became more even and Rennie saw a flash of metal as Junot took a gold cigarette case from a pocket of his tunic. He lit a cigarette and walked off along the beach.

Raw hatred burned in Rennie's brain, hatred of a kind he had never before felt towards another human being. Infiltrating the living wave of odium which flowed from his mind at Junot's departing back, a question insinuated itself. *How had Junot known?* The failure of the escape attempt wasn't just bad luck. *Junot must have known when and where and lain in wait.* So, who had tipped him off? Was it the schooner captain? Had this unknown accomplice simply pocketed Arlette Mercier's money and betrayed the whole venture?

There was another possibility, but Rennie's first instinct was to dismiss it. Bishop had known all about the escape and had forecast its failure—but would he have gone to the length of betrayal just in order to be proved right? Surely not. But what had happened to the man? Where was he? Was it conceivable that he had done a deal with Junot? Had he purchased a comfortable billet or even his own freedom by turning informer?

Rennie suddenly got the feeling that eyes were on him. He looked round to see a huge Senegalese only a couple of feet away. The man was standing looking down at Rennie with lips twisted in a cruel leer. Rennie did not see the boot drawn back. He felt only a quick explosion of pain in the top of his head and then mercifully everything went black.

He was aware of waking and dreaming and then falling back into an abyss of blackness. Sometimes he was aware of light, as if he were swimming near the surface of water. Sometimes he would see faces and hear voices—but the faces were distorted and the tongues clacked at him in an unintelligible babble.

At other times it would be dark. He was aware of being. His mind was still functioning, if strangely and uncontrollably, in a body that was stiff and immobile but a body nevertheless. At these times when all was shadow, it was like waking to endless night. He tried to figure out where he was and who he was but the effort would drain him. It would become too much, and he would allow himself to slide back into the depths of total forgetfulness.

In these moments in the black void, he was a child returned to the womb. There was a comforting security in the oblivion. This would seep away as a compulsion to emerge into light reasserted itself. For with the need to emerge to the light came a nameless dread of the horrors to be found there. For, then, the world became a place without substance and recognizable shapes, peopled by ghostly monsters. Fear filled him, making him cry out. His body would seem to shrink to the size of a child's and the only sounds to penetrate to his consciousness would be the terrified whimpering of a child in abject terror. The whimpering sounds would puzzle him until he realized that he was making them. There was a relief in knowing because, then, he would concentrate on making the sounds and listening to them and, for a time, this would keep the reasons for his terror at bay.

The patterns of his waking and dreaming began subtly to change, inasmuch as each took on different but distinct kinds of reality. He was aware of being stationery at times. At others, there was the unmistakable sensation of movement.

He knew he was lying on a bed. He and the bed were inseparable. Always, it was beneath him, like a raft on which he floated through all the dreaming. At times, the bed was quite still. At others, it rocked up and down as if in a billowing sea. Then his bed would be speeding and swaying through space or bumping along like a chariot, bearing him through an endless tunnel. The movements would cease for long periods. Then they would resume. There would be a bumpy ride, no movement at all, then a pleasant floating as if his bed was a punt gliding over smooth water.

There were patches of nothing and vivid dreaming in between these apparent journeys, but each journey seemed to stir deeper into his consciousness—as if each time he were nearer to finding an answer to a question which obsessed him. The only snag was that when the answer seemed within his grasp, he couldn't remember what the question was.

He awakened to a hazy light, convinced that his bed had wheels and was hurtling along a bumpy road. This time the reality of movement was given an added dimension.

A smell of oil reached his nostrils and there was a continuous sound like a laboring motor.

Then something far more significant broke into his consciousness—the sound of a human voice.

"Poor devil. I wonder how he got in such a mess. He'll probably be like that for the rest of his life—a bloody vegetable."

"As bad as that, is it, Doc? Typical of the French, of course. They only let us have the hopeless cases back. Half of the last lot didn't make it to Freetown. We just get them there to fill the cemetery."

"This one will live all right," said the one called Doc. "He's got a heart as stout as a Serengetti lion's. It's his top storey that's scrambled. Result of cerebral compression. Poor bugger could live another forty years and never know the time of day. How old would you say he is? About thirty?"

"Who are you talking about?" Rennie found himself screaming the question. He was clawing for the surface of reality now with the panic of a drowning man.

"Jesus Christ!" The blasphemy burst from the lips of the man called Doc as he recoiled with such violence that he nearly shot through the canvas roof of the ambulance. He recovered to bend low over Rennie.

"You heard me?" he said with awe. "You heard Inspector McNab and me? We were talking about you."

Rennie forced his eyes open. Through a swirling pink mist he could see a face—a face with hair that was nearly white and had bushy eyebrows and a moustache of the same texture. Rennie felt a surge of great joy.

"I can see your face," he cried happily. "I can see your face."

"It's not a very pretty thing to wake up to, son," came the voice of Inspector McNab.

"It's the most beautiful face I've ever seen," said Rennie. He stretched out an exploring hand. It found and fastened on to the Doc's gnarled paw. Tears welled in Rennie's eyes. He just wanted to hold on to that hand.

"Take a good grip, son. I'm going to stay right here with you. You've been a long, long way away. You've come back from the dead. Welcome back to the world."

Rennie stared at him without speaking. He wanted to say something but could find no words. He wanted to tell this man that he was not afraid any more, that his terror for the swirling darkness from which he had emerged was no more. He felt his eyes closing.

"He's fallen asleep," said Inspector McNab.

"Yes, he has," said the one called Doc. He kept holding on to Rennie's hand.

When Rennie wakened again, his first sight was of a white ceiling. A gentle whirring noise caused him to transfer his gaze away from the point vertically above his eyes. Across the ceiling, his gaze followed a hairline crack in the plaster to the source of the whirring noise. Suspended from the ceiling was a big three-bladed fan. It rotated slowly, disturbing the air and sending cooling eddies over the bed on which Rennie was lying.

He moved his head and found himself looking into the startled eyes of a black-skinned girl in a white nursing uniform.

"Hello," she said. "You've woken up?" Her face broke into a big smile. Her short matted hair was all but invisible under a big starched cap. She had thick lips and a stubby button of a nose. But when she smiled to reveal a wide expanse of gleaming white teeth it was like sunshine after rain.

"Hello," replied Rennie. "Where am I?"

"You're in the Presbyterian Hospital. Are you feeling better?"

"I don't know. I can move my head but I don't know about the rest of me."

"Don't try to move. Does your head ache?"

"No."

"Your chest?"

"A little, now you come to mention it. I feel all tight."

"You're strapped up. You've got four broken ribs."

"How did that happen?"

"Don't you remember?"

"I'm trying to. I was asleep in my bunk when we got the knock. I remember waking up on the deck . . ."

The nurse looked perplexed.

"Don't try to talk now. It'll all come back. I'll get the doctor. He wanted to know if you surfaced."

She was gone about five minutes. When she returned it was with a kindly faced man with bushy eyebrows and a shock of white hair and a moustache to match. Rennie recognized him immediately.

"It's the Doc, isn't it? The one with the beautiful face?"

Dr. Goronwy Evans Lloyd ignored the nurse's attempt not to giggle.

"Right you are, son. Lloyd the beautiful it is. Him of countenance sublime. But everybody calls me Doc and you'd better do the same. You remember me?"

"I remember holding your hand."

The nurse giggled again. The Doc turned on her impatiently.

"Haven't you any work to be getting on with, girl? I can see to this patient without you simpering away like a five-year-old."

The girl's face fell. She seemed ready to burst into tears.

"I'm sorry. Yes, doctor." She turned on her heel.

"Nurse."

"Yes, doctor?"

The Doc looked at her ruefully, regretting his harsh tone.

"Have you ever held a patient's hand, Nurse?"

"Yes, sir."

"And has a patient ever woken up and looked into your smiling face and expressed pleasure at seeing it?"

"Well, I suppose, it has happened, sir."

"And when it has happened, did you dispute it with the patient?"

"Oh no, sir."

"Good," he said, and smiled at her. "First rule of medicine . . . Never argue with a patient. Now, off with you." He turned back to Rennie as she went off in a happier frame of mind.

"She's an Ibo girl, from Nigeria," he said to Rennie. "Lovely people, the Ibos. But how about you? Feeling a bit better?"

"I'm hungry," said Rennie.

"Good, we'll get you some food. The French doctor at the border said they had difficulty feeding you. You kept spitting it out."

"I don't remember a French doctor or spitting out food or any border."

"Don't worry about it," said Doc Lloyd. "You'll feel a bit confused for a day or two but you'll gradually start remembering things. It will all come back, you'll see. What can you tell me about yourself?"

"My name is John Rennie. I remember the ship getting the knock . . ."

"You mean torpedoed?"

"Yes. I was asleep in my bunk and woke up on the deck of my cabin. There was a fire in number two hold."

"What was the name of your ship?"

"The *Oakville.*"

"When did this happen? Can you remember?"

"Yes. It was the day after my birthday. It was the twenty-ninth of July."

Doc Lloyd frowned.

"Can you recall anything that happened after that date?"

Rennie thought about this.

"I don't know. I have been dreaming a lot. It's all jumbled up. I can remember things happening but I'm not sure if I dreamed them or they actually happened. The nurse said this was the Presbyterian Hospital, but I don't know any Presbyterian Hospital or how I got here. How did I get here?"

"To Freetown, you mean? You know you're in Freetown?"

"No, I didn't know."

"Well, you are. You were one of fifteen serious casualties handed over by the French, upcountry near Guekedou . . . I was one of the medical team waiting for you at Pendembu with a fleet of ambulances."

Rennie shook his head.

"Those names mean nothing to me. I've never heard of them before. How did I get to Gay . . . Gay . . . whatever you called it?"

"Guekedou? According to some of the others, you were flown down from Dakar in an ambulance plane, then downriver by boat to the exchange point."

"I don't remember getting hurt. I remember being in the lifeboat. I was all right."

"Don't rush it. It'll come," soothed Doc Lloyd. "There's a big gap to fill but don't worry about it."

"How big a gap, doctor?"

Doc Lloyd hesitated.

"You say your ship was torpedoed on the twenty-ninth of July?"

"Yes—the day after my birthday."

"Don't let it alarm you, son, but this is the seventh of November."

"That's five . . . four months!" Rennie was dumbfounded. A new thought flashed into his brain. "What about Hobart and Jean-Paul? They're dead, aren't they?"

"Who did you say? Hobart and Jean-Paul? Were they on your ship?"

"No, no . . . They were on the island. We were all on the island."

"What island?"

Rennie looked up at him blankly.

"We wanted to escape."

Doc Lloyd patted the covers beside Rennie.

"Take it easy, son. Take it easy. You're trying too much all at once. What you need is rest, lots of it. But, first, I'm going to see about getting you something to eat."

Rennie reached out and caught the hem of his white coat.

"You don't understand, doctor. I've got to know what happened to Hobart and Jean-Paul! I've got to!"

"Of course you do. I don't recall names like that amongst our new arrivals, but I'll check. Do you remember the full names. Jean-Paul doesn't sound English."

"Jean-Paul is French. Jean-Paul Mercier. Hobart's an American. Richard Hobart. He learned commando training at the University of Southern California."

Doc Lloyd's bushy eyebrows shot up.

"A Californian commando, eh? That's pretty unusual. But don't you worry. I've got a Yankee friend who works for the American Government right here in Freetown. If your friend Hobart is anywhere in Africa, he'll know about him or be able to find out where he is. A Californian commando, eh?"

Rennie's eyes clouded with anxiety.

"Did I say Hobart was a commando, doctor? I shouldn't have done."

"Why not, son?"

"It was a thing we had. Not an agreement, just an unspoken understanding. I just didn't ask him any questions about himself. That was the way he wanted it. As far as I was concerned, he was exactly what he said he was—a geologist. I'm not going to say different now."

Doc Lloyd was guiltily aware that he was probably

overtaxing his patient but he was reluctant to pull himself away without trying to fill in more blanks in what was an unusual and highly intriguing case. There was one more question he had to ask.

"Was your friend Hobart and the other one—the Frenchman . . . Were they on the truck you jumped off? When you tried to get away from the French?"

Again, Rennie looked at him blankly.

"Truck? What truck?"

"Don't you worry about it, son," said Doc Lloyd. "It was just something the French doctor up at the border said. I asked him how you came by all your injuries—there's quite a list, you know. I thought you'd been trampled by a rhino. But he said that they'd been taking you to some center for aliens when you'd tried to do a bunk . . . You'd jumped out of a truck that was going fifty miles an hour. But you don't remember it?"

Rennie shook his head. He closed his eyes. His head was beginning to hurt.

Goronwy Lloyd cursed himself for being an inconsiderate busybody and eased Rennie's head by smoothing his pillow for him. He tip-toed from the side ward. He gave orders that some food should be prepared and kept ready unless Rennie wakened again soon. In the meantime he wanted Marie, the young Ibo nurse, to stay with him.

When he reached his office, Doc Lloyd dropped into his chair and sat deep in thought for fully five minutes. Then, he picked up the telephone and dialed a number.

"Is Inspector McNab there?" he asked when he got an answer. There was a pause before a voice said: "McNab here."

"Jock," said Doc Lloyd, "I need your help to solve a mystery. Can you meet me at the club at seven? I'll even buy you a double Scotch."

"Well, I suppose the promise of a dram is the next best thing to getting it from you on prescription. I might be a minute or two after seven but you'll wait, will you?"

"That dram will be on the table when you arrive. Oh, and it'll be a threesome. I'm going to give Lew a ring and ask him to be there, too."

"Lew? I haven't seen the big fella for weeks. I thought he must have gone back to Wolf Creek, Montana, or whatever they call that place he comes from. It must be big if you're bringing in the FBI as well as His Majesty's constabulary."

"Lew isn't with the FBI. He's strictly *Corps Diplomatique*—Department of African Affairs."

"So he's always telling me. Just my little joke, Doc. What's it all about anyway?"

"Remember the young fellow we brought down from the border?"

"The one who thought you were beautiful? How could I forget?"

"He's beginning to piece things together and he's going to need some help. I don't know what the hell happened to him up in Dakar but there's something mighty odd about it. I thought you might be interested. You don't mind, do you?"

"Doc, for the very rare pleasure of seeing you put your hand in your pocket to buy me a drink, I am prepared to show an interest in the life-cycle of the Great Anatolian Lugworm. I'll see you at seven."

Doc Lloyd put down the phone and smiled to himself. Just wait till I tell him about Californian commandos, he thought.

Chapter Seven

A week in the care of Doc Lloyd and the nursing staff of the Presbyterian Hospital brought about an improvement in Rennie's condition that was nothing short of spectacular. He began to remember details of his voyage on the ill-fated *Blairmount Castle* and most of the things that had befallen him on the Island of Thieves. There was still difficulty in relating actual time sequences, which remained confused in his mind—but he was able to recall with clarity the more vivid episodes, if not the precise chronological order of their occurrence.

The cut-off point came at that moment on the beach when he, Jean-Paul and Hobart had been trapped in the search-light beam. Rennie remembered orders shouted in French and the chilling sound of rifle bolts being cocked, but beyond that his mind just would not go. A great barrier of fear would descend and sweat would come out on his forehead. It was as if he stood at an open door, so paralyzed with dread that he could not take the single step which would carry him over the threshold.

Doc Lloyd told him not to think about it.

"Look, son," he said, "I only have the scantiest of knowledge of what happened to you up north. All I have to go on is what I was told by the doctor who brought you and the other casualties from Dakar to the border—and he was only an escort, looking after you on the journey. All he knew about the individual cases *was what he had been told.* He said you'd been a month in hospital in Dakar. *What I can tell you as fact* is that you are one very lucky fellow. That great thick skull of yours was fractured and you had a lump of bone pressing on your brain. The French army surgeon who worked on you in Dakar tried to relieve that pressure but he has no idea how good a job he did. You were brought to him in a coma and, although you came out of it, he gave you up as a bad job. The French prognosis was that you would probably be imbecilic for the rest of your days. And look at you now! Bright as a button. Clear-eyed. Strong as an ox and perfectly lucid. I tell you, son, don't you worry about how you got that clonk on the head or how many days you spent lying babbling on a hospital bed. It's quite natural for the mind to reject the memory and shock of the actual incident of injury, so don't get into a sweat trying to remember what happened. You may never know."

It was on the seventh day that Doc Lloyd brought a visitor to see Rennie.

"This is Lew Peterson," said Doc Lloyd. "He's the American friend I told you about. He has been making some inquiries about your geologist pal from California."

Peterson was a big man, well over six feet tall and would have tipped the scales at close on eighteen stone. He had a moon face, tanned a deep brown. The tan extended over a shining bald head. What hair he had was trimmed to crew-cut proportions and did nothing to relieve the stark spheroid of head. His smile was genial and the massive frame seemed to project a friendly jollity.

"Doc didn't want me pestering you with questions until he gave the okay," said the American. "Otherwise I might have been in earlier. He says you're coming along real fine, John. I'm mighty pleased to hear that."

"Nice of you to say so, Mr. Peterson. Doc's going to let me get up soon."

The American perched a hip on the end of Rennie's bed. He looked at Rennie with an almost perplexed air.

"Look, John, I know you're anxious for news of your friends but I'm not going to be able to help you much. All I can tell you is that we are doing everything we can. Will you take my word for that?"

"I don't have any option," said Rennie, "but, yes, I will take your word for it. Just knowing that your people know is a big relief to me."

Peterson studied Rennie thoughtfully.

"This man, Hobart, John . . . Did he tell you anything about the people he had seen in Dakar? Did he mention any names?"

"Not that I can remember."

"Did he ever mention the Governor-General by name? Boisson? Did he ever hint that he might have met him?"

Rennie shook his head.

"No. I think I would have remembered if he did. He did say that the French accused him of meeting people interested in breaking with the Vichy Government and siding with the Allies—but he said the French couldn't prove anything. He had legitimate reasons for meeting all the people he came in contact with."

Without giving Rennie any reason for asking the questions he did, Peterson continued to pump him in the friendliest possible way. They were interrupted by the unannounced arrival of Doc Lloyd's friend, Inspector McNab, and a severe-looking military gentleman, whose clipped moustache and ramrod bearing proclaimed "Brigade of Guards." The latter, Rennie discovered later, was a Major Ratcliffe.

McNab looked very ill at ease.

"I'm sorry but I'll have to break this up," he said. He looked at Peterson apologetically. "I have to ask you to leave, Lew."

Peterson stood up to his full height. He was mystified.

"You want me to leave? What's this all about, Jock?"

McNab continued to look pained and uncomfortable.

"This isn't a social call, Lew. It's official. Mr. Rennie is to talk to no one until he has been fully debriefed by our own people."

Peterson was unmistakably dismayed and more than a little angry.

"For Christ's sake, Jock, we're all on the same side. Who's put you up to this?"

It was Major Ratcliffe who answered. He, too, was apologetic.

"Jock's acting on orders from London, Lew. It won't help to lose your rag with him."

"I'll get good and mad if I want to," snapped Peterson. "Why the hell is it, Major, that we get along great out here until you guys report back to London and some bastard behind a desk over there starts throwing sand in the works. Just who is the genius who says I can't ask Mr. Rennie here about the whereabouts of an American citizen whose life may be in jeopardy?"

Major Ratcliffe's expression was impassive.

"You know as well as anyone, Lew, that our orders come from some faceless wizard in Section Five. Ours is not to question why—just do as we are damned well told.

In this case, the orders were quite specific. It referred particularly to 'inquisitive Americans'. I apologize for the terminology, which is not the kind that Jock or I would choose. We are just as unhappy as you are about the strain that London puts on our relations."

Peterson's displeasure was not assuaged.

"I bet it's that supercilious bastard I met in Cairo who's back of this. What was his name? Trilby? Philby?"

"I'm afraid we know none of our masters by name," said Ratcliffe.

"Well, I do," said Peterson. "Your Trilby or Philby, or whatever his name was, fancied himself as the world's leading expert on French colonial affairs. Well, he may have known his way around Syria and the Lebanon, but what he knew about French North-West Africa and this coast here you could have written on a five-cent stamp. He treated me like some upstart ignoramus—and these orders of yours reek of his style. Inquisitive Americans!"

Ratcliffe coughed discreetly.

"Perhaps we could continue this discussion elsewhere?" he suggested.

Rennie was staring up goggle-eyed from the bed, shaken and puzzled by the altercation in front of him. It was quite plain that Peterson and Ratcliffe were involved in Intelligence work of some kind for their respective Governments, but why they should squabble over him like dogs over a bone was quite beyond him. He certainly had no military secrets worth knowing about. He resented the intrusion of McNab and Ratcliffe, if only because it seemed to represent a threat to any swift intervention on behalf of Dick Hobart and Jean-Paul. The orders from London—on which Ratcliffe and McNab were acting—seemed petty beyond belief. Why should anyone in London pay even the slightest attention to anyone as insignificant and unimportant in the scheme of things as John Rennie?

Was it just the connection with Hobart? The American had undoubtedly been embarked on more than a simple geological expedition when he had been imprisoned by the French, but surely even that couldn't have been earth-shaking in significance, especially now with the news from Algeria and Morocco of the Allied landings there earlier in the week. Senegal was being by-passed by the war and becoming more isolated from Vichy every day.

Rennie was not the only one taken aback by the officially hostile line being shown to Peterson. It upset Doc Lloyd that, for some very obscure reason, his own people seemed intent on using a patient of his as a political football. What made it worse was that all the men in the hospital room were his personal friends who had drunk and socialized together on the very best of terms.

Doc Lloyd seized on Ratcliffe's suggestion of the discussion being continued elsewhere to usher all the visitors from the room and remind them that he didn't want his patient upset by their stupid wrangling.

Peterson turned to the bed before he left.

"I'm sorry about this, John," he said. "If I can sort things out, I'll come and see you again. In the meantime, I intend to move heaven and earth to do something about the friends you left up north. That's a promise."

He shook Rennie's hand. Rennie had no doubt from the determined glint in the big man's eyes that he meant exactly what he said.

"Thanks, Mr. Peterson. If it's any consolation to you, I'm on your side. You can come back and see me any time you like."

"I'm afraid that won't be up to Mr. Peterson," said Ratcliffe, who was waiting for the American to precede him from the room.

"What the hell can I tell him that's going to make any difference to anybody?" said Rennie angrily. "I don't know anything worth a damn."

"That is very possible," said Ratcliffe icily. "Let me just remind you that you are a British subject and in a colony of the Crown. While you are here, you are—like the rest of us—subject to the ordinances of the Crown's officers."

The Crown's officers showed in the next few days that they were in no hurry to expedite the "debriefing" of John Rennie about his experiences in Senegal. A languid, effeminate man—a civilian who volunteered no information about his identity or governmental function—interviewed Rennie one afternoon. If the man's object was to anger and confuse Rennie, he was eminently successful.

Soft-voiced and with an accent so plummy that it set Rennie's teeth on edge, he questioned Rennie in the manner of a prosecuting counsel bent on discrediting a defense witness. He never asked a direct question nor adhered to any chronology of events, with the result that Rennie found himself floundering and seeming to contradict himself. His questioner seemed deliberately to misinterpret everything he said and, at the same time, to show little inclination to believe any of it.

The interview ended with Rennie losing the last shreds of his temper when his tormentor suggested with a sneering smile that his head injuries had left him without any capacity to distinguish between reality and the vivid workings of his imagination. Almost blinded by a raging headache, Rennie called the man a very rude name and, in the most basic of language, told him to go off and perform an act which was not only sexually improbable but anatomically impossible.

Rennie's outburst seemed only to amuse the man and broaden the self-satisfied smirk on his face. He got up from his chair by Rennie's bed as if he had already forgotten Rennie's presence. He looked around with an abstracted air, then minced from the room with the purpose of one whose lipstick needed freshening and who had suddenly remembered where the powder room was.

Rennie's anxiety over the fate of Hobart and Jean-Paul increased as day after day passed and his frustration at the absence of activity or information increased. Peterson's promise that the Americans would not be idle was his only consolation. What Rennie could not understand was why the British authorities, having made such a fuss about him talking to Peterson, now seemed to have lost interest in him but were still making sure that the Americans had no contact with him.

By the end of November, Rennie was up and about and declaring to Doc Lloyd that he was as fit as a fiddle. His ribs were still bound but were healing remarkably well. Outwardly, he bore little sign of what he had been through. Even the scars on his face had begun to blend with the craggy character of his features. There had always been a quality of weather-beaten ruggedness about his looks. Now, they were more so.

Convalescence bored him. He had been shown nothing but kindness by Doc Lloyd and his staff but he longed now to be uncaged and free. Mingled with this longing was a growing obsession that he must do something about the comrades he had left on the Island of Thieves—but just what he might be able to accomplish on is own he had no idea. His powerlessness angered him, but it did not temper his resolve to knock on doors and make a nuisance of himself until someone paid attention.

He read such newspapers as he could obtain from end to end, devouring every snippet of information about France's African territories. It was a great encouragement to know that both Algeria and Morocco had been restored to the Allied fold and that the Eighth Army was racing west from El Alamein. The shadow of Vichy still bedeviled the situation in Algiers, however, where Admiral Darlan had somehow contrived to run political rings round the invading Allies and remain all-powerful.

In Dakar, the North African landings seemed only to have hardened attitudes against the British and Americans and there had been no slackening of the Vichy grip.

Early in December, when Rennie was beginning to feel that the British authorities in Freetown had forgotten that he existed, things suddenly began to happen. They were foreshadowed by news from Doc Lloyd, who looked in at the hospital late one night after a visit to his club. There, he had encountered the American, Peterson.

"Lew wanted me to pass on a message to you," Doc Lloyd told Rennie. "Major Blood-and-guts Ratcliffe would do his nut if he knew that I was acting as go-between but I couldn't care less. I know how much you've been worrying about the pals you left in that prison camp and I am more concerned about your state of health than any stupid feuds between our cloak-and-dagger boys and the Yanks."

"What did Peterson say?" asked Rennie. "Has he found anything out?"

"Only that the French in Dakar were denying that they knew anything about an American called Richard Hobart. He said not to give up hope, however, because his investigations were not restricted to orthodox channels and he was hopeful of results from another quarter very soon. Lew also said that he had created hell in London and Washington about being banned from talking to you and that pressure was being brought to bear to have the ban lifted. He was hopeful of getting the okay to see you within the next two days."

Rennie shook his head in puzzlement.

"Why should somebody in Whitehall go to a hell of a

lot of trouble to keep me from talking to Peterson, Doc? It just doesn't make any sense. I'm nobody. I don't know anything."

"Beats me, son," said Doc Lloyd, "but there's very little these hush-hush boys do that does make any sense. I'm supposed to be blind and deaf to all their goings-on, but I see a lot and pretend I don't. I'm pretty sure that Lew Peterson thinks that somebody is deliberately causing friction between their cloak-and-dagger people and ours, but that's only because I can put two and two together and make four. If Whitehall left our people out here alone, it would be fine but, recently, they've been going out of their way to make life difficult for the Yanks. Usually, it's something quite petty and unimportant—like stopping Peterson from talking to you—but those niggles mount up. They're all too bloody sensitive, if you ask me. It's a Civil Service malaise. Every little Napoleon has his own little empire and gets as jealous as hell of anybody who strays into it."

Doc Lloyd's wry assessment of the situation was accurate up to a point. His belief, however, that Peterson carried enough muscle to produce the necessary results in London was wrong. Peterson was never given the opportunity to resume his conversation with Rennie—for the simple reason that, within twenty-four hours, Rennie was on his way to England in a Sunderland of the RAF. The big flying-boat touched down briefly at Gibraltar before continuing to a Coastal Command station near Milford Haven in South Wales.

Rennie arrived in London on a gray, cheerless winter morning after a long and uncomfortable journey from Wales which involved three changes of train. He took a taxi straight to Leadenhall Street and the head offices of the *Oakville*'s owners. Everyone at the office, from the Marine Superintendent to the tea-girl, treated him like a long-lost hero. It was both gratifying and embarrassing: good to be made to feel important but embarrassing because he felt in no way heroic.

Blenkinsop, the Super, was particularly concerned about Rennie's injuries, fearing that he might no longer be fit for sea-going duty. Rennie hotly denied that he wasn't a hundred per cent fit but, on Blenkinsop's insistence, agreed to a full check with a Harley Street specialist later in the week.

The office staff fell over themselves to do things for Rennie. Hargreaves, the ancient accountant, made sure that he had £100 to stick in his pocket while the formalities of calculating backpay and survivor allowance were undertaken. He also telephoned a firm of tailors to arrange a complete re-kitting session for Rennie at the shipping company's expense. The problem of where Rennie might stay was resolved by no less a person than the rather dragon-like lady who was the Chairman's private secretary, Miss Montgomery-Tod. Cooing over Rennie like an elderly aunt with a favorite nephew, she tried six hotels before finally getting a room for him at The Howard in Norfolk Street.

At lunchtime, almost the entire staff adjourned to fete Rennie in a nearby pub. Bloated with beer and wartime bangers, his next stop was the tailor's for clothes. Then it was on to The Howard, where he had time for a short nap, a bath and a shave before Blenkinsop collected him to wine and dine him at his club in St. James's.

Blenkinsop insisted on introducing him as a war hero to every club member who tottered within hailing distance. Modestly assuring a succession of elderly gentlemen that they had endured far greater hazards in London from Hitler's bombers than he had encountered at sea. Rennie was moved by the genuine pride with which so many strangers seized his hand and shook it. He graciously accepted the outpouring of tributes, not as garlands for him personally, but as a spontaneous expression of the high regard which the Merchant Navy enjoyed in the public estimation. It's standing had never been higher.

"You must have quite a bit of leave coming to you, John," said Blenkinsop. "What are you going to do with it all?"

Dinner past, they reclined in high-backed leather armchairs, glasses of brandy on the table before them. Rennie pondered the question.

"Well, I don't think I'll be going north. I've sort of lost touch with the old home town since my folks died. There's nothing to take me back."

"I don't blame you. There's still a lot of life in London. There are good times to be had in spite of the bombs and the black-out."

"I won't be looking for a good time. I have things to do."

"Like what?"

"I left a couple of good friends behind barbed wire in Senegal. I want to find out what the hell can be done to get them out."

Blenkinsop's face clouded.

"I can understand how you feel, John, but don't build your hopes too high on seeing your friends again before the war's over. Just count yourself lucky that your knock on the head earned you a ticket home. You've reported what conditions were like on that island. There's nothing more that you can do."

"You don't understand," argued Rennie. "You never met that bastard Junot. My mind may be a blank about how I got my head bashed in, but I'm one hundred per cent certain that Junot was responsible. Somehow I know it."

"Has it crossed your mind that you may have ome out of it lightly? The other two could be dead, John. You could be getting yourself worked up about something that nobody can do anything about."

Rennie sighed wearily.

"I know. I know. Don't think that I haven't thought they might be dead. But until I know for sure, I'm not going to have any peace of mind. I have the feeling that they are alive but that every day that passes is vital. The more time that passes and nothing is done about it, the less their chances of getting off that island alive."

Next day, after an exhaustive examination by the specialist in Harley Street—who said that there was no reason why Rennie shouldn't resume his sea-going duties early in the New Year—Rennie strolled in the direction of Baker Street. It was cold, with a squally wind blowing sleet in his face. He turned along Bentinck Street to escape the wind, and the lights of the Coachmaker's Arms proved an irresistible haven in the winter gloom.

The lunch-time rush had thinned. He ordered a half-pint of bitter and looked round for a seat. There were three empty stools at a table where an army officer was sitting alone reading *The Times.* He nodded politely as Rennie took one of the vacant stools, and smiled before taking a sip from a glass of white wine in front of him.

The officer wore British battle-dress uniform with the insignia of Captain. Rennie's interest in him, which had gone no further than registering his presence, suddenly quickened. A tab on the Captain's shoulder carried the one word, "France." Rennie hesitated only a moment.

"Excuse me, Monsieur," he said, speaking in his more than passable French, "I hope you don't mind me asking you, but I have been wondering how to find the Free French headquarters in London. Perhaps you could help me?"

It was the French captain's turn to study Rennie with interest. He saw a man in a new-looking grey civilian suit, a man about his own age and one who, strangely, did not have the winter pallor of the other Londoners in the pub. This man had a near mahogany complexion, with scarring around one eye and down one cheek. He had blue steady eyes which invited trust. The face was open, honest.

"Why do you want to know, Monsieur?" the officer replied. "I should like to tell you, but . . ." He pointed to a poster on the wall. It warned that careless talk cost lives. "You may be a German spy," the officer ended with a smile.

Rennie returned the smile.

"I have identity papers—brand new ones as it happens. The reason I want to speak to someone on the Free French side is because I'm very anxious to do something about a friend—a French friend. He was in your Navy, on the Vichy side, but wanted to get away to join up under de Gaulle. He . . . We both tried to get out of French West Africa . . . We were prisoners together . . . He didn't make it."

The French captain's interest was now keen.

"You were a prisoner in West Africa?"

"I'm an officer in the British Merchant Navy. The ship I was on was torpedoed. A Vichy destroyer landed us at Dakar."

"From the *Castle* ship? The one with the Italian prisoners?"

"You know about it?" said Rennie in astonishment.

"Monsieur, Berlin and Vichy have tried to tell the world about it. It is a *cause célèbre*. Hitler has ordered his U-boat captains to stop picking up survivors as a result of it. But that is getting away from your French friend . . . I am interested, Monsieur. I should like to hear all about it—but this is not a good place to talk. I work from offices in Baker Street, not far from here. Perhaps we could go there and talk in private?" He drained the last of his wine and stood up.

Rennie hesitated. The French captain's obvious interest made his hopes soar that at last someone was prepared to do something about Jean-Paul, but why an army man, a Frenchman whom he had encountered by the merest of chances? All he had asked was the whereabouts of Free French headquarters. An address was all Rennie wanted, nothing more. Given that, he could go direct to someone with authority.

The French captain was smiling down at him.

"Now, you are wondering why I am so interested, Monsieur? If it would not be better to talk to someone higher up, eh? Well, do not worry. I think it is a stroke of luck for us both that we met. I used to be a journalist and my job now is with the Information Service which the General himself set up here in London. I know for a fact that the General would be intensely interested in the smallest piece of information from inside Dakar. He might even want to talk to you himself."

Rennie hesitated no longer. He sank what was left of his drink in one go and put the glass on the table. He reached for his navy raincoat and stood up.

"Let's go," he said. "Oh, my name is Rennie, by the way. John Rennie."

"And I am Pierre Bernard," said the Frenchman. "For some strange reason, my English friends call me Barney."

Rennie smiled.

"Trust me to step into a pub and walk into a Barney?"

The Frenchman looked at him, puzzled.

"Sorry," said Rennie, "I was making a not vey good joke with an English slang expression. When an Englishman talks about a barney, he means a brawl, a rumpus, a fight, a row, a punch-up. In short, trouble."

The Frenchman laughed.

"Ah, now I see. Do you have a habit of walking into 'barneys', Monsieur Rennie?"

"Oh, I never go looking for trouble," said Rennie with a grin, "but it has a nasty habit of finding me. My problem is walking away from it."

One officer in the British Secret Service became convinced, in the next few days, that John Rennie was asking for trouble. That officer was Kim Philby. In seven years,

Philby—since his recruitment into the Soviet espionage network—had burrowed away in London like an industrious mole, consolidating a front for his nefarious activities in the most sensitive of all British government establishments.

Only recently, just before the Allied landings in North Africa, his industry had been rewarded by the people whom he was betraying with promotion to a key post in Section Five of the Secret Intelligence Service, the department dealing with counter-espionage.

Philby had been warned by his Kremlin masters that he should do nothing to jeopardize his good standing in Whitehall. His main value—and it was considerable—was in keeping Moscow posted on the secret activities of HM Government's agents. It was suggested to Philby, however, that should opportunities occur to create friction between the British and the American secret services—without undue attention being drawn to himself—then situations would be created which the Kremlin could exploit.

The intense activity, at diplomatic level and of a more clandestine nature, which had preceded the "Torch" operations in Algeria and Morocco, had provided ideal opportunities for Philby's mischief. He was aided in this by a certain amount of existing rivalry between British and American organizations. There was also a trait—almost an inbuilt occupational trait—in secret governmental servants, which made them resist encroachment from any quarter. Encroachment from a foreign, albeit friendly, power generated the most profound distrust.

So, at a time when both Churchill and Roosevelt had ordered the maximum of co-ordination of effort and purpose between the secret services of their two countries, there had been great areas of fertile ground where Philby had been able to plant seeds of discord in a most inconspicuous manner.

When a colleague had grumbled about closer working with counterparts in the American OSS, it had been a simple matter for Philby to commiserate and perhaps offer his own view that the Americans were "still bloody amateurs." He would subtly encourage obstructionist tactics, often when little encouragement was needed.

So, a file which the Americans wanted urgently would be inexplicably mislaid, or the wrong one sent. Messages to particular individuals would never reach their destination because they were never passed on from the department where they arrived.

The fact that America had continued to have diplomatic links with Vichy and its African empire, while Britain did not, created all sorts of problems for those doing their best to improve the Anglo-American partnership in Intelligence. Feeling that their sources were superior, certain State Department elements were reluctant to be too forthcoming with the British in case the British interfered and spoiled things. On the British side, there were angry mutterings that the Americans were freezing them out in French North Africa and a monumental political mess would result if they were left to their own devices.

The situation was such that Philby, with a word in an ear here and a throwaway comment there, was able to frustrate months of careful Anglo-American co-operation and, in some cases, sabotage it to the point of irretrievable breakdown. And it was all done subtly enough to leave no direct link between the mischief and its true orchestrator.

Philby might never have heard of John Rennie but for the legend he liked to build around himself that he was something of an authority on French colonial affairs. Thus, a colleague handling a low-priority signal from Freetown sought out Philby to pick his brain.

The signal briefly sketched in the story of John Rennie's repatriation from French West Africa, with head injuries of such severity that recovery beyond a partially comatose state of babbling incoherence was not anticipated. He had apparently sustained his head injuries by leaping from a moving truck on his way to an internment center, while in French hands. The man, however, had made a startling recovery in Sierra Leone and told a garbled tale about trying to escape from an island with a Frenchman and an American who was a geologist or posing as a geologist. The American was using the name Hobart.

The signal went on to say that Peterson of the American OSS had shown considerable interest in the repatriated seaman. The name Hobart obviously made some kind of sense to the Americans. The suspicion was that Hobart was one of Peterson's agents or, more likely, an agent from whom Peterson had been expecting contact. Peterson, however, would not admit to knowing anything about Hobart or what he might have been up to.

The author of the signal was of the opinion that the doubtful mental condition of the seaman made him a most unreliable source of any worthwhile information and that his story about escaping from some island prison could be the ramblings of a confused brain. It was his belief that the Americans were welcome to question the man, for all they were likely to get out of him that made sense. For the time being, the hospital was allowing no interrogation because of the seaman's condition. It was proposed that Peterson be given a clear field to follow up the American connection when the patient was fit to answer questions. London approval was sought to take no further action in the case or, alternatively, to advise if their sources divined any significance and the need for further investigation.

"Do you know this fellow, Peterson?" Philby was asked.

"Yes. Met him in Cairo not long ago. Big man with a bigger mouth. Typical Yankee pain in the neck. Do we have anything on this Hobart?"

"Not a thing. The whole thing is a non-starter if you ask me. I was just going to tell Freetown to forget it. If the Yanks hadn't shown an interest, I doubt if Freetown would have even bothered to report it."

"It's not my show," said Philby, "but I wouldn't let Peterson within a mile of that injured seaman, certainly not before the man had been fully debriefed."

"You think there could be something in the story?"

"Not necessarily, but I know Peterson. He has a genius for making smoke without fire. It would make us look pretty silly if he did get on to something and then did his usual inflation act and blew it up out of all proportion to its importance. You're the one who'd have a fire lit under his seat, old boy, if it was discovered that this seaman fellow's story hadn't even been checked out by our people on the spot."

"Hmm, I see what you mean. The whole thing could still be a load of rubbish."

"It probably is. I'd tell Freetown not to get hot under the collar about it but I'd make certain the Yanks were locked out and told to go and sniff around somewhere else. You can bet your boots that if that had been an American seaman, our people wouldn't have been allowed within twenty square miles of him."

"What if Peterson starts screaming to Washington?"

"If he does that," said Philby, "then it could mean he knows a damned sight more about an American geologist called Hobart than he's letting on. It could mean that the OSS have been playing games in Dakar and keeping us completely in the dark. If they scream, old boy, you have the best justification possible for freezing them right out of the picture. Co-operation is a two-way thing. If they're not going to be perfectly frank with us, why the hell should we make life easy for them?"

Having implanted his words of wisdom, Philby had not expected to hear any more of John Rennie. But Peterson had made waves all the way to London.

Philby had been unofficially consulted a second time by his colleague.

"What the hell am I going to do?" he had asked. "I've got a full rundown on this Rennie from Freetown but I can't make up my mind if they've given me the facts or simply what they think I wanted to hear. They say that the man's mental condition rules out the possibility of placing any credence on his story. But if his story is rubbish, why is Peterson running round like a maniac getting more and more excited?"

"I told you he has a genius for blowing things up out of proportion," said Philby.

"Well, I'm not going to be able to stall him any longer. I've had a heavy hint from on high that if I don't give him access to Rennie, I'll have to start producing very good reasons. Peterson is almost camping on the hospital steps in Freetown waiting for us to let him in."

"Do the dirty on him then," suggested Philby. "While he sits on the front steps, get Rennie out by the back door. If the man's well enough, fly him home and send him on a long sick leave. Then go and see him yourself and make your own mind up about him. Leave the Yanks guessing."

His colleague's delight at the idea of spiriting John Rennie away from Freetown and out of Peterson's reach left Philby in no doubt that this was the course he would adopt. The Americans, of course, would be furious, but if the powers-that-be started making noises Philby was certain that his colleague—rather than appear unequal to his job—would insist that he had acted entirely on his own initiative. The name of Philby would not be mentioned. And, as far as Philby was concerned, no more would be heard of John Rennie.

But he was wrong.

With Christmas only two weeks away, the name of John Rennie cropped up for a third time in Philby's life—and, this time, it was not incidental to a colleague's problem but suddenly central to one of his own. For some time now, he had been occupied with the clandestine activities of the various factions elbowing for power in Algeria.

This struggle, even at the highest level, was putting severe strain on Anglo-American relations. The Americans wanted General Giraud to take command of the territories now freed from Vichy, while the British—much as they were dismayed by his arrogance—backed General de Gaulle as the natural leader of all Free French. Both countries were embarrassed, however, by the *de facto* political control of French North Africa remaining firmly in the hands of the Vichy turncoat, Admiral Darlan.

In order to protect his base of operations in Algiers and get his armies east to face the Germans in Tunisia, General Dwight D. Eisenhower, the Allied military commander, had had to recognize Darlan as the only man capable of maintaining any kind of political stability in the area. The Allied reliance on Darlan had created a world-wide outcry. In order to fight the Germans in Tunisia, Britain and America seemed to be prepared to prop up a Nazi-type regime in Algiers.

Since the occupation of Algiers in November, British agents had been sending back a stream of reports. Philby's department had been concerned mainly with those relevant to the counter-espionage war. These and other reports from Military Intelligence had been the basis of a special memorandum to the Prime Minister.

As a result of the memorandum, Churchill had seen fit to cable Roosevelt on 9 December saying how disturbed he was by reports from North Africa. He detailed the behavior of Vichy sympathizers and others whom he labelled as "kindred Fascist Organizations" against French who sympathized with the Allies. Churchill wrote: "Not only have our enemies been thus encouraged but our friends have been correspondingly confused and cast down."

Philby had taken a calculated risk, in various analyses of intelligence, to be openly critical of American activity in North Africa, whether it was overt or undercover. Arguing from what his overlords took to be a profound faith in the superiority of British expertise over American, Philby neglected no opportunity to blame American political naïvety and diplomatic blundering for every trouble that bedeviled the North African situation.

His contempt for the American effort in the secret war had already, he knew, aroused the suspicion in some American quarters. Hoover, the head of the FBI, had already pinpointed him as a thorn in the flesh of Anglo-American co-operation and had sought his dismissal.

Philby felt secure, however, in the belief that he would not be dismissed simply for repeating views which he knew many of his senior colleagues shared: that the Americans were clumsy and amateurish and seeking far too great an influence in a field of activity where the British, with their long experience, reigned supreme. He realized that neither the British nor the Americans had the slightest awareness of the presence of a Russian finger in the pie. Nor could they have comprehended the truly inimical nature of Russian designs, believing as they did that the Russians were their staunch allies and friends.

When someone like Hoover had the nerve to suggest that somebody on the British side was deliberately trying to wreck Anglo-American co-operation and that that somebody was Kim Philby, few on either side took the accusation seriously. Hoover was obviously overstating the issues. He would suspect his own grandmother.

Philby realized, however, that if someone in the OSS started pointing a finger at him, his security could be threatened. If Peterson weighed in to voice the same kind of suspicions as Hoover's, there was just a chance that someone senior enough in the British Secret Intelligence Service might begin to think that Philby's antipathy to Americans was becoming too much of an embarrassment.

The affair of John Rennie suddenly brought this possibility nearer.

Without officially involving himself, Philby had twice been responsible for frustrating American interest in John Rennie. Now, this unknown and quite unimportant Merchant Navy officer had precipitated a crisis which had landed the whole matter in Philby's lap.

John Rennie had become a damned nuisance. While he had been a minor problem for the West African branch of "The Firm," there had been no connection between Philby and Peterson's anguished cries of British obstruction. But, now, there might be. Philby's chief had broken the news to him in surprise fashion.

"De Gaulle's been kicking up hell with the PM again, Kim. It's something you'd better look into."

"What bee has the General got in his bonnet this time?" asked Philby.

"I don't quite know. He was on again about the Vichy lot still running the show in Algiers and persecuting his supporters. He was agitated too, though, about a talk he had with some Merchant Navy chap who fell foul of the French in Dakar."

Philby was instantly on the alert.

"A Merchant Navy chap? If he has been to see the General, we'll know about it. We've been keeping tabs on all the General's visitors."

"This chap didn't call on the General. He bumped into him at the Free French place in Baker Street and apparently was closeted with him there for over an hour."

"Nothing earth-shaking in that," said Philby.

"Maybe not," said his chief, "but a number of interesting names were dropped in the conversation. It appears that this fellow—his name's Rennie, by the way—was incarcerated with a French naval lieutenant called Jean-Paul Mercier."

"And?"

"And Jean-Paul Mercier is the son-in-law of Admiral Bousquet."

Philby made a whistling noise as an indication that he was impressed.

"Bousquet's son-in-law, eh? That makes a difference. What do you want me to do about it?"

"I want the whole story, Kim. It turns out that our people have already run the rule over this fellow Rennie in Freetown and decided he was a head case—but it hasn't stopped them whisking him away from under the noses of the Americans, who were extremely interested in him. The Yanks are as angry as hell. And if that wasn't bad enough, the fellow turns up in London and goes shooting his mouth off to de Gaulle. I want to know just what the hell is going on, Kim. This Rennie may have no connection with what's going on in Algiers right now but you, yourself, have said that Bousquet has more influence in North Africa than even Darlan. I want to know if the Americans or the French know something that we don't but bloody well ought to."

Kim Philby left the interview with his chief with a slim folder under his arm. The folder held all the information which the SIS had so far documented on John Rennie. In the privacy of his own office, Philby went over that information several times. He decided that John Rennie was more of a nuisance than a threat. But even a nuisance can be very tiresome. It was time something was done about the man.

He made several outside telephone calls, then dialed an internal number.

"Superintendent Latimer's office," said a voice over the wire. "Sergeant Park speaking."

Philby identified himself and then said: "I've got a job for you, Sergeant Park. I'm rather anxious to have a chat with an individual who is staying at the Howard Hotel in Norfolk Street. His name is John Rennie. He's an officer in the Merchant Navy and shouldn't give you any trouble."

"Is he likely to be armed, sir?"

"That's most unlikely. No, the most dangerous thing about Mr. Rennie is his tongue."

"I see, sir. Shall we bring him to the usual place?"

"Yes. I'll get over there right away. Oh, and Park . . ."

"Yes, sir?"

"I don't want any bones broken but you don't have to be too gentle with him. Lean on him a bit. I want him to appreciate what a nice fellow I am. So, it will help if you put the fear of death in him first."

"I understand, sir. Been blabbing about our shipping movements to the enemy, has he, sir? I got no sympathy for bastards like that. I know just what to do, sir."

"I'm sure you do, Sergeant," said Philby and hung up the phone.

Chapter Eight

RENNIE trembled with anger and a sense of outrage. He sat wedged between the two big men in the rear seat of the heavy-engined Austin as the car sped west along the Victoria Embankment.

He had offered no resistance when the two men had burst unannounced into his room at the Howard. He had been rinsing shaving soap from his face at the wash-basin and had turned, half bending, as the door had been flung open. His startled query was silenced by the less intelligent-looking of the two men, who had thrust a police identity card in front of his face and said: "Special Branch."

"How can I help you?" Rennie had begun to say, when the man who had flashed the card seized his wrist, twisted his arm behind his back and forced him face-down on the bed.

"Go through his things, Bert," the big man muttered over his shoulder.

Rennie had tried to protest, but every time he tried to speak, the big man grabbed the back of his head and held his face pressed against the bed coverings so that Rennie could scarcely breathe.

"Nothing here, Sarge," the second policeman announced, after he had rifled through Rennie's few belongings.

Rennie's captor did not relax his hold. He took a fistful of Rennie's hair and turned Rennie's head round so that his mouth and face were free of the covers.

"Been flogging convoy secrets to the Jerries, have you?" snarled the Sergeant. "Shooting's too good for you bastards."

"You've got the wrong man. I don't know what the hell you're talking about!" cried Rennie.

The Sergeant's answer was to twist Rennie's hair in his hand.

"That's what they all say." The Sergeant suddenly let Rennie's hair go. He stared at the patch of new growth which was still quite short on Rennie's scalp. "Somebody been hitting you on the head, then?" he inquired. "Look at this, Bert. He's been cut up real good."

The other man peered at Rennie's head.

"Better leave off, Sarge. He's had surgery there—and not long ago."

The Sergeant let Rennie go and got up. Rennie felt dizzy and his head ached. He got off the bed and swayed on his feet. The second policeman was regarding him anxiously. He reproached his Sergeant:

"One of these days, you're going to kill some poor sod, Sarge." He turned to Rennie. "You all right?"

"I'll live," muttered Rennie. He stared at the Sergeant. "There was no bloody need for that. Now, maybe you'll tell me what this is all about."

"We're taking you to meet somebody," said the Sergeant. "Get your coat—and no funny stuff."

"Where are you taking me? I told you you've got the wrong man."

"You're John Rennie, aren't you?"

"Yes."

"Well, we've got the right man. Are you going to come quietly or do we have to put the cuffs on you?"

"Tell me what it's all about."

"Mr. Smith will explain."

"Who's Mr. Smith?"

"The man who wants to see you."

"I don't want to see him," said Rennie stubbornly. "If the invitation had been put a little more politely, perhaps . . . But I've never heard of your Mr. Smith and I don't know what he wants to see me about. Why don't you go back and tell him to phone and make an appointment?"

The Sergeant took a step forward. "Put his coat on him, Bert. We're going to have to do this the hard way."

Rennie made no struggle, but he was held and his arms forced into the sleeves of his raincoat.

"Aren't you going to let me put on a shirt and a jacket?" he asked.

"You should have thought of that before. You had the chance," said the Sergeant.

People in the lobby stared in astonishment as Rennie was propelled out of the hotel by the two men. A big Austin was parked at the kerb, a driver inside. Rennie was bundled into the back seat and the car moved off down Norfolk Street towards the Embankment. He sat uncomfortably between the Special Branch men, his arms still held, while his fury boiled within him.

The car did not slow as they reached Scotland Yard but kept on going towards St. James's. Finally, it turned sharply into a cul-de-sac and was braked to a stop in the forecourt of the St Ermin's Hotel.

Rennie was led in by a side door and taken straight to a lift. He was taken to a room on the third floor and ushered inside.

There was little furniture in the room: a table with two telephones, four straight chairs and a leather couch. Patches on the wallpaper showed where a couple of wardrobes had once stood. A man in a dark suit was standing at the window, staring out. He turned.

"Ah, Mr. Rennie. How good of you to come. Won't you take a seat?" He nodded towards the Special Branch sergeant. "Thank you, Park. No need to stay."

The two police officers exchanged slightly puzzled looks and went out. Rennie made no move to sit down.

"You are Mr. Smith?" he said.

"Smith, Brown, Jones. It's not important." The other man smiled. 'Won't you take off your coat?"

"Thanks, but I'll keep it on. I was shaving when your two gorillas called. I didn't have time to throw on a shirt."

The other man sighed.

"Sergeant Park is rather enthusiastic. You must forgive him. He's used to dealing with dangerous criminals. I hope you didn't upset him."

"I'd like to upset something over him—like a barrel of hot tar."

The man who called himself "Mr. Smith" made a shrugging gesture.

"Oh—then you did upset him? I'm sorry."

"You're going to be . . . Unless you can give me a damned good reason why I was frog-marched out of my hotel and pushed around like I was Jack the Ripper. Hansel and Gretel said they were from Special Branch."

"Quite true," said Smith. "They were acting on my orders. You could say they are the long legal arm of the department of Government which employs me."

"Security?"

"Something like that. It's unimportant. What you should understand, of course, is the power which our branch of Government wields and the latitude we have to exercise that power—especially in wartime. It is sometimes necessary to forego such niceties of procedure as courts of law. You do understand, old chap, don't you?"

"I think I'm beginning to . . . But I still don't know what you want of me. The big fairy—the one who looked like Tommy Farr's punchbag—said something about me selling convoy secrets to the Jerries. He's out of his tiny mind. And you're crazy, too, if that's what you think."

"Oh, I don't think you're a wilful traitor, Mr. Rennie. Not that that would stop me having you locked up under the War Emergency Act. I think that, at the worst, you were probably just very indiscreet."

"Feel free to elaborate on that," said Rennie with irony.

"Let's sit down first, shall we. Would you like me to order some tea?"

Rennie sat down on one of the hard chairs with the air of one whose patience is near exhaustion.

"Let's skip the hospitality," he said curtly.

The one who called himself Smith was in no hurry. He sat down opposite Rennie and adopted almost a praying attitude: placing his hands together just below his chin, so that the fingertips met. He stared thoughtfully up at the ceiling.

"Did you know that the last merchant seaman we hanged was a man called George Thomas Armstrong? It was just about eighteen months ago."

"What did he do to deserve that?" asked Rennie. "No, don't tell me. You caught him eating peas with a knife."

"No, he's one who did sell convoy sailing times to the Germans. He belonged to the wrong political party, too, of course. He was a Communist. Do you belong to a political party, Mr. Rennie?"

"No. In that respect I'm an atheist. No political party commands my soul, Mr. Smith-Brown-Jones. That doesn't mean that the right party doesn't exist. I just haven't found it."

"Then it would be more correct to say you are a political agnostic?"

"It would be correct to say that we're not getting anywhere very fast. You were going to tell me of my indiscretions. How about getting on with it?"

"Very well. Your trouble, Mr. Rennie, is that you talk too much—and to the wrong people. First, you tell a fantastic story to an American Government agent called Peterson. Then you go repeating the same wild stuff to a refugee foreign general who is the unbidden guest in this country of His Majesty's Government. We really cannot allow it, Mr. Rennie."

"You mean that that's the cause of all this nonsense?" cried Rennie. "You've brought me here because I've tried to get somebody, anybody, to help two friends of mine to escape from West Africa."

"There's no need to raise your voice, Mr. Rennie. I can see now that you obviously have no idea of the damage you may have done."

"You're dead right about that!" flamed Rennie.

"You don't seem to appreciate," countered Smith, "that the interests of His Majesty's Government and those of America and the Free French may not coincide. You can be forgiven for not knowing just how delicate the political situation in French North Africa is at this very moment—but it's something you'll have to get into your head. Please take my word for it, you have been interfering in matters that are away over your head. I can tell you in the strictest confidence that as a result of the seemingly *harmless* conversation you had with General de Gaulle, that same gentleman is making strong political pressures on both the British and American Governments and exploiting for his own political ends differences of opinion in the Allied camp."

"But that's absurd," said Rennie. "For heaven's sake, aren't we all on the same side . . . French, American, British? I don't know any State secrets. All I know is that I got out of Senegal and left two good friends behind—one a Frenchman and one an American. I want somebody to do something to get them out before it's too late."

The man who called himself Smith sighed.

"Aren't *you* being a little absurd now, Mr. Rennie? We're engaged in a global war and thousands of men are dying every day. I can understand your anxiety for your two friends but they're no different from the tens of thousands of prisoners held by the Germans and the Japanese. We'd like to rescue them all but we've got to face reality. There isn't really very much we can do about them."

Rennie bowed his head dejectedly. Smith-Brown-Jones, or whatever his name was, was right. It had been preposterous to think that anyone could really do anything to rescue Hobart and Jean-Paul. What had driven him to think that as much as a finger might be raised to help them?

He closed his eyes and a terrible fear and helplessness seemed to envelop him. He put his hands over his face but still the nameless dread enclosed him, making him want to cry out. He slid from the chair on to the floor. The sound of the chair opposite him being pushed back echoed in his ears—but it did not sound to him like a chair's legs bumping over the floor. It was like the rapid clicking of rifle bolts being drawn back.

A voice said: "Good heavens, man, are you ill?" But these words did not reach him. Instead, he was hearing orders shouted in French and a fierce light was dazzling his eyes. Then the face of a Senegalese soldier was looming before his face. He could see the butt of the man's rifle raised to club him and he could hear the scream coming from his own lips as the rifle thudded into his own flesh and bone. He could taste blood and sand in his mouth. From the corner of his eye he could see Hobart's body further along the beach—and there was Jean-Paul, with four soldiers pinioning him. Now he saw the hated figure of Junot come into view. He watched him take a rifle and bayonet from a soldier. The weapon was raised and then thrust at Jean-Paul. Rennie closed his eyes and pressed his face into the sand. Then he felt a hand gripping him by the shoulder and turning him over.

Again the light was dazzling his eyes, although he kept them tightly shut. Now a finger was poking at his eyes. An eyelid was forced open. He was staring straight into the light. The light seemed to be only inches away from his eyeball. He jerked his head away and dared to open both his eyes. Then a voice spoke.

"He's coming round."

Rennie turned his head slowly. The speaker was bending over him. He held in his hand what appeared to be a pencil flash-light. He had been shining the light in Rennie's eye.

"Just lie perfectly still," said the man. "Give yourself time to come to."

Rennie slowly took in his surroundings. Smith-Brown-Jones was standing a few feet behind the man nearest him. A doctor? An open black medical bag stood on the table.

"You were out for the count," said the doctor. "Has this happened to you before?"

"No," said Rennie. He struggled to a sitting position. "I'm all right now. I . . . I feel . . . calmer." He rubbed his eyes like a man who was woken from a long sleep. "I can remember everything now. Everything."

The doctor turned to Smith-Brown-Jones.

"The black-out was obviously an after-effect of that head injury. Have you any idea how he got it?"

"He jumped from a moving truck, as far as I know."

"That wasn't what happened," said Rennie quietly. "I can remember it all now. Every detail."

"Couldn't you remember before?" asked the doctor.

"Not everything. I couldn't remember how I got the knock on the head or what had happened immediately before. But I do now. I can remember the Senegalese soldier clubbing me with his rifle and kicking me. Hobart was lying on the beach as if he were dead. Maybe he was dead. I don't know what they did to him. Jean-Paul was being held by four soldiers and Junot was screaming at him like a madman. Then Junot bayoneted him. I thought at first that Junot was going for his guts—but it was the upper leg. First one thigh and then the other . . . The bayonet went right through."

The doctor was gazing at Rennie with a horrified look on his face. He turned his head and threw a questioning look at Smith-Brown-Jones.

"Do you know what he's talking about?"

"Perhaps. He spent some time in the hands of the Vichy French and obviously had an unpleasant time. Some of our people thought the knock on the head caused hallucinations."

"I know what happened to me," said Rennie, an edge of anger in his voice.

Smith-Brown-Jones was instantly apologetic.

"Of course you do, old chap. I admit I had doubts, but

not any more. When the French returned you to our people in Sierra Leone, the last thing they expected was that you would ever again be well enough to tell the tale on them. They obviously invented a cover-up story for how you got your injuries. Well, with your help we'll see that the blighters responsible don't get away with it. I want you to tell me everything you know."

The doctor looked questioningly at Smith-Brown-Jones. "Can that wait? I think this man should be in hospital, if only for observation."

"I'm not going to hospital," put in Rennie. The doctor's eyebrows shot up at the vehemence of his interruption. "I'm sorry," said Rennie, "but I've had enough of hospitals in the past few months. I'll be all right now, honestly."

"It's your decision," said the doctor. "I can't force you. But at least go and see your doctor pretty soon. He should know about your blacking out. You'll be running unnecessary risks if you don't check with him regularly and keep him fully in the picture."

Smith-Brown-Jones accompanied the doctor out to the corridor. Rennie heard him thanking him. There was also a whispered conversation which Rennie could not make out. The doctor was probably being reminded to keep his mouth shut about his emergency call, Rennie surmised with accuracy.

When Smith-Brown-Jones returned, he was most solicitous about Rennie, attributing the black-out to the rough handling he had experienced at the hands of that ox of a Special Branch sergeant.

Then the real questioning began. Smith-Brown-Jones wanted to know everything that had happened to Rennie from the moment the *Blairmount Castle* had been sunk. He was particularly interested in Bishop and his failure to get along with just about everybody. He was curious, too, about Bishop's strange vanishing act and a possible connection between it and the betrayal of the escape plan.

He wanted to know everything about Arlette Mercier and her revelation to Rennie of belonging to an anti-Vichy organization in Algiers. He tried to get Rennie to recall every scrap of remembered conversation about Jean-Paul's father-in-law, Admiral Bousquet. Smith-Brown-Jones seemed to feed on names. Boudin, Junot, internees at L'Ile de Voleurs . . . his appetite was insatiable.

Lastly, came Rennie's interviews with Peterson, the

Frenchman, Barnard, and the formidable General de Gaulle, whom Rennie had found to be the most charming and sympathetic of men, nothing like his public image.

Rennie told Smith-Brown-Jones that Peterson, too, had had an insatiable appetite for names—in particular, those that Hobart might have mentioned.

"I remember him trying to get me to recall if Hobart had said anything about meeting the Governor-General," said Rennie. "The name's gone . . . It started with a B."

"Boisson?" prompted Smith-Brown-Jones, with an air of surprise.

"Yes, that's it, Boisson. Peterson was quite insistent about knowing if Dick Hobart had ever mentioned Boisson's name or given an indication that he had met him."

Smith-Brown-Jones digested this thoughtfully.

"And had Hobart met Boisson?"

Rennie shook his head.

"No. I had never heard the name Boisson before Peterson brought it up. And I'm damned sure Dick never said anything to me about the Governor-General. He just didn't talk about himself at all. And I didn't ask."

At last, it was over. Smith-Brown-Jones had made copious notes. Now, he put them all into a brief-case.

"I'll get a car to take you back to your hotel," he told Rennie. "I'm very grateful to you for all your help. Will you accept my apologies for the way you were brought here?"

"It's in the past now. I'll try to forget it happened."

"There's a lot you should try to forget. What happened in Africa, the people you met, all you've told me. I want you to forget you've even met me."

"There are some things I won't forget easily," said Rennie.

"Try all the same," said Smith-Brown-Jones. "It's over for you now, done with. I've got to ask you to say nothing about it to anyone—French, Americans, anyone who tries to approach you. They'll be warned not to bother you, of course. I'll see to that. Have you signed the Official Secrets Act?"

"No."

"Then I'll get you to do that before you go. It's just a formality, of course, but an important one. Once you've signed it, your lips have to remain sealed. You understand, don't you?"

Rennie stared hard at the other man.

"I'm not signing anything. I'm funny that way. I just can't bring myself to put my name to promises I might not be able to keep. The Vichy French wanted me to sign a piece of paper, too. Remember?"

"This is different."

"Is it?" said Rennie drily. His eyes mocked Smith-Brown-Jones. "What happens if I don't sign?"

"If you don't sign, you might leave the authorities with no option but to place you under restraint."

"In other words, I might be deprived of the liberty that we Britons are supposed to be fighting for."

"That is a fairly accurate assumption," said Smith-Brown-Jones.

Rennie's eyes sparkled like icicles in sunlight.

"I've always believed that a signature obtained under threat was worthless."

"No one is threatening you."

"Well, that's fine," said Rennie, the steely brightness in his eyes never wavering, "I'll sign your piece of paper . . . And any promise I make in it will be as valid as the absence of threat in inducing me to sign."

Smith-Brown-Jones met Rennie's unblinking stare. They stood locked in silent combat of will. Rennie's tongue-in-cheek acceptance of the demand for his signature was more openly provocative and challenging than would have been his continued refusal to sign. It left Smith-Brown-Joses in no doubt of Rennie's position. The Merchant Navyman was making it plain that he would be no more bound by a vow of silence obtained under duress than any law court would be influenced by a confession extracted on the rack.

It was Smith-Brown-Jones who ended the silent confrontation. He turned away with an impatient snort.

"Well, that's that," he said. "We understand each other." He stood deep in thought for a moment, temporarily as distracted as a miner who has been drilling in soft earth and struck granite. A different approach was needed.

"Look, Mr. Rennie," he said with false heartiness, "it hasn't been my intention to try to intimidate you. You're not the kind of man who is going to be bullied into doing anything he doesn't want to do . . . I applaud that." He shrugged. "But it's difficult to caution you against imprudence without seeming heavy-handed. All I want you to do is leave things with us from here on. We know that you have been motivated by concern for your two friends and I want to assure you that we share that concern. We realize that the chances of Hobart and Mercier being still alive are very slim—but we won't let matters rest. Bousquet is an important man in North Africa and it's inconceivable that any of the Vichy crowd would go so far as to have his son-in-law murdered. That may be the only comfort you can take out of this."

"A small hope is better than nothing," said Rennie. "There's not much more I can do about it, is there? Just hope."

"There's nothing you can do, Mr. Rennie." The flat statement was delivered with such finality that it became more than just a statement. It warned John Rennie against any future involvement. The matter was now out of his hands.

Kim Philby's chief—a man known to his intimates as Ginny because of a predeliction for drinking gin neat and the capacity to go through bottles of the stuff without turning a hair—laid the report down on his desk and buzzed the internal phone.

"That you, Philby?" he said into the mouthpiece. "Can you spare me a moment? I've been through your report and I'd like a natter about it before I show my face upstairs. Come through, will you?"

Philby was apprehensive when he arrived and was invited to "take a pew," but he covered it with a show of smiling deference.

"Anything wrong?" he enquired.

"Not at all. It's an excellent report. You've done damned well."

Philby smiled.

"You do appreciate, sir, that some of the conclusions I suggest we can draw are more conjecture than anything else. I can't come straight out and say that the Americans have been deliberately misleading us about what they were up to in Dakar—and in North Africa, too, probably—but they've probably been doing their damnedest to pull the wool over our eyes."

"I think we can make that assumption—even if we don't have all the facts we need to back it up. They're still being absolutely bloody-minded over de Gaulle. They won't let us forget the cock-up de Gaulle made when he tried to return to Dakar like a conquering hero, but it's damned shabby of them to try their own stunt in Dakar without saying a rod to us about it."

"That is conjecture, sir, on my part," said Philby. "I tried to piece together the few facts we have and form a picture that made sense."

"Well, you made a damned good job of it," said his chief. "I think it's high time the Yanks were put in their place. We're being pressurized all the time to co-operate with them. Tell them this, tell them that—and all the time they're doing things like this behind our backs. It's bloody galling."

"It would be wrong to over-react, sir. I mean, without having absolutely solid facts."

"Who's over-reacting?" demanded the other, whose face—florid enough from that day's gin—was turning a deeper red. "There's no doubt that this fellow, Hobart, was doing exactly what you suggest he was doing."

"Well, it made sense to me," said Philby, "although all I did was to put two and two together. We know that Boisson, the Governor-General of French West Africa, is a man for whom Roosevelt has the very highest regard. Roosevelt must have believed that the whole of French West Africa would have come right over bloodlessly to the Allied side if Boisson could be won over secretly. The snag from Roosevelt's point of view was our distrust of Boisson and de Gaulle's. If he had tried to do a deal with Boisson through normal diplomatic channels, either our people in the States or de Gaulle's in Dakar would probably have got wind of it and tried to stop it. That's why a secret envoy was sent. This man Hobart. But the whole thing obviously got fouled up. The Vichy spy-catchers got on to him before he got anywhere near Boisson. They thought he was organizing de Gaulle supporters but they didn't have a shred of evidence to support it—so, they just took the American out of circulation. The Americans must have been laying eggs wondering what had happened to their man. It explains why Peterson got all excited when Rennie, the British seaman, turned up in

Sierra Leone with some wild story about being held prisoner with an American called Hobart."

Philby's chief frowned.

"The damnable thing is that we'll never be able to come right out and accuse the Yanks with the story. They would deny it point-blank."

"They would have to, wouldn't they," said Philby, who was far from displeased at the likelihood. There was probably only one person in the world who could effectively contradict his ingenious but quite unsupported treatise, which had the capacity to aggravate further the growing disharmony between the British and American Intelligence Services. That man was Richard Hobart. And Hobart, in all probability, was quite dead.

"What about this John Rennie?" asked the man behind the desk.

"He wants to get back to sea as quickly as possible. He's a bit bewildered by everything."

"The Americans still want to talk to him."

"Well, we'll just have to tell them to get stuffed—in the nicest possible way, of course. We put on our stupid look and say we can't understand why they are making such a fuss. We only need to show them a copy of one of the Freetown reports to show that the man's mental condition leaves a lot to be desired. No useful purpose could possibly be served by pursuing the matter further. Unless, of course, there's *something* they know about that we don't . . ."

"Such as a mad stunt to do a deal with a Vichy French G.-G. who is not noted for his love of Britain? You're a crafty bastard, Philby."

Philby smiled slyly.

"If that doesn't do the trick, we can always wave de Gaulle in their face. Tell them that Rennie has already given us a red face by getting de Gaulle's ear and providing him with ammunition to fire at the dear old United States. We just cannot run the risk of a repeat of this kind of embarrassment with anything he might say to them."

The man behind the desk chortled.

"You'll get this department a bad name, Philby. Upstairs will get the impression that we don't like Americans."

"Of course, sir, that impression would be quite erroneous. We love the Americans but we have our own way of doing things. The fact that they are waving dollar bills all over London doesn't give them the right to jump into bed with us."

"And so say all of us," said the man behind the desk. He reached inside a drawer and produced a bottle of gin and two glasses. "Can I offer you a wet?"

"Thank you, no, sir. Sweetened with some Italian, perhaps—but on its own, no."

"Suit yourself," said the other, splashing gin into his glass. "Cleanest drink there is, gin." Philby wrinkled his nose and shuddered as his chief took a big swallow from the glass.

"Was there anything else, sir? I've got quite a lot on my plate."

"No, there's nothing else. I was just going to comment that it's odd the way Bousquet's name keeps cropping up. Our people are trying to get the old fox on our side in Algiers and, here, he crops up in this Dakar thing. You can't see any connecting threads, can you?"

Philby shook his head.

"The Bousquet connection makes it interesting, especially the daughter's tie-up with an anti-Vichy group and her husband's Free French sympathies. I intend to ask for more information. But it's just coincidence, I think, that Bousquet should turn up alongside the Hobart enterprise and what the Americans were up to. It just shows the extent of Bousquet's influence. Our people are doing the right thing going after him. He might not be such a Darlan-lover as the Americans seem to think. They certainly don't trust him an inch."

"It would be quite an eye-opener if we found that Bousquet had been secretly against Vichy all along, but I doubt very much if he was. Our people are finding him a very awkward customer indeed. He treats us and the Americans as if we had no right being in North Africa, but manages to give the impression he would rather co-operate with the Yanks than with us."

"And the Yanks don't want to know?" said Philby.

"No, he's too much of the old imperialist for them. Murphy hates his guts."

"Franklin D.'s special plenipotentiary?" asked Philby.

"The same. He's on record as saying that whatever

Bousquet professes to be and whatever colors he flies at his mast, the old man himself is a Fascist at heart."

Philby's chief finished the gin and poured some more. "Talking of Murphy. Any fresh light on that OSS man of his and the Barbary Consignment?"

Philby squirmed. He had hoped that his chief would not have brought up that sensitive matter. Ideally, of course, he would have liked to lay the entire blame for the missing Barbary Consignment at the door of the OSS as yet another example of American incompetence—but that was difficult when the whole thing was such a baffling mystery. He said:

"I'm sorry we're no further ahead on that, sir. We've had a team in Algiers working on it ever since the 'Torch' landings but they've come up with nothing. It could be another American botch-up. We landed the stuff safely enough near Oran—that was back in July—and Murphy's man took delivery. It was loaded into a truck and the OSS chappie was to deliver it to our French friends in Algiers. But it never arrived in Algiers."

"No, *it* didn't," said Philby's chief, "but the OSS man *did,* with his throat cut! I would think twice, Kim, before accusing the Americans of fouling this up. We asked for their help, they gave it, and they wound up with one of their best men dead. I surely don't need to emphasize to you how embarrassing it could be if it transpired that we had put our trust in the wrong people in Algiers."

"Please don't misunderstand me, sir. I'm not blaming the Yanks, even though it was their end of the operation that went wrong. But there's absolutely nothing to suggest that our Algiers contacts are anything but snow-white. They're completely baffled by the whole thing. They thought we had let them down. We had promised them a truck-load of the most sophisticated sabotage gadgets ever tied up in one parcel and they waited and they waited and it never came. We don't know if the truck ever reached Algiers or was hi-jacked before it got there. It just seems to have vanished off the face of the earth. Nobody knows where, how, or even when."

Philby's chief sighed.

"Well, the purpose of the consignment has been achieved without it. The French handed Algiers to us on a plate. But we can't leave a shipment like that lying around waiting to be found by any Tom, Dick or Harry.

We've bloody well got to get it back, Philby, or there's going to be hell to pay."

"Yes, sir, I know."

Mention of the so-called "Barbary Consignment" drove from Philby's mind all the delight he had been feeling at his handling of the John Rennie affair. He retired from his chief's sanctum in a bitter and angry mood.

Back in his own office, he took the Rennie file from a drawer. Most of the stuff could now be returned to the West Africa department and filed away. He extracted his own copious notes for his own file and made a note of the reference number of the West African folder.

He threw it down on his desk. That was that. It was most unlikely he would ever have to refer to the folder again. The whole thing had been a diversion in triviality, but useful enough if—in the end—it lubricated the endless petty feuding between the American and British Services.

The odd thought crossed his mind that John Rennie was a fool to be in such a haste to get back to sea. He had been torpedoed twice but still he wanted to go back for more. Next time, the sea or the U-boats would probably get him for good. Well, that would be the poor dupe's bad luck. In a way, it would be a satisfactory way of closing the file.

If Philby nurtured any human feeling for John Rennie, there was no charity in it—only contempt. One thing was fairly certain. Once the folder was back in the file, John Rennie could be forgotten.

Philby was quite sure he would never hear of him again. Philby was wrong.

Chapter Nine

THE pilot throttled back on the Liberator's powerful 1,200 h.p. Wasp engines and brought the big aircraft on course for the final run-in to Gander airfield. Below, the rocky wooded slopes of the Newfoundland wilderness lay white in the morning sunlight. The snows had come early this year, with a heavy fall in November, but the blizzard of yesterday—Christmas Eve—had died out as suddenly as it had begun, and Christmas morning had started with bright blue skies and no wind other than frost-laden gentle airs from the north.

Rennie had remained huddled in his duffle-coat, a blanket pulled around him, in the unheated and cramped passenger section since the aircraft's take-off from Prestwick some twelve hours before. One way or another, no fewer than fourteen passengers had been shoe-horned into the converted bomber. Nearly all of them were pilots of Ferry Command making return trips to Canada after delivering a fleet of Lockheed Hudsons to Aldergrove, near Belfast. The exceptions were Rennie, a middle-aged man who was a King's Messenger, and a thirty-five-year-old Canadian who had been introduced to Rennie as Dr. Kerslaw.

In spite of the cold and the discomfort, the journey across the Atlantic night had been far from cheerless. Rennie had been filled with a rare exhilaration ever since the Super had come to him with twin items of exciting news. The first was that, after further checks by the Harley Street doctor, he had been passed as fit for sea duty. Not bad, he thought, for someone who had been written off by a French surgeon as a vegetable only a couple of months before. Rennie had carefully omitted to tell the doctor of his black-out in the room at the St. Ermin's but, even if he had, the great man might not have altered his verdict all that much. He believed that the actual damage to Rennie's brain, although dangerous, had been minimal in a physical sense. It had created some cerebral pressure, inducing semi-coma rather than deep coma. The Harley Street man, while acknowledging the French surgeon's skill in repairing the physical injury, believed that Rennie had been in much greater danger from shock. Shock had complicated his semi-comatose condition and caused temporary derangement. It explained his total lack of awareness at times when he was obviously fully conscious and performing simple bodily functions such as eating and drinking and urinating and talking. Shock had caused the amnesia which had made it so difficult for Rennie to piece together the events leading up to the attempted escape, and had left him oblivious of four or five weeks of his life which were and would remain a complete blank.

The second item of news had been the company's decision to give Rennie his first command. He was now Captain John Rennie. The ship he was to command was brand new. She was currently undergoing trials in Vancouver Sound, the latest product of the West Coast Shipbuilding Company of Canada, and he was to take her over on 8 January. She was the *Fort Daring*. Technically, the ship was the property of the US War Shipping Administration, but she was to be crewed and managed by the British company and sail under the red ensign. A full complement of officers, crew and gunners had sailed in mid-December to New York, en route to man the ship, but a radio message from mid-Atlantic had advised that the original Master had died of a heart attack. Rennie was to be flown out as replacement.

Rennie was over the moon at his promotion and, in the frantic rush to organize himself and get to Prestwick for a Christmas Eve take-off, the nightmare of the past few months was forgotten. The returning Ferry pilots were an exuberant bunch and the cold discomfort of the Liberator's interior was dispelled by their good company and the liberal sharing of bottles of Scotch whisky which they produced from their flying bags.

Perhaps because they were in the minority, Rennie and the two civilians attracted much of the banter and good-humored interest of the airmen. But the intent was kindly. The fliers did not want to appear to be excluding the strangers in their midst.

When it was discovered that the Canadian doctor was a psychiatrist, it produced a rash of outrageous jokes about "trick-cyclists" which—in the event—the Canadian was nearly always able to cap with anecdotes from his own experience. This led to a spate of amnesia jokes. One of these provoked a great deal of hilarity with everyone except Rennie.

"What's the matter, Captain?" roared the teller, scarcely able to control his own laughter. "Don't you get it? This guy said to the nurse: 'Hey, I've got one of those but I can't remember what it's for!' "

Rennie grinned apologetically.

"Sorry," he said. "It's a good story but it's too damned near the truth. I got a knock on the head not long ago and I suffered amnesia. And what you were saying reminded me of something the doctor in London said about it. I've been lying awake at nights ever since, wondering about it."

There was a chorus of demands that Rennie should reveal the cause of his sleeplessness.

"Well," he said, "I have four or five weeks which are a complete blank when, as far as I'm concerned, I just wasn't in this world; but the doc said it was like I was drugged with shock. I was physically conscious and talking and eating and my body was functioning normally in spite of the fact that I didn't have control of my mind. And that's what's been bothering me. I'm wondering how many times I wet the bed!"

The pilots guffawed with laughter. They were curious to know more about his amnesia but Rennie dismissed it lightly: "Oh, I got a knock on the head. Somebody tried to kick my brains in. He came off worst. He broke four toes!"

Later, in the quieter watches of the night, as the aircraft had forged west into head winds high above the dark Atlantic and the passengers had quietened and dozed, the Canadian Kerslaw raised the subject of Rennie's amnesia with him.

"I'm interested," he said. "Like to tell me the whole story?"

Rennie looked at him quizzically.

"What *is* your interest, Doctor?" Preposterous as it seemed, the thought had flashed into his mind that Smith-Brown-Jones had somehow spirited Kerslaw on to the aircraft to spy on him and see he kept his mouth shut about French West Africa. Alternatively, could the Canadian doctor be the instrument of the Americans who—according to Smith-Brown-Jones—might make some kind of approach to him? The next thought that occurred to Rennie was that his encounters with the hush-hush people in Freetown and London had finally turned his brain, making him outrageously suspicious of every stranger who engaged him in conversation. He could see that this suspicion had registered with Kerslaw, who was eyeing him with surprise.

"You could say my interest is professional, Captain Rennie," came the Canadian's reply. "My working life is devoted to a study of the human mind and what happens to it as a result of stress or injury. Do you not want to talk about it?"

"I'm sorry," said Rennie. "It's not that I don't want to talk about it. Medically, it must be quite unusual. The company doctor wanted to do a paper on it for the *British Medical Journal*. Unfortunately, there are political aspects to the circumstances which I've solemnly sworn not to say a word about."

"I haven't the faintest interest in the political side," said Kerslaw. "It was what you said about being drugged with shock and having no memory of what happened to you for four or five weeks. Were you at sea when this happened?"

"Good grief, no! I was in a hospital most of the time and, as far as I can gather, flat on my back. A piece of bone was pressing on my brain—but the London doctor I saw seems to think that my scrambled mental condition was due more to shock than the actual injury. He said I started physical recovery quickly, as soon as they relieved light pressure on my brain caused by the bone splinter, but that my mental recovery was much slower because of severe shock."

Kerslaw made a hissing noise with his tongue against teeth.

"You must have had one hell of a shock, Captain Rennie. Tell me about it, for Christ's sake! Surely to God it isn't a political secret how you got a kick in the head!"

Rennie grinned.

"Not really. And it wasn't true about the other fellow coming off worse with four fractured toes. I suppose the cause of the shock was man's inhumanity to man. I witnessed some rather nasty brutality and I was on the receiving end, too. It's not very nice getting your face kicked in, Doctor Kerslaw."

The Canadian was silent for a moment. In the blue-lit interior of the blacked-out cabin, Rennie could see from the other's face that he was reading implications from his words. There was a quick and lively mind behind Kerslaw's pale staring eyes. Although the other occupants of the cabin all seemed to be asleep, the Canadian's voice came as no more than a whisper above the relentless roar of the Wasp engines.

"Were you taken by the Gestapo?" he asked.

Considering the little Rennie had told him, it was shrewd reasoning.

"Not the Gestapo," said Rennie. "But perhaps the next best thing. The Vichy French . . . In West Africa. Three of us tried to get out of one of their prisons, but we were caught and roughed up. I passed out and have no idea what happened to me until I woke up in an ambulance in Sierra Leone more than a month later. The French had thought my brain was permanently damaged and they'd shipped me over the border."

"Fascinating," said Kerslaw. "Fascinating. You've made a complete recovery?"

Rennie laughed.

"Yes. I'm now as crazy as I was before I got kicked on the head!"

Kerslaw screwed up his face thoughtfully.

"You know, I would have thought our propaganda boys could have got a bit of mileage out of your story—particularly in the States, where the public have taken some convincing that Laval and the Vichy-ites are worse thugs than Hitler. Yet you've obviously been gagged. It doesn't make sense."

Rennie shrugged.

"Does it have to make sense? What happened to me isn't all that secret or even important, but others were involved, too, and I've been warned that chatting about it will be a contravention of the Official Secrets Act. For all I know, I've already qualified for ten years behind bars for chatting to you about it."

"There aren't any secrets between a psychiatrist and his patient," said Kerslaw with a smile, "even if you're not my patient and I've been away from my practice since the first week of the war!"

Rennie eyed him with mock suspicion.

"Just what does a psychiatrist do who rates a transatlantic flight in an RAF plane? They don't come that easy."

"Now, you're prying into my secrets," said Kerslaw roguishly. "I'm sorry I can't tell you what I do, Captain, but, if it's any comfort, I work for the British Government and have a high security clearance. Anything you say to me is unlikely to be repeated where it will do you or the country any harm. I would really like a longer talk with you . . . In less draughty surroundings and where conversation isn't quite such a strain."

"I think I've been much too talkative already," said Rennie. "What is it about whisky that lubricates the jaw muscles and makes the tongue babble? Doctor, please do me a good turn and don't repeat anything I've said to you to anybody. It won't do me any good . . . It won't do anybody any good."

"Okay. Suit yourself. I won't press it right now. If you like, we'll summon up a little amnesia. By the time we get to Gander, we'll both have forgotten we ever had this conversation."

The likeable Canadian was as good as his word. There was no more mention of head injuries or West Africa from the moment the Liberator touched down on a snow-cleared runway and a team of parka-clad mechanics welcomed the new arrivals to Newfoundland.

Rennie found himself next to Kerslaw, doing justice to a monstrous breakfast of steak and fried eggs in the airfield canteen hut, and then again two hours later, when they had adjacent seats in the RCAF passenger plane which was to take them on to Montreal. There, they said good-bye to the Ferry pilots who had shared their flight from Scotland and to each other and made their way to separate hotels.

The friendliness and out-going goodwill of every Canadian was a warm and live thing to Rennie. It was intensified by the spirit of Christmas, shown first by the mechanics who had greeted the Liberator at Gander with genuine welcome and echoed by every Canadian Rennie encountered on arrival in Montreal.

There were Christmas parties going on all over the hotel during the night. Dining alone in the hotel restaurant, Rennie found himself on the receiving end of several invitations from groups of complete strangers to join the fun. He politely declined them all. He was mindful that he had a train for Toronto to catch in the morning and he had had next to no sleep in three days. He was in bed and asleep by ten and heard little or nothing of the revelry going on in nearby rooms well into the early hours.

He had the dining-room to himself at breakfast next morning. Half an hour later he was on his way to the railway station, in a taxi driven by an émigré Scot who still had a thick Glasgow accent. Rennie was paying him off when another taxi pulled in alongside. From it alighted the tall, lean figure of Dr. Kerslaw.

The psychiatrist, too, was for the Toronto train. So, once again, Rennie found himself in the company of the likeable Canadian. They sat together looking out at the white snow-scape as the express hurtled westward.

Kerslaw, it transpired, was not going all the way to Toronto but getting off at the last stop before the Ontarian metropolis, at a place called Oshawa. He neatly sidestepped Rennie's conversational query about what he would be doing in Oshawa and asked Rennie how long he intended to stay in Toronto.

"Oh, a week. Maybe ten days. The Marine Superintendent of the company back in London suggested it when I said okay to flying out on Christmas Eve. I don't have to be out in Vancouver until the eighth of next month and he reckoned, with all the leave that's due me, I ought to have a break somewhere along the line. I've got some long-lost relatives living in Hamilton, Ontario. So, I'll maybe take the chance to look them up."

"If you're going to be at a loose end any time, maybe we could meet," said Kerslaw. "We could take in a hockey game, or just have a few beers and go for a meal. I know lots of good eating places."

"Sounds like a good idea," said Rennie. "How will we get in touch?"

"I'll ring you at your hotel. Where are you staying?"

"I'm booked into the York Regency."

"I know it," said Kerslaw. "You'll like it there. It's got a couple of nice restaurants and the bar on the first floor has a reputation that might interest you."

"What kind's that?"

"It's supposed to be a good place to run into well-heeled unattached women."

"Hmm. Maybe I could get lucky and wouldn't be available for a stag night with you later in the week," said Rennie with a smile.

Kerslaw smiled back.

"Get lucky and we could always make it a foursome. Toronto is full of pretty girls just waiting the chance to date me."

"What's your secret?"

"Well, I used to think it was my effortless charm. But it's not. The word got around that a date with me was good for a private analysis thrown in for free. The prices psychiatrists charge nowadays, I just can't miss."

Light snow was falling when Kerslaw left the train at Oshawa. Rennie gave him a final wave as the tall Canadian hitched his coat collar, picked up his suitcase, and threaded his way through a crowd of soldiers pressing towards the train. From what Rennie had been able to see of the place, Oshawa wasn't a big town. It seemed a strange destination for a psychiatrist employed by the British Government.

It was funny the way Kerslaw had avoided giving any indication of why he was visiting the town. Of Oshawa itself, he'd said: "Oh, there's not much there . . . An automobile factory, a brewery and not much else." Of his business there, he'd said nothing.

Rennie settled back in his seat. In another thirty minutes he would be in Toronto and he was looking forward to discovering that city's delights. There was something deliciously exciting about places unknown but with names that had been familiar since childhood. The need to see them and discover them for himself had had a lot to do with Rennie's choice of the sea as a career. Now, in spite of years of voyaging and having tasted the sights and smells of many lands, his compelling wanderlust had not diminished.

While Rennie pleasurably contemplated a week or more of relaxation, his late companion, Dr. Kerslaw, was exchanging pleasantries with the attractive blond driver in FANY uniform, who had met him in Oshawa. Kerslaw piled his suitcase into the trunk of the black Buick sedan and climbed into the passenger seat beside the girl.

"Good to have you back, Doctor Kerslaw," said the girl. "How were things in New Brunswick?"

"Where?" said Kerslaw.

"New Brunswick. That's where you've been this past month, isn't it?"

It dawned on Kerslaw that someone at the Camp must have passed off his absence by saying he was in New Brunswick.

"Oh, yes, yes," he said. "New Brunswick was fine. Fine."

The girl put her foot down when they were on the Toronto-Kingston Highway. They were on it only a short distance before taking a cut-off through dense bushland. The Highway had been clear of snow but the side road had not been ploughed. Here, there were three or four inches of hard-packed snow. The red lights of a barrier across the road signaled the first check-point.

Soldiers in parkas surrounded the car as an NCO checked Kerslaw's and the driver's special identity cards. Finally they were waved through. The identity check was repeated at the Camp gates.

A squad of Commandos, with blackened faces and carrying sub-machine-guns, filed past the car as the checking formalities were taking place. They trooped off down a track to the shore. Beyond, gleamed the black waters of Lake Ontario.

"It all looks just the same," sighed Kerslaw.

They drove on through a complex of hutted buildings.

"There are still lights on at the office," said the girl driver. "Do you want to stop off there or will I drop you at your quarters?"

"Drop me at the office," said Kerslaw, "and be a pal, will you, and dump my suitcase at the cabin with Wiley. Tell him I'll be round in half an hour."

"No problem, sir," said the girl.

A great-coated figure in naval uniform emerged from "the office" as Kerslaw got out of the car and signaled it on its way with a couple of gloved thumps on the roof. Kerslaw turned to recognize Commander Lomax, an expert in underwater warfare and the man in charge of training British Security Co-ordination agents in the sub-aqua use of explosives.

"Hello there, Kerslaw," greeted the Commander. "Nice to see you back. How was Saskatchewan?"

"Where?"

"Saskatchewan. Some blighter told me you'd gone off to Saskatchewan for a few weeks."

"Oh," said Kerslaw, "Saskatchewan was fine."

"Anyway, welcome back to Camp 'X'."

"Nice to be back."

The overwhelming nature of Canadian hospitality was something that Rennie had not anticipated. On his first day in Toronto, he had decided to telephone his remotely connected relatives in Hamilton. As a result, he had seen very little of Toronto. He had travelled down to Hamilton intending to stay overnight and return to Toronto next day. Instead, he had been prevailed upon to remain in Hamilton, while the fiery cross went out to a whole clan of cousins, twice and thrice removed, so that he could be the honored guest at a gathering of the clan. Resistance to their kindness would have been futile. They made him feel that the greatest kindness he could show in return would be to settle down permanently with them in Hamilton and allow them to wine and dine and fête him for the rest of his life.

Tempting as the prospect was, he knew that he would never get away unless he took firm and positive steps to get himself back to Toronto. Even at that, a total stranger—a neighbor of a second cousin—insisted on having the honor of driving him all the way to Toronto and seeing him safely restored to the York Regency. This Samaritan then declined Rennie's invitation for a drink and a meal—which would have salved his conscience a little for accepting so much hospitality—and insisted on returning to Hamilton straight away. The weather forecast was bad and there was a chance the roads could become tricky.

"Thanks for letting us know that you were held up in Hamilton, Captain Rennie," said the desk clerk. "Lots of folks wouldn't have bothered to take the trouble."

He handed Rennie his room key.

"Oh, by the way, a Doctor Kerslaw phoned a couple of times. He said he wanted to see you urgently. He left a number to call." The clerk pushed a slip of paper across the desk. "The phone booths are over there, at the end of the lobby. Or you could make the call from your room if you'd prefer it."

"Thanks," said Rennie. "I'll phone from upstairs." He

wondered what Kerslaw could want that merited the label "urgent." There was only one way to find out. He called him immediately he reached his room.

"I want to see you, John, and it *is* urgent—but I can't discuss it on the phone. Will you be at your hotel all evening?"

"I could be," said Rennie. "I've nothing planned for tonight. Why? What's it all about?"

"I'll tell you when I see you. I'll be on my way to Toronto in ten minutes. Just promise that you'll stick around until I get there—and I'll explain everything."

It was just after seven when Kerslaw appeared. He found Rennie in the bar, where he had lingered more than an hour over the one glass of beer.

"Would you like a drink?" Rennie asked the Canadian. "I've been marking time on this one."

"I'd love a drink, a beer—but could we go to your room? What I have to tell you is rather private."

Rennie gave him a long look.

"I'm not sure I like the sound of that. Is it going to take long or are you going to let me have it in a short sharp burst?"

"It . . . It could take some time," said Kerslaw deliberately.

Rennie turned to the barman.

"Could I have some bottles of that beer sent up to my room? The same as this one." He held out his empty glass.

"It was a Frontenac you had, sir. How many do you want? I'll get Room Service to bring it up, sir."

"It's room six-two-one. Better make it half a dozen bottles."

The six bottles of Frontenac and two glasses were sitting on a tray at Rennie's bedside by the time the two men reached the sixth floor. There was also a bottle opener, a bowl of nuts and two books of matches bearing the hotel's name.

"That's what I call service," said Rennie as he opened a bottle and poured one for Kerslaw. "Now, Larry"—they had been on first names since Gander—"you'd better tell me what the hell this is all about."

Rennie's voice was calm and even but Kerslaw, for the first time since he had known him, could sense a degree of hostility just below the surface. He chose his own words with care.

"Look, John, I don't know quite how to tell you this, because the last thing I want to do is to fall out with you. You're the kind of man I would choose to be my friend—and I want you to understand that. I still want to be your friend. The fact is that I've been doing some checking up on you."

"I see," said Rennie. His tone was icy.

"I don't think you do see," said Kerslaw. "You're captain of a ship and, for the past three and more years, you've been risking your life for your country. You're a brave man, John. I've seen the whole record. You've been bombed, torpedoed, imprisoned, gone through God knows what kind of horrors and you keep coming back for more."

"So?"

"My job doesn't involve me in the same kind of dangers as you face, John. I can't even tell you much about it. But it's important in its own way, too. I am using all my talents, inconspicuous as they may be to you, with only one end in view—and that is winning this war. I've been trained to heal minds but a lot of my work has been searching for the frailties in men and using these frailties to destroy them. I'm involved in a dirty war, John, but it's a total one. I'm not particularly proud of what I do. But I do it because I love my country and I know that all the things we cherish are not going to survive without some people getting their hands dirty. I haven't been able to convince myself that I should be exempt from having my hands soiled."

There was no doubting Kerslaw's sincerity. Rennie was not unaffected. The other's honest passion was something he could understand. But Kerslaw had still not come to the crunch. *What* did he want of him?

Glass in hand, Rennie stood gazing out of the window. In daylight, the sixth-floor vantage-point gave a wonderful view south over Lake Ontario but, now, the great expanse of water was invisible in the darkness. The city stretched below, a carpet of colored lights, with an endless stream of traffic on Yonge Street several blocks away sending up a faint hum of sound. Rennie turned to face Kerslaw.

"Larry, what is it that you've got to tell me that is so

contentious that you can't come to the point? Are you afraid I'm going to punch you on the jaw?"

Kerslaw grinned.

"You'd be welcome to if it meant we could still stay friends. The truth is, John, that I've gone behind your back . . . Taken advantage of a confidence, if you like . . . And the result is that I've been asked . . . No, I've been told to get you to do something—which I don't think you're going to like."

"What, for God's sake?"

"I want you to talk to some American newspapermen about what happened to you in Dakar. The whole story of how you nearly got kicked to death."

Rennie stared at him in disbelief.

"You must be out of your bloody mind!"

"I said you weren't going to like it. But will you do it?"

"Not in a million years! Hell's bells, I've already been jumped on from a great height for talking out of turn . . . But to talk to newspapermen! American newspapermen! I'd get myself shot!"

"No, you won't. I've talked it over with my boss and he has a direct line to the War Cabinet in London. The hornet's nest has already been stirred. A lot of people are wanting to know why the propaganda people didn't go to town on you long before now. You've got celebrity value, John, and you don't seem to realize it. And you could help the war of words that's just as important as the war with bullets. A lot of people still don't believe that Vichy wants Germany to win the war. You can help them see the truth."

"Who the hell is interested in the truth?" growled Rennie angrily. "Look, Larry, I'm sick to death of faceless bastards questioning me and pushing me around. I've been told I was a liar and the next best thing to a traitor. I've been bullied and lectured, until I don't know any more whose side I'm supposed to be on in this war. From now on, I'm not going to say anything to anybody until somebody levels with me!"

He was so worked up that he was breathing hard. His expression was fierce.

"How can I convince you that you can trust me?" said Kerslaw wearily.

"By trusting *me!*" Rennie cried. "Look, Larry. I know there have to be secrets, but I'm not a bloody child. If I'm fit to take charge of a ship and the lives of all the people on it, I'm fit to be told why I must say this or why I must say that—instead of being fobbed off with bullshit about meddling in things that are away over my head and can't begin to understand. If you want me to go along with you, Larry, you're going to have to tell me all about what you're doing and what your boss does and why it's so bloody important. I'm not going to run round the houses shouting out all your secrets, but somebody has to tell me what is secret and what bloody isn't and then they are going to have to trust me to behave like a responsible citizen."

Kerslaw let Rennie's words sink in. He watched Rennie through the curl of smoke rising from the cigarette in his hand. He crossed to the table next to Rennie's bed and crushed the cigarette out in an ash tray.

"OK," he said. "Mind if I make a phone call?"

"Be my guest," said Rennie.

Kerslaw picked up the receiver but kept a finger over the twin connecting buttons on the cradle. He stared across at Rennie.

"I'm sorry to have to ask, but would you like to take a walk as far as the john? This one has to be private."

Rennie smiled resignedly.

"I'll take a walk as far as the lobby. I haven't seen a newspaper since I left London. I'll see if I can get one downstairs."

Kerslaw was asking the operator for a number as he left the room.

He bought a paper in the lobby kiosk and opened out the front page as the elevator purred back towards the sixth floor. He read the stark headlines with a shiver that raised the hair on the back of his neck. Here he was in a safe city, far from any battlefront, but the problems of Africa and Vichy France were reaching out to him with bloody fingers. There seemed no escape from them.

The headline proclaimed: YOUNG OFFICER DIES BEFORE DAWN FIRING SQUAD: Swift Justice For Admiral Darlan's Assassin.

The story was datelined 26 December, from Algiers, and told how a young French Army officer had been tried and executed for killing the celebrated Vichy turncoat within hours of the politically sensational assassination.

Alongside the news story on page one was a profile of

the dead Admiral. It was boxed off and titled: DARLAN, THE GREAT ENIGMA—Was He Friend Or Enemy?

In another column were quotes from well-known statesmen. Few, it seemed, mourned Darlan's passing although some acknowledged his importance as an historical figure and suggested that his stature in world affairs could be measured by the size of the political vacuum he left behind. One American Senator was quoted as saying: "Love him or hate him, he [Darlan], by carrying the whole of French North Africa with him after the Allied landing, prevented a fratricidal bloodbath of incalculable dimensions. The problem now is who is big enough to fill his boots?"

Rennie returned grim-faced to his room. Kerslaw had completed his telephone call and was waiting for him.

"OK, John, I've got more or less what you wanted," he announced. "I've been given permission to tell you something about my work and the organization I work for. But I have to caution you that it *is* privileged information and *most secret*. Under no circumstances must you repeat what I tell you in part or whole. And that doesn't just apply to this year and next year. It applies for the rest of your life."

Rennie was suitably awed.

"If that's supposed to scare me stiff, Larry, it does. For God's sake, don't tell me anything I don't need to know. Just enough to help me understand what the hell is going on."

"Secrets are a heavy thing, John. I wanted you to be quite sure. You can't just unload them when you want to get the weight off your shoulders. And you have to take care that they don't slip off accidentally. In my work, a careless word can cost a hundred lives."

In the next couple of hours, Kerslaw told Rennie a little about his work for British Security Co-ordination, without giving him anything like the full picture of the world-wide extent of its organization or the range of operations undertaken by this most sophisticated and most secret intelligence service.

He did not tell him that from its base at Camp "X," near Oshawa, BSC trained agents, assassins and saboteurs and sent them to every quarter of occupied Europe. Nor did he tell him that, from Oshawa, BSC's executive master-minded espionage and counter-espionage activities in every major city in the world and co-ordinated the work of the intelligence-gathering services of Great Britain and the United States.

Instead, Kerslaw told Rennie how he had come to be involved in secret work. He had been on holiday in London at the outbreak of war in 1939 and, in a flush of tionaire by the recruiting officer. The outcome was that had wanted to become a fighter pilot.

In this connection he had been invited to fill in a questionaire by the recruiting officer. The outcome was that the RAF had turned him down but he had been invited to attend an interview at certain Government offices. There, he had been asked to help set up a new and secret establishment called the Psychological Warfare Department. He took the job, after it had been explained to him that his training as a psychiatrist made him eminently suited to the Department's function of "reading the enemy's mind" and devising operations aimed at sapping enemy morale.

After a year with the PWD, he had become personal assistant to a man responsible for co-ordinating intelligence services. Then he'd joined BSC at their New York headquarters, setting up liaison with US Government agencies and establishing both public and private channels to the media. Here, he had discovered how essential to the war effort it was to supply the American news media with stories which kept American public opinion sympathetic to Britain and countered German efforts to undermine the Anglo-American relationship.

When BSC had established its secret base in Canada, he had moved north to plan training schedules and find instructors for the growing number of agents needed to operate behind enemy lines.

"I'm pretty high up the totem pole now, John," he concluded. "I know how far my responsibility goes and I'm near enough the top to know exactly what official thinking is on certain matters. That's why I was so surprised when you hinted that some of our people in London had put a gag on you instead of exposing you to newsreel cameras and reporters. I couldn't believe that you wouldn't come across well or that you would say something that would blow up in our faces. There had to be a damned good reason for sweeping you under the carpet and I wanted to find out what the hell it was."

"And have you found out?" asked Rennie.

"Oh, I think I have the reason all right, but it's not a good one. It's not one that I wear and it's not the one my boss wears. And it's something nobody will take the blame for or admit or even get their arse kicked for. You had the Secrets Act thrown at you in London, John, because of inter-service bloody-mindedness. I hate to admit it but a lot of people in my business who ought to know better feel that their own little departments are sacrosanct and that the rest of the world is bent on doing them down. They trust no one, co-operate with no one and generally behave as if the world would fall apart if their strange little ways are questioned. You were leaned on in London, John, because the American OSS wanted to talk to you. Not because you were in possession of some nugget of information which was going to shake the British Empire to its foundations. You just came between two departments that are jealous of each other."

"That doesn't comfort me much, Larry," said Rennie. "It frightens me."

"It frightens me, too. If supposed friends can't get along together, what hope is there for us? Some people in London aren't going to like you for it, John, but I want you to tell me exactly what happened back in London. And in Dakar. You won't be going back on any promises you may have made because I'm in on this now, officially. Right up to my neck."

Rennie had no qualms about telling everything to Larry Kerslaw. He liked the Canadian instinctively. And he trusted him. Which was more than Rennie could say for Smith-Brown-Jones and his methods of persuasion.

Kerslaw heard Rennie out, asking only an occasional question. At the end of it, he said,

"You realize, John, that I can't make heads roll. I'd dearly love to weed out the bastards who gave you such a rough time in London and have them kicked out on their ears but I know what will happen. The guys on top will think they're under attack and they'll cover up for the guys underneath. There may be hard words spoken in private and a few ears will ring but, in the end, nothing much will be changed."

"I'll be quite happy if they don't try to get back at me. I'm not the vindictive type, Larry."

Kerslaw was thoughtful.

"The guy who called himself Smith or Brown or Jones was probably from Section Five. What we'll never find out is just how high up the tree the word went out to warn you off. They might acknowledge that someone in the department showed excessive zeal or even stepped out of line but you can bet your last dollar they'll have a bucket of whitewash and a big brush at the ready. They'll produce ancient directives ordering them to run a mile from anything likely to attract publicity to their department. They'll say the case was low priority, no account, and everybody's getting burned up over nothing. They'll want to know why everybody is ganging up on them and sniping at them when they've got their hands full fighting the enemies of the Crown on a hundred secret battlefields. In short, they'll throw so much bullshit around the yard that we'll all be knee-deep in the stuff. Only one thing will be clear at the end of it—and that will be that whatever went wrong, it sure as hell wasn't the blame of anybody in Section Five."

In spite of the trust which had been established between the two men, Rennie's diffidence about publicizing his brutal treatment at the hands of the Vichy French did not disappear. It was a personal thing. He just didn't want to be thrust into the limelight. And wasn't it possible that Smith-Brown-Jones, or whatever his name was, might have a point about this kind of thing complicating the Giraud—de Gaulle squabbling and further estranging Anglo-American relations, to say nothing about the political crisis in North Africa, as a result of Darlan's assassination?

Rennie indicated the newspaper lying where he had thrown it on the bed.

"Things do seem to be pretty messy over there in Algiers," he said.

Kerslaw conceded that there were a lot of new things to be considered.

"When it was first mooted that you should talk to the American press, John, I didn't have anything like the full picture. Now that you've told me your side of it, I realize it's not quite so straightforward as I supposed. That doesn't mean to say that telling people what happened to you is an idea that should be dumped. Germany is still using Vichy to pump highly damaging stories across North America and it's not enough for us to deny them, we've got to nail their lies by producing eye-witnesses and good solid evidence. Goebbels had a field-day over the rescue of the Italian prisoners from that torpedoed ship you were on. Hell, there isn't an editor between here and the Rio Grande who wouldn't give his teeth for your version of what happened. The same goes for your story about the French officier who defied his captain over firing on a British ship. You say they bayoneted this poor guy when he was caught! The world ought to know, John, that the people responsible for atrocities like that are the people who are running France today."

Kerslaw agreed, however, that press interviews could wait until he had done some checking. Rennie had provided him with several leads which had to be followed up. Those which offered the most immediate results were in his provision of the names Hobart and Peterson. BSC had excellent connections with Washington and Kerslaw was confident that the full extent of Peterson's interest in Hobart and the nature of Hobart's activities in Dakar would be known to him within twenty-four hours.

In fact, it took several days. Rennie was at breakfast in the dining-room of the York Regency when the tall Canadian appeared in the doorway and scanned the tables, obviously looking for him.

Rennie saw him and gave him a wave.

"Happy New Year, Larry," he greeted him. "Pull up a chair. Can I order you breakfast or have you had it?"

"A Happy Nineteen-Forty-Three to you, John." He offered his hand. "I'm afraid the celebrations passed me by. How about you?"

"I got to bed at three," said Rennie. "There was a bit of a party but I'm not as fragile as I deserve to be."

Kerslaw declined breakfast but said he'd welcome black coffee, lots of it. He had been working all night.

"I've got good news for you, John," he announced. "I could have phoned you before now but I've been waiting confirmation. I got it a couple of hours ago. I have located Richard Hobart."

Joy lit Rennie's face.

"He's alive?"

"He turned up in Morocco a week or two ago. Rather strange circumstances though. He didn't know there was a hue and cry for him and still doesn't. And the military group he ran into at some village or other just took him for what he said he was, a prospecting civilian geologist heading for the Atlas Mountains. Washington isn't too pleased with him for not reporting in—you guessed, of course, that he was OSS."

"I was pretty sure he wasn't a geologist," said Rennie.

"That's where you're wrong," said Kerslaw with a smile.

"He is a geologist, and a damned good one from all accounts. He was roped in for—er—other work because of his background. And he knows his way about Africa. Anyway, you may be pleased to know that your other friend, Peterson, wasn't letting the grass grow under his feet. He meant to find out if Hobart and the Frenchman were still on that island."

"What did he do?"

"Well, diplomatic channels drew a blank, so Peterson mounted an operation to land a dozen marines from a sub and get your two friends off. Washington cancelled it when they heard Hobart was in Morocco. Peterson was sore as hell. He's still kicking up hell about it and saying the operation should have gone ahead and not been cancelled until there was proof that the guy who'd turned up in Morocco was definitely Hobart. Well, it took me to get that proof for them."

"From five thousand miles away?" said Rennie. "That's quite impressive."

"You need it up here," said Kerslaw, tapping his temple. "Washington told me that the news of Hobart being in Morocco had first come in a story radioed to New York by Mike Roberts, the war correspondent. He had been with this flying column showing the military presence in a string of outlying villages when they'd run into Hobart. He filed a story about the lone American civilian whose work took him into the backlands and deserts and how he had been given a breath of home by his first bottle if Coca-Cola in six months. He doesn't know that Washington killed the story before it reached the newsdesk. What Washington didn't do and should have, because it was obvious, was wire Mike Roberts and ask him if he had taken any photos of this Hobart."

"And you did?" asked Rennie.

"I've got them right here in my pocket," said Kerslaw. He patted his jacket. "Roberts didn't wire the photos because they weren't that great, but I had a word with his editor in New York and they were radioed yesterday. I got the prints two hours ago."

Kerslaw fished in his pocket and produced an envelope from which he emptied four five-by-eight prints onto the table. Rennie picked them up. They showed a group of helmeted GIs behind a hatless figure in bush clothes, who was holding a bottle of Coca-Cola.

"Hobart's in the center, the one with the beard," said Kerslaw.

Rennie stared at the photo, a look of complete puzzlement on his face. He was sure of only one thing. Whoever the man in the photograph was, he was certainly not the man he knew as Richard Hobart.

Chapter Ten

HARDLY a day of the year 1943 passed without momentous events tumbling one on another and competing for their own special place in the pages of history. They went almost unheeded by John Rennie. He was like a haunted man. For the ghosts of 1942 would not leave him be.

There were lonely nights when he would be seized by bouts of depression, a new and strangely terrifying thing for a man who had gone through his years on the earth as one of life's eternal optimists. There were times when he wished he could take a sponge and erase the year 1942 from his mind. It was not a year of happy memory. He had been twice torpedoed. Then had come the ordeal of his imprisonment and the nightmare aftermath.

His appointment as master of the *Fort Daring* was the one bright landmark. But even that had been soured by the past that would not let him go. He could recall his elation in Toronto on the first day of the year when Larry Kerslaw had brought him the news that Richard Hobart was alive. How short-lived that joy had been. It had lasted only minutes, dashed by the realization that the man in the war correspondent's photograph bore no resemblance whatsoever to the man he knew as Richard Hobart.

Larry Kerslaw's shock at the revelation was considerable. There were implications which Rennie could not even begin to guess at, but which were real and significant to this man steeped in secret war. Kerslaw could not explain the mystery. He only knew that he had stumbled, almost by accident, on a totally unexpected development of a story that had started many months before—when an American agent called Richard Hobart had embarked on a secret and dangerous mission. Kerslaw, as yet, did not have the details of that mission but—because of Rennie's revelation—he was now in possession of a certainty that the mission's directors did not yet have. That certainty was that the whole thing had gone terribly wrong. The stink of disaster was strong in Kerslaw's nostrils.

He had taken leave of Rennie without delay, in order to return to his operational base near Oshawa. Rennie had watched him go, agitated and white-faced still at the import of Rennie's insistence that the man in the photograph was not Hobart. Rennie had not seen Kerslaw again.

The Canadian had telephoned the following day to say that he was flying to Washington. He wanted to wish Rennie bon voyage and all the luck in the world in case he didn't get back to Toronto before Rennie had to leave for Vancouver. Thus Rennie had been left like an actor in a long-running radio soap opera who had fallen out of favor with the producer. He had been written out of the story.

That understates, however, the depth of Rennie's immersion in the part destiny had handed him unasked. Into his role had gone his blood and broken flesh and tears. And, although he set himself resolutely to face the rigors and considerable demands of a completely new chapter in his life, he could not free himself from the chains of his immediate past. Too many ghosts peopled his dreams. Too many questions screamed within him for answers.

The nature of his private torments were unknown to the officers and men of the *Fort Daring*. They found their new young captain a strange and brooding man. Rennie was resented even before he arrived.

Captain Lockhart, the first choice to command the *Fort Daring*, had been highly popular. He had handpicked the men for the new ship and there wasn't one who hadn't jumped at the invitation to serve with him. His sudden and tragic death had been taken very badly, with the result that his replacement could have been the Archangel Gabriel and large fault would have been found with him.

Rennie did not go out of his way to court popularity. He set out to run an efficient ship and to exercise his authority fairly, but he made no attempt to bridge the resentment which waited for him and grew as he familiarized himself with his ship.

The *Fort Daring* left Vancouver with ten thousand tons of grain and steamed south to the Panama Canal. Then she port-hopped—sometimes in convoy, sometimes unescorted—through the Caribbean and up the eastern seaboard of the US to Halifax, Nova Scotia. Canada's snows were melting in April sunshine when the great east-bound convoy sailed out into the North Atlantic and began the slow trail home.

West of Ireland, the armada separated into two sections and the *Fort Daring* joined the southern portion destined for the Bristol Channel. By the first day of May, her grain cargo was fully discharged at Avonmouth docks.

All the time the ship was in the UK, Rennie half expected to see his cabin door flung open and a couple of bruisers from Special Branch come charging in. There was no Kerslaw and his authority here to protect him from the retaliatory arm of Smith-Brown-Jones, whose carefully framed threats he had chosen to ignore.

But no one came near him. And there was no enquiry he could make to ease his troubled, questioning mind. He had unwittingly stepped in and out of a hornets' nest, and he carried the stings to remind him. But the war of Kerslaw and Hobart was not his war. It was none of his business.

It hurt Rennie that none of the officers of the *Fort Daring* elected to sail with him again. Instead, they all opted to take the full leave due to them. This meant that when the *Fort Daring,* light and high in the water, sailed north to join a west-bound convoy at Loch Ewe, she had a brand new complement. The new men took Rennie as they found him, making no unfavorable comparisons to an affectionately regarded shipmaster snatched from their midst by untimely death. The result was that the *Fort Daring* was a happier ship. Rennie found new heart.

For once, the Atlantic was at its most benign. Anticyclonic weather stretched from Labrador to Scandinavia, giving cloudless skies and a sea like a mill-pond. Smiled on by the element which was his home, Rennie felt renewed. For the first time since he had taken up his command, he felt he could concentrate on the horizon ahead and not look back.

The trip was uneventful—no losses to U-boats as there had been on the east crossing—and the *Fort Daring* tied up in Manhattan on a glorious day of early summer sunshine. Her stay in New York was brief. Within four days, she was fully laden with the munitions and machineries of war and outward bound once more. This time, there was the short journey south to Hampton Roads to become part of a sixty-ship convoy destined for Mediterranean ports. Final destination orders would be relayed from Gibraltar.

A day out from Gibraltar, the convoy encountered a fleet of Spanish fishing boats. This was bad news to the old hands who knew these waters. They knew that the Spanish boats acted as the eyes of the German agents who were to be found throughout the Iberian peninsula. News of the convoy's presence would be relayed by various means to U-boat Command in Brest before nightfall and word would also have been passed to every German airfield between the Pyrenees and the Straits of Messina.

The armada of ships slipped past Gibraltar into the Mediterranean at two in the morning. The great rock stood gaunt and shadowy against the northern sky. Necklaces of twinkling lights beribboned the Spanish coast nearby.

Once inside the Mediterranean, a strange uneasiness took possession of John Rennie. He could not sée the shore of French North Africa but its very propinquity seemed to exert an influence which reached out and pressed on his mind. It re-awakened in him a terrible brooding, aggravating wounds he was forgetting and reminding him of mysteries that he had tried to lock firmly in the past.

Exercising himself by parading his bridge-deck alone, he found himself drawn to the starboard side—where he would stand for long periods of time, looking south. The land just beyond the horizon seemed to mock him. It held the key to so many secrets and it taunted him with its silence.

At a steadily maintained eight and a half knots, the ships kept eastward. Rennie knew that French North Africa would keep its secrets from him despite the tantalising closeness of the land. The *Fort Daring's* orders—relayed by the new escort leader which had met the convoy from Gibraltar—had disclosed the ship's destination as Alexandria. The Mediterranean was no longer a closed sea. With the whole of the North African shore now in possession of Allied forces, the ports if Egypt had once again become accessible without the long haul round the Cape. Allied mastery of the Mediterranean was being even further consolidated with the massive invasion of Sicily which had begun in the same hour as the *Fort Daring* had slipped past Gibraltar.

For two days and two nights, the shore that was only twenty miles away cast its disturbing spell on Rennie. He became preoccupied and silent, toying with the food that was set before him and becoming distant and unhearing when anyone spoke to him. Adding to his unease and the total distraction of unburied memories was a sense of impending evil. The whole sky of his mind had become black and overcast with heavy lowering clouds. The Mediterranean sky was cloudless and the air clear, but Rennie was like a man weighed down by the stifling oppression of atmosphere which heralds imminent storm.

It was as if Nature was offering him prescience of events to come. For, already, the random shuttling threads which are men's destinies were weaving and inter-weaving the irregular and unpredictable patterns that defy prescription or explanation. In the normal course of events, Rennie's ship would have sailed on past the French territories and any reunion with the links to his traumatic past. He would have lived out his life without re-involvement in a circle of affairs, which that life had briefly touched but left again at tangent course. But that was not to be.

The force that, in Rennie's case, was to bend the tangent and upset the predictable course of his destiny was an Italian called Ricardo Minelli. He was the commander of the submarine on patrol near Algiers who was advised that on the morning of 10 July a large eastbound convoy had passed through the Straits of Gibraltar. Minelli got the news when he surfaced just before midnight on the 11th about 150 miles north-east of Algiers. The convoy was believed to be further reinforcements for the Allied armies now streaming ashore on both sides of Cape Passero in Sicily.

Minelli set course towards the approaching convoy, making good speed until just before daylight when he took his craft deep to avoid detection from the air. He made contact with the convoy at dusk on the evening of the 12th but made no attempt to engage. Instead, he surfaced and ran east ahead of the convoy under cover of darkness. Using the lights of Cherchel as a positional guide, he took the submarine into shallow water and hove-to within three miles of the shore. Here, the coastline curved in a long bight which stretched to Algiers at its easterly end. Minelli chose his position well, taking advantage of a headland at the west tip of the bight to conceal the submarine from vessels approaching from the direction of Gibraltar. Half an hour before sunrise,

Minelli submerged in the lee of the headland and allowed his craft to settle on the seabed. Before long, the hydrophones were picking up the drumming engine noises of many ships to seaward. Glancing repeatedly at his watch, Minelli waited. Finally, making dead slow speed ahead, he brought the submarine to periscope depth.

In the first grey light of morning, the convoy was stretched over several miles of ocean to the north. The corvette guarding the convoy's starboard flank was already east of Minelli's position, and the heart of the flock of ships lay exposed. The Italian Commander fired two torpedoes from the bow tubes and, then, ordered the submarine to be taken gently to a greater depth. There was no frenzy of an emergency dive. Calmly, gently, and with engines stopped, the submarine was allowed to settle once more on the sea floor.

Minelli's maneuver, with the object of driving home his attack and remaining undetected, required great skill and courage. Its success was spectacular. From seaward came the deep rumble of two explosions, one much heavier and of greater duration than the other.

The greater explosion came from the thundering end of a tanker as its cargo of high octane ignited and sent a column of fire a thousand feet into the air. The other occurred when the second torpedo was passing thirty feet astern of the *Fort Daring* and its acoustic warhead was detonated by the deep pulsing percussion of the ship's screw. The blast sent a plume of water skywards at the *Fort Daring's* stern and hurled shock-waves of energy and released force at the ship's rudder. The great rudder was torn from its stock and its buckling mass thrown forward into the thrashing propeller, where both merged with a grotesque screaming and rending of metal. Such was the stress imposed on the spinning shaft that the heavy screw sheered off at the stern as if cut through by a cheese-wire. Now, the great engines of the *Fort Daring* continued to rotate the propellerless shaft in a screeching frenzy of unbearable sound.

In the engine-room of the *Fort Daring,* the Second Engineer—conquering the numbing shock of the explosion and the sensation of feeling the ship jump from the water as if picked up by the stern—hastened to shut off steam from the main engine and end the crazy racing of the shaft.

Rennie had rolled from his bunk at the first sudden wave of sound. He did not need to be told the meaning of the deafening bang which had wakened him from sleep and had been followed by an agonized shuddering of the ship. He was quickly on the bridge.

Cole, the First Officer, met him white-faced at the top of the ladder. Rennie's mouth framed one word:

"Torpedo?"

"I think so. Right up the arse," said Cole.

"Get aft and let me know the worst as soon as you can," Rennie ordered. "I'll look after the bridge."

The telephone was jangling as he entered the wheelhouse. It was the Second Engineer to say that he had stopped the engines because the screw had gone. The Chief Engineer had joined him in the engine-room and would remain on the platform. He, himself, was going aft to assess the damage.

Rennie told him that Cole, the First Officer, was already on his way aft to make a similar inspection. "I want to know if we're making water. And, if so, how much and how fast?"

Rennie threw down the phone and thumbed the alarm button on the bulkhead beside it. Six times he pressed out the letter "b" in Morse, the signal for boat stations. It was too early yet for the signal to abandon ship.

The ship was now drifting helplessly. Other ships in the convoy altered course to avoid collision. Then the ranks closed as the convoy steamed on, leaving the *Fort Daring* alone to her fate.

Cole's first report was encouraging. The ship was taking water at the stern but was not holed, most of the damage had been external. The screw was gone and the rudder, but the ship had a good chance of staying afloat, if the buckled plates of the counter could hold.

The Second and Third Mates had arrived on the bridge close on Rennie's heels. He now detailed the junior of these two officers to answer the urgent flashing of a corvette which was circling the *Fort Daring* like a mother hen. Rennie stood at the young officer's side as the corvette winked its message.

"She wants to know if we are in danger of sinking and if she can be of assistance. Senior Officer Escort has ordered her to stand by."

"I got it," said Rennie. "Tell her we've lost our rudder

and propeller but most of the damage is external. We need a tow. We are not in immediate danger of sinking."

As the corvette maneuvered close to the *Fort Daring's* bows, Cole returned to the bridge.

"We've been bloody lucky," he announced. "Only one casualty and he's not bad. One of the firemen got tossed out of his bunk and he's got a broken arm."

"The Navy's going to give us a tow," said Rennie. "What about damage? Is she going to stay afloat?"

"She'll stay afloat all right. The worst of the damage is well beyond the after watertight bulkhead. And I think that the worst that can happen is that we could lose our arse-end beyond the aftermost transom. The rudder post has a bloody great bend in it and this is putting a hell of a strain on the arch-piece of the stern. The whole of the poop is sagging down towards the sea and the cant frames are twisted to hell."

Rennie was visualizing in his mind the skeleton framework of the ship's stern and trying to picture the effects on it of the explosion.

"There's a lot of weight on that poop," he said. "The four-inch, the mooring winches, all that armor round the accommodation . . . The whole bloody lot could go."

"I don't think so," said Cole. "You know how thick they make these transom floors. They're almost indestructible. Mind you, I thought the same about rudder posts—but you should see ours. I don't know if it's actually fractured underwater but it obviously buckled forward in the blast, rudder and all, and got tangled with the screw. Christ, did you hear the noise? It was like dropping railway lines into a ten-ton mincing machine. I don't know if the rudder post sliced up the propeller or if it was the propeller that sliced up the rudder post but I hate to think what it looks like down there."

"What about damage to the stern tube?" asked Rennie. "The screw must have sheered clean off and taken a piece of the tail-end shaft with it. Either that or the boss piece came adrift and the damned thing just dropped off."

"There's no way of telling outside of a dry dock. The lucky thing for us is that there's not much water getting through the stuffing box into the tunnel. Where we are taking water is in the after peak. We can handle that if plates don't start springing all over the place with the pressure."

"Thank God we're carrying so many trucks and not a bulk cargo," said Rennie. "We're high enough in the water to keep some kind of trim. You'd better do a few sums and work out what kind of adjustments we can make to keep the taffrail from dragging in the drink."

"What about the tow?"

"Leave that to the Second Mate just now. I sent him for'ard just before you got here. The bosun and some of the crowd are getting towing lines from the fore peak. I don't know what the hell we're going to do about steering. You managed to put the brake on the quadrant all right?"

"Yes, it was jumping around all over the place. How about a jury rudder?"

"You're a bloody optimist," said Rennie. "Have you ever rigged one? Apart from the fact that it would take us a week to build one, I don't think we have the wherewithal to do the job."

"It's going to be tricky for that corvette trying to tow us. We'll sheer all over the bloody ocean."

Rennie was thoughtful.

"If that happens," he replied, "we'll improvise a long tow to try to keep the tail steady."

"With what?" asked Cole gloomily. "What have we got that's heavy enough and will float fairly deep?"

"How about the number one lifeboat? We could half-fill her with water and float her out astern. Or one of the big life-rafts? There's a fair weight in them."

Cole brightened.

"That might just work," he said. He grinned broadly. "And it'll give us something to swim for if the ship sinks under us!"

It was seven in the morning when the corvette, HMS *Lavender*, finally took the *Fort Daring* in tow. As both Cole and Rennie had suspected, the chunky little escort vessel had its work cut out and its heavy tow was almost unmanageable. Then the experiment of streaming a heavy life-raft three hundred yards astern of the merchant ship was tried with moderate success. The corvette was able to proceed on a slightly erratic but reasonably straight course instead of tending to loop round in semi-circles.

Ricardo Minelli did not know of the easy target which presented itself only a few miles from where his submarine lay doggo on the seabed. He was satisfied that he had achieved two hits with two torpedoes and that was pretty good hunting for one day. The need to confirm his sinkings was less pressing than the need to preserve the safety of his ship and his crew. He had no doubt that the British Navy would leave an escort skulking around in the area to play a cat-and-mouse game of detection with the marauder who had struck at the convoy.

Minelli was aware that, in the shallow water, the maximum chance of discovery was from the air—but he had considered the odds carefully. His closeness to the North African shore could work in his favor, because few hunting aircraft would search there. They were much more likely to concentrate on deeper water. And, even if they did spot the submarine, its very proximity to the land might fool them into thinking that, in that location, it must be a wreck.

So, the Italian Commander kept his craft silent and immobile on the seabed until the air in its interior was foul and scarcely tolerable. Not until the sun had gone down beyond the near headland did he bring his vessel to the surface and head west towards Oran to see if the comings and goings from the port offered any worthwhile targets.

By that time, HMS *Lavender* and her tow were twelve miles to the east and crawling slowly but surely towards the safety of Algiers harbor.

It was not until just before dark on the following day that Rennie brought the *Fort Daring* to anchor in Algiers Bay. The *Lavender* had been aided in this operation by a tug from the harbor. When it was complete, the *Lavender* steamed slowly past her late charge, so that her Captain could exchange courtesies with Rennie and bid farewell. There was to be no respite for the Navy ship. She had been ordered back to sea with instructions to proceed at full speed in pursuit of the convoy from which she had been detached.

The lamp on the *Lavender*'s bridge winked out the message: "Goodbye Darling. Correction—Daring. Parting is such sweet sorrow."

The compliment was returned with: "We'll miss you, too, Lavender. Yours is the prettiest backside we have ever followed. Godspeed and a safe voyage."

The crew of the *Fort Daring* raised a cheer as *Lavender* made her final pass and headed for the open sea.

A launch from the shore brought aboard more than the usual number of port officials. In addition to officers of Health, Wharfage, Military Control and Pilotage, there was a covey of engineers, damage assessors and cargo inspectors. The *Fort Daring* immediately became the center of a debate on what was to be done with her. Rennie was left in no doubt that his crippled ship was an unexpected and unwelcome problem to the busy and harassed port authorities. The harbor was already congested and more than seventy vessels were expected and would be requiring berth facilities within the next two or three weeks.

It was agreed, however, that the *Fort Daring*—with a mixed cargo valued at just under ten million dollars—could not be allowed simply to rust in the roads and possibly sink there. The immediate priority, therefore, would be the discharge of the *Fort Daring*'s cargo. The fate of the ship thereafter did not rate much consideration. Rennie got the impression that, once the cargo was out, the ship would likely be towed out to the bay again and left to rot. The prospect was disagreeable, but he wisely decided to face the longer term problems when he came to them. For the time being, he would take one step at a time.

No berth was to be available that night or even the next day, so Rennie decided to keep the crew on full sea watches while in the anchorage. Just before noon on 16 July, the *Fort Daring* glided past the mole: a harbor tug straining ahead of her and two others strapped to her flanks. Nearing the berth waiting at the Quai Dakar, one of the flanking tugs detached. Then, in tandem with its partner, they pushed the crippled merchantman against the wharf with fendered noses. By two in the afternoon, the *Fort Daring* was securely moored and the deck-hands were stripping the hatches in preparation for discharge of the cargo.

Rennie dealt swiftly with a succession of port officials who came and went from his day-room in a constant stream. They left in their wake a mass of paperwork and forms to be filled and he was about to make a start when Cole stuck his head round the door.

"Port Security Officer to see you, sir."

"You'd better show him in," said Rennie wearily.

He rose to meet the new visitor, a tall lean figure with a sallow face and bony knees protruding from beneath neatly laundered white shorts. The three gold bands of Commander, Royal Navy, adorned his shirt epaulettes.

The newcomer came forward with hand outstretched. "Good afternoon, Captain, I'm Commander . . ." The words died on his lips. He stared at Rennie, jaw sagging and mouth open. Rennie, too, was staring like a man transfixed. He completed the Commander's introduction for him.

"Bishop!" he said.

Chapter Eleven

BISHOP continued to stare at Rennie as if he were seeing a ghost.

"Well!" he said. Then repeated it: "Well!" He kept staring at Rennie. "Well, this is a surprise!"

A confusion of memories and unanswered questions flashed through Rennie's brain. A shared cell at Fort Cap des Tigres. Conflict over an escape plan. Bishop appealing to Junot for new quarters and his subsequent disappearance. The horror of the island beach—and the sure knowledge of treachery and betrayal. Was this the betrayer? This man in his crisp white uniform? Was it guilt written on his face? Was that what tied his tongue and made him stare and stare and stare?

When Rennie finally found his voice, he could scarcely believe that it was himself speaking in a calm, polite tone. He felt strangely detached, as if someone else was inhabiting his body and he was an invisible eavesdropper. His tone was almost hearty.

"Not an unpleasant surprise, I hope, Commander. I've been looking forward to meeting you again. It calls for a drink . . ." As he spoke, Rennie realized for the first time that another officer had followed Bishop into the day-cabin. He was standing, cap in hand, at the doorway; a perplexed look on his boyish face. Bishop seemed to remember his presence at the same time as Rennie became aware of it.

"Oh, this is Lieutenant Clifford, my exec. He usually does the round of the ships, but I'm making the calls myself today. I thought you Merchant Navy chaps would pay a bit more attention to someone with a bit of scrambled egg on the cap, eh?"

Bishop's bonhomie was as forced as ever, and as grating as it was false.

"Would you like that drink? And you, too, Lieutenant," said Rennie.

Clifford looked deferentially at Bishop, then back to Rennie.

"Thanks, I'd give my arm for something long with ice in it. Or a cold beer, if you have one."

Bishop glared at the younger man. He had obviously spoken out of turn.

"I should like a drink, too, Clifford, but this isn't a social call. Perhaps we can accept Captain Rennie's invitation at a later date." He turned to Rennie. "Your offer is appreciated, Captain—but we have a lot of calls to make."

"Can't they wait?" said Rennie. "You and I have a lot to talk about. I'd like to hear how you got out of Senegal."

Bishop's eyes narrowed.

"I can't think why." In an aside to Clifford, he said: "Captain Rennie and I had the misfortune to be interned in West Africa."

"Oh," said Clifford, "you two are old friends?"

"You could say so," said Bishop. "But apart from a shared spell of captivity, we didn't have a great deal in common."

"That's true," said Rennie, an edge to his voice. "Commander Bishop's distaste for my company was so marked that he asked for a change of quarters. He got it, too. I've often wondered what he had to do to return the favor."

Clifford was looking from one man to the other, mystified by the currents passing between them but sensing a mutual hostility. Bishop was the first to let real anger show.

"Just what the hell are you insinuating?" he snapped at Rennie.

"That we still have a lot to talk about," replied Rennie. "Surely you must have wondered what happened to me. Or do you *know?*"

Bishop eyed him suspiciously.

"I don't know what the hell you're driving at. As far as I know, you had an accident. At least I took it from what they said that it was you . . . About the other Englishman being taken to hospital."

"I'd like to believe you, Bishop," said Rennie.

Bishop gave an impatient snort. He glanced at his watch.

"I don't really care whether you believe me or not," he said shortly. "And I don't have time to discuss it. I have five more ships to visit after this."

"I want you to find time to discuss it. There are some things I've got to know the answers to."

There was a fierceness about Rennie's insistence that got through to Bishop. He relented.

"Very well. But I honestly don't have time to talk about it just now." He considered possibilities. "Look, why don't you come out to my place tomorrow evening, say about seven? I've got a bungalow a mile or two along the coast. Clifford can confirm it's a delightful spot. It's on the Bousquet estate . . ."

"Bousquet estate?" echoed Rennie.

Bishop looked at him with dawning recollection.

"Why, of course, you met Mercier's wife didn't you? She's Admiral Bousquet's daughter. Perhaps I can arrange for her to look along later. Or we could pop up to the Villa to say hello."

Now, Rennie's eyes were wide with surprise.

"Arlette Mercier . . . You've met her? Does she know what happened to Jean-Paul?"

Bishop glanced again at his watch.

"Yes, of course I've met her. It was through her I got a decent billet away from the Naval Barracks. But look, it's a long story about her and her husband. It'll have to wait till tomorrow." He turned impatiently to Clifford. "Look, it's really time we got going."

"We'd better tell Captain Rennie why we're here, sir," said Clifford with an apologetic grin.

"Yes, yes, of course," said Bishop absent-mindedly. He turned to Rennie again. "I really am sorry about the rush," he said, "but I am personally visiting every captain in the harbor, in my capacity as Port Security Officer, to make sure that every step is taken to tighten anti-sabotage security. The Navy can only do so much with dock-gate checks and mobile patrols, so it's up to every shipmaster to organize adequate shipboard measures."

"I see," said Rennie, deflated at the realization that any talk about Jean-Paul was obviously going to have to wait.

Without specifying how the Port Security Office had come by the information, Bishop said that a warning had been received of possible sabotage attempts against shipping in Algiers harbor. His office was taking the warning seriously. Consequently, every ship was being instructed to institute round-the-clock gangway watches and regular shipboard patrols. The suggestion was that merchant ships use their DEMS personnel—army and navy AA gunners—to do this work, and that they should be armed. Also, intensive anti-sabotage searches were to be made from stem to stern of every ship, prior to sailing.

Clifford handed Rennie several sheets of duplicated typescript. These were marked "Confidential" and listed mainly those vulnerable areas of merchant ships where sabotage might be attempted. There was also a list of methods known to be used by saboteurs against shipping.

"Now, we really must be on our way," said Bishop. He looked again at his wrist watch. "It's gone a quarter past three. What's the next ship, Clifford?"

The Lieutenant consulted a list.

"Five more to do, sir. There's the Norwegian coaster, *Bjorkhaug*—I think that's how you pronounce it—and another of these Fort ships, the *Fort Confidence*. Then there are the two American Liberty ships and the heavy-lift ship, the *Empire Icelandic*. She's the next ship up."

"Good, then we'll . . ." Bishop never finished the sentence. The words died in his mouth as a wave of cataclysmic sound rent the air. The ship beneath their feet seemed to lift and fall in a sickening movement as further cascades of booming thunder eddied at them in ear-splitting waves. The temperature in the day-cabin seemed to leap thirty degrees as the ports and metal fitments shook, a book-case was shaken from the wall, the light fittings rattled, and the air was filled with an acrid stench.

"Good God!" breathed Bishop. All three men rushed for the door. Clifford was first to reach the bridge-deck, but only seconds ahead of the other two.

The first thing they saw was a pillar of smoke and flame. It was high, and still rising like an opening umbrella over the harbor. It completely blotted out the sun. Its base was less than half a mile away along the quay.

Almost with puzzlement, Rennie became aware of rapid, patternless crashing sounds. Some were no noisier than hailstones on a corrugated iron roof. Others were grinding thuds of varying pitch, echoing and reverberating in hideous discord. It took Rennie a moment to associate the sound with what he could see with his eyes. Even then, he could not quite believe it. His arms went out to catch the other two men as they made towards the ladder leading to the deck.

"Wait!" he shouted. "Get under cover!" The puzzled frowns on Clifford's and Bishop's faces vanished and turned to horrified understanding as a single mass of metal, twice the size of a man, fell from the sky. It struck the midships gunwale of the *Fort Daring* opposite the number three hatch and disintegrated into several pieces. The object was a ship's winch and must have weighed three tons. It fell like a monstrous bar-bell, one drum-end smashing into the ship's gunwale. The impact caused the center-shaft to fracture in several places like a stick of candy rock. Pieces flew in all directions. A massive gear-wheel rocketed high in an arc and plunged through the roof of the quayside cargo shed, leaving a jagged hole. One winch-drum, with a piece of shaft attached—and looking for all the world like an outsize potato masher—was flung into end-over-end flight before smashing through the wind-screen of a truck on the quay and plummeting through seat and metal and rear axle. The truck lurched and sat down on its tail like a tired work-horse whose rear legs had given way.

Ironmongery rained from the sky in a storm which killed and mutilated indiscriminately at distances up to a mile from the heart of the explosion. Rennie crouched low on the bridge-deck with Clifford and Bishop, numb with shock at the terrifying spectacle. As the death-storm subsided, Clifford was the first to move. He ventured towards the rail and peered astern of the *Fort Daring* to where the pillar of smoke still billowed up into the atmosphere and spread a widening shadow.

"What can you see?" Bishop asked hoarsely. Rennie had followed Clifford out into the open and Bishop now ventured tentatively after them.

"That Norwegian coaster . . ." Clifford's voice was barely a whisper. "There's no sign of it. Just smoke."

"She was loading explosives, wasn't she?" said Bishop. Clifford nodded his head.

"German land-mines. The whole bloody lot must have gone up. Oh, my God!" The last exclamation was wrung from him as a spurt of orange flame appeared at the roof of a cargo shed further along the quay. It darted out like a lizard's tongue, licking swiftly along the guttering of the roof. Then the roof itself seemed to swell like a balloon before erupting skywards. The air shimmered visibly in waves of refracted light, then this wobbling haze seemed to bubble outward in trembling opaque clouds towards the watchers. The blast hit them in a rushing wind of oven heat, throwing them down and scorching at their skin.

The disintegration of the far cargo shed triggered a chain of fresh explosions and fires as showers of burning metal and liquid fire landed amongst stacks of petroleum fuel and ammunition. Shells and bullets began to explode crazily in all directions like rogue fireworks. A huge oil holder beyond the sheds was holed in a dozen places by maverick fireballs and spewed up a dense black mushroom of smoke edged with orange. The black cloud bubbled and expanded upwards, obliterating from sight the city on the hillside beyond and swirling in seconds to a height of two thousand feet.

For those near the center of the holocaust, death came at a merciful speed. Those drawn by duty or curiosity towards the first center of explosion were caught or found themselves cut off by tidal waves of fire and blast leaping out from the epicenter. No official death roll would ever be published, although one conservative estimate numbered the dead at "not less than two hundred and possibly in excess of three hundred." The catastrophe left two square miles of dock and storage area in complete devastation.

Considering how close the *Fort Daring* was to the initial explosion, the ship and her crew survived remarkably unscathed. Bishop was a desperately worried man when he and Clifford finally took their leave of Rennie to brave the flames and rubble of further along the quay and investigate what had happened.

"Looks like your sabotage warning may have come just too late," Rennie observed. "Watch how you go along there. I can still hear stuff popping off."

Until that moment, it had not crossed Bishop's mind that a saboteur had caused the holocaust. He looked sharply at Rennie.

"Sabotage? Didn't you hear aircraft? Jerry's been sending hit-and-run raiders over every other day. It was a bomb surely."

But neither Rennie nor Clifford could recall hearing

aircraft. And there certainly hadn't been any anti-aircraft fire. Bishop was shaken. In spite of the fact that he had been in the process of personally warning every ship-master in the harbor of expected sabotage, he seemed reluctant to believe that the very thing he feared could actually have happened.

"You did say you took the warning seriously," Rennie reminded him.

Bishop was staring at the pall of smoke. He made a limp kind of gesture with his hands.

"But all this, no. De Gaulle's supporters wouldn't go this far. They talk tough and might go so far as to throw a thunder-flash through a barracks window . . . But not this. Unless Bousquet was right."

Rennie raised his eyebrows.

"Bousquet?"

"He's had threats made against his life, because he still won't declare for Giruad or de Gaulle. He has warned our people repeatedly that de Gaulle's agents will stop at nothing. He said that if we didn't round them up, they would burn Algiers to the ground and every ship in the harbor."

It was Rennie's turn to stare in disbelief.

"The old man must be senile," he said. "That really is stretching it. Have you asked de Gaulle what he thinks about Bousquet?"

"I don't suppose there's any love lost," said Bishop thoughtfully, "but I'm inclined to agree with Bousquet when he says that de Gaulle is a political opportunist who is interested only in his own self-aggrandizements." He looked sharply at Rennie. "In any case, these are hardly matters which need concern you."

With that, he left. Rennie watched the two men make their way along the dockside. Bishop baffled him. The man was as arrogant as ever. By what strange quirk of fate had he landed in Algiers? It did not surprise Rennie that the navy had not given Bishop another ship. He had fallen some way short of distinguishing himself in the *Wyvis*. But he had got his promotion and been given an important job, even if it was shore-based. Maybe there's a scarcity of Port Security Officers, thought Rennie. He recollected that Bishop had once mentioned being in that line before.

Bishop's one gracious act had been the invitation to his-bungalow. Rennie would have liked to have all the answers there and then, when Bishop had put in his unexpected appearance—but the very fact that Bishop was prepared to talk about events on the Island of Thieves was something. It was not the act of a guilty man, nor consistent with the possibility that Bishop had anything to hide. The invitation to talk was more the concession of patron to humble petitioner. They had survived bad times together and the high and mighty one acknowledged that some explanation was only proper. It was a case of *noblesse oblige*.

For the time being, Rennie had a great deal more to think about than the shadows of past events. The demands of present were all-pervading.

The fact, however, that the *Fort Daring* was totally without automotive power greatly simplified the problems facing Rennie in the immediate aftermath of the blowing up of the coaster, *Bjorkhaug*. His ship could not be moved without the help of tugs—so, the *Fort Daring* was obliged to sit out the emergency while, all around, ships began to evacuate from the harbor.

The most immediate danger came from the numerous fires onshore spreading to the ships alongside. Having ascertained that small pieces of burning debris on the *Fort Daring* had been adequately dealt with, Rennie mobilized fire-fighting teams from his own crew to protect the immediate vicinity of the ship. Soon, long lengths of hose were stretched along the wharf from the *Daring*'s decklines and the seamen were supplementing the dock fire and rescue services, whose resources were strained far beyond their limits. In army camps around Algiers, volunteers were being recruited to reinforce the overstretched emergency services but, for several hours, the battle to save the harbor was critical. On shore, the great arsenal of warehouses—piled to the roofbeams with munitions—were under the direct threat of the blazing oil storage tanks while, in the harbor, the congestion of ships was exposed to no less significant a menace. When the *Bjorkhaug* and its cargo of land-mines had blown up, burning debris had started a fire on the nearby *Fort Confidence*—and it suddenly became the *Fort Confidence*'s turn to threaten the safety of every ship in the harbor. Her holds were full of cased petroleum.

The port authorities were thus faced with a massive

problem: what to do about this 10,000 ton incendiary bomb which was already ablaze? The alternatives were: to clear every ship out of the harbor and try to control the fire, or to try to get the *Fort Confidence* out of the harbor before the docks became a sea of fire and burning ships.

Several shipmasters, deciding that their first consideration was the safety of their vessels, immediately began putting to sea. This did not simplify matters when it became apparent that the fire on the *Fort Confidence* was beyond control and the decision was made to tow the ship out of the harbor.

With smoke and flames belching from her, the touch-and-go battle began to tow the ship out past the mole before she, too, exploded. When darkness came, the operation had been successfully accomplished and the *Fort Confidence* lay in shallow water to the east of the harbor. Flames rose from her from stem to stern. A pall of smoke from the dying ship hung over the whole of the city of Algiers. She was to be a long time dying. For three more weeks, she was to burn.

For three long weeks, the smoke rose and spiralled while the interior of the ship became an inferno of molten steel. By night, the hull of the beached ship glowed white-hot in the dark waters of the bay, and watchers—a mile away on the shore—could feel their faces flushed by the scorching heat emanating from the tortured wreck.

Finally, to put her out of her misery, a destroyer and a submarine of the Royal Navy pumped shell after shell into the pitiful hulk. The remains of the *Fort Confidence* broke and settled on the sea bottom, to lie like a dismembered whale: a sorry mass of twisted metal to be washed and tumbled by the waters of the bay.

A hot gusting wind from the Sahara whipped flurries of smoke across the harbor and out to sea. Clouds of it still poured from the oil storage area where, at last, the battle was beginning to turn in favor of the fire fighters. But it would be days yet before that battle was finally won. The morning light brought with it stark evidence of the extent of destruction to the docks in the vicinity of the Quai Dakar. Great areas were flattened. The twisted skeletons of huge sheds lay black and smoking in the warm winds of dawn. Alleys and open spaces, which had been awash with water and foam from fire pumps, quickly muddied and dried to leave a dirty yellow scum. This grayed and blackened as the charred dust was lifted in the gusts of wind and settled overall.

Soon after dawn, great armies of American and British soldiers moved in to start the massive clearing operation. Teams sorted and salvaged. Engineers with bulldozers toppled tottering shells of buildings. A mortuary detachment combed for human remains and their grisly finds were carried in blankets to be laid in the open, prior to disposal. Gangs of Arab laborers, noisy as magpies as they organized their efforts, performed by hand the lifting and lowering and moving operations that machines could not tackle.

These activities were at their height when, in mid-morning, Rennie made his way on foot to the nearest dock exit. He had several calls to make, most of them necessitated by the facts that his ship's cargo was to be discharged a long way short of its destination and that his ship was immobilized by enemy action.

The round of port offices—British, French and American—proved frustrating in the extreme. All were overworked, understaffed and neck-deep in the problems of handling a shipping situation that would have been impossible through excessive demands if it had been static; but it was one which was constantly changing with the floodtide of war and being daily complicated in its fluid state by the dictatorial pressures of High Command planning. On a day when things were running with the strains tolerable, Rennie with his crippled and unscheduled ship would have provided an unwelcome complication. On the day following a major explosion which had laid waste half the docks, he was as welcome as a life insurance salesman at a funeral.

He was hot, perspiring and foot-weary by the time he reached the shipping agents in the commercial heart of the city adjacent to the docks. They had offices in the impressive Delta-Afrique Company building, home of a vast conglomerate of enterprises ranging from banking and construction to vineyard ownership and petrochemical industrial development.

Gerard Blom, the agent, was a sad-faced man with a sense of humor that totally belied the set lugubrity of his features. He won Rennie's friendship instantly by making it clear that he was there to help him and that nothing would be too much trouble to undertake. He would blast his way through bureaucracy, charm his way through locked doors, seduce the Governor's wife, anything that was necessary to get things moving on behalf of the *Fort Daring*.

Rennie needed money to pay out advances to his crew. Blom took a check book from a desk drawer. How much? Rennie thought about £10 per man. Blom shook his head. They would be back for more in a couple of days. He wrote out a check for a quarter of a million Algerian Francs and thumped a bell on his desk.

A pretty olive-skinned girl in a blue frock appeared from the outer office.

"Violette," said Blom, "run across to the bank and give this to Fontaine. Tell him I want cash in new notes—and within the next half hour. I want a hundred thousand in five hundreds, a hundred thousand in one hundreds, and fifty thousand in fifties."

"Yes, Monsieur." The girl made no move to go.

"Well, what are you waiting for?" asked Blom.

The girl glanced uncertainly at her watch.

"Monsieur, it is late in the afternoon to ask for so much money. You know what they are like."

Blom stared at her solemnly.

"That's why I told you to see Fontaine. Now go."

She clicked out on her high heels. Blom sighed.

"In Algiers, Captain, what you know is unimportant. Who you know is everything. Before the British and Americans came, this was the most bureaucratic city in the world. Now, it is the most bureaucratic city, in triplicate. It is a jungle of red tape. A stranger stumbling into it would become hopelessly lost. That's why I hope you won't hesitate to call on me for anything at all. If I hadn't learned how to beat the system I would have gone out of business long ago."

Rennie smiled.

"How do you do it? Bribery and corruption?"

"I wish it were that simple," sighed Blom. "Oh, admittedly, a gift here and a gift there often helps, but I like to think it's sheer hard work. People have come to know that I will work twenty-four hours a day to be of service. I just don't give up because some *fonctionnaire* says I've got to get a permit from another department, or it's not his pigeon, or letters of authority are needed from the British and the Americans as well as the Civil Authority. I just keep hacking through the jungle."

Rennie sat back and watched with admiration as Blom went into action on his behalf. There were cables to be sent to London, Alexandria and New York, all of which had to meet censorship and coding requirements. There was a huge order list from the *Fort Daring*'s Chief Steward for fruit, vegetables and other supplies. There was the question of the ship's seaworthiness and the necessity to have the damage surveyed by approved assessors so that decisions could be made on repair, dry-docking, or whatever. The shipping company had certain obligations to fulfil as a result of Board of Trade regulations and insurance requirements, but the final word would remain with that section of the naval administration responsible for shipping and shipping facilities in the area.

Rennie had made a long list of all the items of ship's business requiring attention. Blom sailed through it, making phone calls here and phone calls there, and giving a simultaneous running commentary on the difficulties or otherwise of obtaining results. The tricky problems were immediately soluble, it seemed. The impossible ones might take a couple of days.

At the end of it, a glimmer of pleasure flickered across his sad face when Rennie expressed his thanks and admiration.

"I am at your service," he said, shrugging away Rennie's praise. "Now, all I have to do is get you safely back to your ship with that money for your crew. I'll drive you down to the docks—that is, if you don't mind riding in my delivery truck—and then, perhaps, you would do me the honor of having dinner with me at my home?"

Rennie accepted the lift but, with real regret, had to decline the dinner invitation. He explained that he was meeting a naval friend from the Port Security office. Then he suddenly remembered something.

"I should really look in at the Port Security office on my way back to the ship. My friend has a bungalow somewhere along the coast, but he didn't tell me exactly where. Or how I was going to get there."

"No problem," said Blom. "We'll look in at Port Security on our way to the ship."

He led the way from the office, carrying the attaché case with the money. Rennie followed him along the corridor, past frosted glass doors bearing the names of companies which were all part of the Delta-Afrique conglomerate. Ahead of them, one of these doors opened and a young woman in a white dress came out. Rennie halted as a thrill of recognition ran through him. Then he hurried forward as the woman, without a glance in their direction, walked quickly towards the main stairway.

"Madame Mercier! Arlette!"

The clicking footsteps halted. The young woman turned, icy surprise written on her face, as Rennie made up on her. He realized immediately he had made a mistake. This was not Jean-Paul's wife. The shape of the nose was slightly fuller. She was not unattractive, but without the flawless symmetry of feature of Arlette Mercier. She stared at Rennie.

"Je ne vous connais pas. Connaissez-vous Arlette?"

Rennie flushed with embarrassment. He blurted an apology, stumbling with his French, which for once seemed strangely inadequate.

"I'm sorry . . . I thought you were someone I knew."

"My sister would not be pleased to know that you have mistaken the ugly duckling of the family for her, Monsieur."

"You are not ugly," protested Rennie.

The young woman shrugged. "It is of no importance. I do not flatter myself quite so readily as you seem prepared to do. Are you a friend of Arlette?"

"Yes. Yes, I am."

"And you are English, no?"

"Yes. My name is John Rennie."

Fiery lights of contempt danced in the young woman's eyes.

"Then forgive me if I do not say it has been a pleasure to meet you. Good day, Monsieur."

She turned on her heel and walked quickly towards the stairs without a backward glance. Rennie stared at her departing figure, his mouth hanging open in bewilderment. Blom, a silent witness to the brief encounter, regarded Rennie with a flicker in his sad eyes that suggested amusement.

"I did not know you were acquainted with the Bousquet family, Captain Rennie," he observed.

"What did I say to deserve that?" muttered Rennie. "Did you see that look she gave me? As if I'd crawled up out of a drain. Do you know her?"

"I know of her," said Blom.

"What did I do to offend her?" said Rennie.

"You committed only three unforgivable offenses that I can think of," replied Blom. "First, you were in bad company—mine. Secondly, you mistook her for her sister—whom she hates. Thirdly, you're English."

Rennie was still mystified.

"I don't understand. What has she got against you?"

"I'm a Jew," said Blom. "The Bousquet family doesn't like Jews." Blom waved an arm. "They've been trying to get me out of this building for long enough. With some of the Vichy regulations, they would have succeeded, too. I would have lost my offices for sure if the Americans hadn't landed here. Thankfully, I have some American friends with a bit of weight."

"But how could Bousquet get you thrown out? Isn't this building all Delta-Afrique? Aren't you part of it?"

Blom's look sympathized with Rennie's seeming naïvety.

"My father was part of Delta-Afrique. That was thirty years ago, when this place was built. He was one of the original members of the combine that built these premises—but they were all independent companies, an association of companies rather than one great amalgamation. It wasn't until just before the war that Bousquet started empire-building on his own . . . Buying out all the independents and getting his greedy fingers into every pie. My father refused to sell and I reckon that the pressures Bousquet put on him sent him to an early grave. I inherited the business—and the pressures. They haven't been quite so vicious since Bousquet discovered I had American friends."

They walked slowly down the stairs as they talked.

"Jean-Paul didn't think much of the old boy either," said Rennie.

"Jean-Paul?"

"Jean-Paul Mercier. Arlette's husband. We spent some time together in the same prison in Senegal. Neither of us cared very much for the Vichy idea of hospitality."

Blom looked at Rennie with a new intensity of interest.

"I had no idea that you . . ." He let the sentence die in mid-air. Rennie broke the silence that followed.

"That's how I came to know Arlette Mercier," he explained. "I only met her once. She came to see Jean-Paul."

Blom was thoughtful. He hesitated before saying: "Arlette is all right."

"You know her?"

"No," said Blom, "just what I've been told. I was with a Resistance group before the landings . . . One with American connections . . . Another group—one with English connections—let it be known to us that they didn't want any accidents happening to Arlette because she was hobnobbing with certain members of the German Armistice Commission. She was obviously working on the side of the angels."

"She certainly struck me as being something special," said Rennie. "What about the other sister? You said they hated each other."

"It's well known that there's no love lost between the two. The odd thing is that the father dotes on Arlette and doesn't have much time for the younger one, Geraldine. Yet it's Geraldine who seems to be more of a chip off the old block. She's not married—a bit of a man-hater apparently—and she has the reputation of being a task-master in the mold of Simon Legree. She runs the wine side of the family business in Bilda with a rod of iron."

"What has she got against Englishmen?" asked Rennie. "You said I committed three unforgivable offenses in her eyes and that the third one was being English."

Blom had led the way from the foot of the stairs through a series of corridors and out into the bright sunlight of a yard at the rear of the building.

He blinked as he replied to Rennie.

"Geraldine was very close to her brother. Didn't you know about the brother?"

Rennie shook his head.

"Until we bumped into Geraldine upstairs, I didn't even know that Arlette had a sister. Is there a brother, too?"

"Was," corrected Blom. "He was killed at Mers-el-Kebir, when the British Navy bombarded the French fleet in nineteen-forty. Geraldine Bousquet has never made a secret of her hatred for the British since Mers-el-Kebir,

Captain. As far as she's concerned, you belong to a nation of bloody murderers. You killed her brother."

Three years had passed since that day of infamy at Oran in the immediate aftermath of France's defeat by Germany. Rennie could recall how he had felt sick to the stomach at hearing the news over the radio of British sailors firing on the French sailors who, days before, had been their allies and comrades-in-arms. He had, however, accepted Winston Churchill's agonized defense of the British action: that the French had been entreated to sail out and join the Royal Navy and continue the fight against the Germans or, alternatively, to escape to the French West Indies or the USA. Churchill had said that the consequences of allowing the might of the French Navy to fall under German control were too frightful to contemplate, inasmuch as the balance of seapower would be tipped overwhelmingly in favor of the Nazis. It could not be allowed to happen. And, for this reason, it had been necessary for the offer made by HM Government to the French Mediterranean Fleet to be couched in the terms of an ultimatum: "Join us or we must destroy you." Rennie had no doubt at all that the agony of Churchill's decision had been very real.

All of this coursed through Rennie's mind at the thought of a girl understandably outraged by the senseless death of her brother. He could understand the bitterness which the very sight of his British uniform could evoke in her. He was sad that it should be so. War, he knew, fed the nationalistic prejudices and false prides which are the seeds of hate, but he had never learned to hate another human being on the basis only of his tongue, his faith, his color or the uniform he wore. It was easy enough to hate—with a hate born of fear—men and nationalities arrayed against you and bent on your destruction, or even a single enemy with the same intent, but it was a different matter to hate by proxy: to hate a son for the sins of a father or an entire clan for the crimes of its chief. For Rennie, hate had to be as selective as love. A Montague could love a Capulet. It didn't follow that a Montague had to be enamored of every Capulet who walked the earth. And as with love, so with hate.

He became so lost in his own thoughts that he stopped and stood almost trance-like in the middle of the yard. Blom had kept on walking towards a blue utility van with the words, BLOM MARINE Cie., painted in white on the side. The agent brought Rennie back to earth with an oath exploding from his lips.

Rennie caught up with Blom, who pointed angrily at the van. The tires on all four wheels were flat.

"This happens now about twice a week," said Blom angrily.

"You mean it's deliberate?" said Rennie.

"I told you about the pressures. This is the petty kind of thing they get up to now."

"Haven't you gone to the police?"

Blom laughed.

"They'd look me straight in the eye and tell me I was mad. I had a petrol bomb thrown at my house last October. Communist terrorists, they said. They get the blame for everything the police can't solve or can't be bothered looking into."

Rennie stared at him, askance.

"Petrol bombs! They play pretty bloody rough, don't they?"

"Oh, it's not so bad now, although I could give you a list as long as my arm of some of the tricks they've got up to. Bousquet hasn't turned the strong-arm mob loose on me since he found out I had friends at American military headquarters. In G-two. Supplying ships is important to the war and the Yanks will come down like a ton of bricks on anyone fouling up the process."

"So, what do we do now?" asked Rennie.

Blom grinned.

"We get out the foot-pump and blow some air in these tires."

Chapter Twelve

THE Port Security Office's white-washed exterior was half in shadow as the late afternoon sun dipped southwest beyond the rabbit-warren lanes of the Casbah and the huddle of cavern-like dwellings stepped into the hill above the harbor. Blom's van was still some distance away from Bishop's headquarters when Rennie realized that a naval officer in earnest discussion with two civilians in light-colored suits was Bishop himself. The three men were standing on the cobbled road which fronted the Port Security Office.

"That's a bit of luck," said Rennie to Blom. "There's the man I wanted to see—the Navy officer."

Blom crawled the van in second gear as they approached.

"Your friend keeps bad company," he observed. "I know the two with him. They are very bad medicine indeed."

Rennie threw a sideways glance at his companion.

"Who are they?"

"Deuxième Bureau—both of them. They used to spy for Darlan. God knows whose payroll they're on now."

Blom stopped the car and remained sitting behind the wheel while Rennie got out. Rennie crossed towards Bishop, who turned at that moment and recognized him. There was a thunderous scowl on Bishop's face.

"And what the bloody hell do you want?" he greeted Rennie. His tone was more than rude. It was tense with rage. Rennie halted as if he had been slapped.

"I'm sorry," he said. "Am I interrupting?"

"Of course you're bloody well interrupting," Bishop snapped back. "What are you doing in this part of the dock anyway? Your ship's at the other side of the harbor and that's where you should be!"

Rennie could feel the blood rising to his face, but he kept a grip on his anger.

"I wanted to find out how to get to your place tonight," he said evenly.

"You can forget it!" snapped Bishop. "Good God, man, half the dock went up in flames last night, or don't you remember? Do you think I'll have any time to chit-chat with you with all that's going on. Now, be a good fellow and just piss off out of my sight!"

Rennie's temper was now just a fraction of a degree below flash-point. It reached it when Bishop pointedly turned his back on him and began to say something to one of the two civilians. Rennie stuck out an arm and propelled Bishop round by the shoulder to face him. What followed next, surprised even Rennie. Bishop seemed to lose complete control of himself and flew at Rennie with fists and elbows flailing in all directions. The momentum of his sudden assault sent Rennie to the ground. He did not remain there long. He scrambled to his feet and crouched, murder in his eyes.

"Now, I'm going to bloody kill you, Bishop," he ground out. Bishop was staring at him, wild-eyed as a rabid dog, and giving vent to great grunting sighs. He flew at Rennie again. This time, Rennie was ready for him. He stepped inside the flailing arms and, with a punch that travelled only nine inches, crashed his right hand into Bishop's midriff. Bishop snapped together like a jack-knife and hit the ground folded double. He skidded backwards over the cobbles on his bottom.

Rennie followed up and tried to drag the other man to his feet by seizing his shirt front, but there was no fight left in Bishop. He was gasping painfully for breath and hung limply, fingertips trailing on the ground, suspended in the grip Rennie had of his shirt. Rennie let the shirt go and Bishop collapsed in an undignified heap on the ground.

The two Frenchmen had watched the episode without interfering, all the time exchanging puzzled glances. Now, one of the men—the more thick-set of the two and the owner of a short Hitler moustache—drew a revolver from inside his jacket.

"Assez!" he hissed at Rennie. "Rien de plus!"

His companion ran and helped Bishop to his feet.

Rennie retrieved his uniform cap, which had rolled on

the ground at the start of the struggle, and—ignoring the gun—walked back to face Bishop from a distance of two feet. Bishop backed away but succeeded only in bumping into the man who had helped him to his feet.

"We're still going to have our talk, Bishop," said Rennie, "or, so help me, I will thrash the living daylights out of you. You know where my ship is. I'll give you four days to come and see me or let me know where we can meet. If I don't hear from you, I'm going to come looking for you. Just you see that it doesn't come to that. Because if it does, I'm not going to be fussy how I get the answers out of you."

"You can't threaten me," Bishop shrilled, in what was intended as a defiant snarl but came out more as a blustery squeak.

"I *am* threatening you," Rennie said evenly. "*You* are going to talk to me whether you like it or not. And sooner rather than later."

"What can I tell you? What is it you want from me?" Again, Bishop's tone was shrill.

"I'll tell you what I want to know. I want to be sure —one hundred per cent sure—that you weren't the bastard who sold us out to Junot. I want to know if it was because of you that I got kicked half to death and Jean-Paul got skewered on a bayonet . . ."

"You're out of your mind," screeched Bishop, eyes wide and frightened. By now, little knots of passers-by, mainly British navymen, were halting at a polite distance and watching. It was a rare sight to see two British officers —one a Naval Commander and the other a ship's captain —bawling the odds at each other in broad daylight. A civilian with a revolver in his hand added spice to the drama.

"You'd better clear out before you're arrested," said Bishop. "I only have to wave a finger and a guard detail will have you locked up in ten seconds flat." His fear of Rennie was receding quickly as it became clear that the Merchant Navy captain did not intend to do him further bodily harm. And with the return of some composure came the realization of the undignified picture he presented to the growing number of interested spectators. Embarrassedly, he ran a hand through his tousled hair. The Frenchman with the gun picked up his uniform cap from the ground and handed it to him without a word.

The two Frenchmen were obviously still bemused by all that had happened and hesitant to interfere in an all-British argument.

Rennie looked about him. He detested scenes in public and it gave him no pleasure to be at the center of this one. Although at a distance, the gallery seemed to have sprung from nowhere. He stared hard at Bishop.

"You've got four days, Bishop. I'll expect to hear from you."

He turned on his heel and strode quickly towards the van. He got in, slamming the door closed after him.

"Sorry about that," he said to Blom. "I'm afraid I lost my temper."

Blom started the motor and engaged the gear.

"I suppose it was none of my business," he said. "But I had a bad moment when that hood pulled his gun. It may be no consolation, Captain, but if he had tried to use it, I was going to run him down with the truck."

Rennie grinned.

"Thanks."

"And the argument?"

"It was personal."

Blom nodded sagely.

"If the British officer was a friend, Captain, I hope I never become your enemy."

"It has settled one thing," said Rennie.

"It has?"

Rennie smiled.

"I can take you up on that dinner invitation. I'm going to be free this evening, after all."

Six days passed and Rennie neither saw nor heard from Bishop. The time gave him the opportunity to reflect on the ultimatum he had made to Bishop. In the sobering light of the following days, the threat he had made seemed empty and foolish and it made Rennie wonder if it was the consequence of seeing too many western films. What was he going to do if Bishop failed to respond? Load his six-gun, mount his white horse, and go galloping round the docks looking for him? It was all too melodramatic.

At the same time, the maggot in Rennie's brain, which was his concern for Jean-Paul and Hobart and the uncertainties surrounding their fates, continued to gnaw at his mind and demand some kind of positive action. Here, in Algiers, there had to be some of the answers to the questions which haunted him.

Standing in the way of indulging himself in such strictly personal matters, of course, was the fact that Rennie had a ship to command. The ship demanded and got his conscientious attention. Events conspired, however, to reduce greatly the demands made on Rennie as shipmaster.

At the end of six days, the *Fort Daring*'s cargo had been completely discharged and she had to surrender her berth alongside the wharf to one of the waiting queue of ships in the anchorage. Rennie feared that the *Fort Daring*'s consequent fate would be to be towed out to the bay and to be left at anchor out there indefinitely—but this fear was not realized. Instead, the ship was moved across the harbor to be moored stern to the mole, with bow ropes out to one of the string of buoys which ran parallel to the sea-wall.

Here, within the harbor, preliminary repairs were to begin on the ship's damaged stern. By trimming the water tanks and loading ballast in the forward holds, it was proposed to raise the stern tube free of the water so that work could start. The immediate task would be to make the ship seaworthy and assess the full extent of any structural damage. The question of replacing the rudder and propeller was to be left in abeyance until after this preliminary work was complete.

One thing was clear. The *Fort Daring* was to be in Algiers for a very long time. In a cable to Rennie, Blenkinsop advised a start to the arrangements for paying off the majority of the crew and providing them with passage to the UK. He sugegsted that Rennie remain aboard with such officers and men as might be required to look after the ship on a care and maintenance basis. The difficulty in obtaining dry-dock facilities in the foreseeable future meant that the *Fort Daring* might be laid up in Algiers for anything up to a year.

Thus it was that the question of what to do about Bishop was forced by circumstance, if not by choice, to the lower end of Rennie's list of priorities. It was not until his ship was safely moored stern to the mole and the future promised only months of enforced idleness that Rennie felt he had any freedom to devote time and thought to the unsolved mysteries of his Senegal experience.

Then, out of the blue, a note came from Bishop. It was handed aboard late on a Friday evening by Lieutenant Clifford, together with a batch of official security instructions for ships at buoy moorings.

The note was written in a spidery long-hand, but its outstanding feature was its conciliatory tone. It read:

Dear Rennie,

I must ask you to forgive my inexcusable behavior the other day. There were extenuating circumstances. I had gone 48 hours without sleep and was at my wits' end as a result of the explosion on the Norwegian ship. I am sorry I was so rude to you and flew off the handle. It was simply a case that I had so much on my plate and had had such a trying day that I wasn't my usual self. I honestly don't know what came over me.

Having said that, I don't think that any useful purpose would be served by us meeting for a talk about my release from internment. There really is nothing to tell. Major Junot acceded to my request for new quarters on the Island of Thieves by putting me in a filthy cell in the barracks at Fort Raphael. I shared it with a Polish colonel, who spoke no English and was quite mad. No doubt, this was Junot's idea of a joke. I did not find the experience amusing.

Anyway, I only spent a week or two at Fort Raphael before being taken back to Dakar and, from there, on to a big internment camp for Royal Navy personnel outside Casablanca. The Americans landed at Fedala soon afterwards and our camp was liberated on 9 November. I volunteered my services to the naval people on General Patton's staff and stayed on in Casablanca until just before Christmas. Then my promotion came through and, with it, my official posting to Algiers. That's the whole story.

Yours,
Matthew Bishop, Commander, Royal Navy.

P.S.

I have just come across something in the Philippeville traffic program which may interest you. It's not urgent. If you want to see it, look into my office some time you're passing.

* * *

The letter was almost an anti-climax. If it were true—and it had the ring of truth—Bishop could obviously have had no part in betraying the escape plan to Junot. One part of the letter baffled Rennie—the postscript. What on earth was the Philippeville traffic program and in what possible way could it be of interest to Rennie?

He brooded over the letter and its implications for the rest of the evening. He knew in his heart of hearts that, although circumstances made Bishop the number one suspect as Junot's informer, he had never really believed that Bishop would stoop so low.

Bishop was pig-headed, arrogant, egotistical to the point of paranoia, a volatile and unstable man, but he was too much of an old-fashioned snob in the Colonel Blimp mold to descend to cold-blooded treachery. Yet Rennie's accusation of treachery six days before had frightened him. Why? The answer to Rennie was that Bishop was guiltless. He had reacted with fear, not because there was any truth in the accusation but because of the accusation itself and the possible damage it could do to his standing as a serving officer.

It explained, too, perhaps, the handsome apology for his behavior. Rested and given time to reflect, he had done the gentlemanly thing—said he was sorry, patched things up with an explanation that would put the record straight, and politely suggested there was no reason why he and Rennie should ever meet again.

But the postscript invited further contact. Was this just an empty gesture? An afterthought? "I'm not slamming the door in your face, old chap. Just closing it gently." He had picked on some inconsequential snippet of information in official bumph, which might interest Rennie as a ship's captain and in no other capacity, and had thrown it in as a sop. No hard feelings, old chap.

Rennie, who found little pleasure in solitary drinking, made an exception that night and worked his way through half a bottle of whisky as he brooded over Bishop and Jean-Paul and Hobart and a man who had turned up in the middle of Morocco calling himself Hobart. He didn't know what startling revelation he had expected from encountering Bishop again, but, now, Bishop seemed to represent a dead end. That note from him answered nothing.

By the time he had sipped his way through several glasses of whiskey, the strung-up tautness he felt began to ease. At the back of his mind, the haunting images he had of Junot plunging a bayonet into Jean-Paul faded—to be replaced more and more by softer but equally haunting images of a lovely blond girl cradling his head in her lap and gently bathing his face. He felt vaguely ashamed that he could not think of Jean-Paul's wife without stirrings of desire.

For a week now, he had lived with the knowledge that Arlette Mercier was, if not in the city, somewhere close by—and he had wanted to go to her. It was a logical thing to do if he were to obtain news of Jean-Paul. Time and the opportunity had not occurred to do so, but more than that had held Rennie back. Now, in the solitude of his cabin and with the tranquillizing effects of the whisky anesthetizing the guilt pangs of being brutally honest with himself, he acknowledged the reason.

His wanting to go to Arlette Mercier had less to do with Jean-Paul than the disturbing fantasies which she roused in him when he allowed himself to think of her.

Before, when he had fantasized about her, he had deluded himself that it had no significance. The monastic existence of life at sea, the fact that no woman had anchored his affections, the need to people dreams with remembered faces, all these were ready and rational explanations why his subconscious mind should bring her to him subliminally as an eager partner to a deep recurring lust. Now, he deluded himself no more. He felt a disgust at himself at the knowledge but, accepting that he was what he was—a man who constantly fell short of his own expectations of himself—the faint intimations of guilt lost their restraining grip. He would seek her out, regardless. He would go to her because he *was* concerned about her husband and he would go knowing that this alone was not the sole motivation. Why should it inhibit him? Hell, probably every man who clapped eyes on Arlette Mercier got the urge to bed her. Why should he think he was any different?

At ten the following morning, he was in Blom's office. Characteristically, Blom showed no curiosity at Rennie's unscheduled appearance and sudden request for help in locating Arlette Mercier. Instead, he consulted a telephone directory, chatted briefly on the phone with an operator and then handed Rennie the receiver.

Their conversation made an inauspicious start. She got the impression that it was René somebody or other on the line, and it was a moment or two before she was finally able to identify her caller. Rennie had a feeling of disappointment. He had somehow thought that she would place him instantly and react with excitement and delight. But it wasn't like that at all. She seemed to have difficulty recalling any John Rennie in her acquaintance and then, when the penny did drop, she had to excuse herself from the phone and rush off to attend to something. Rennie waited for fully five minutes before she returned full of apologies.

'I'd like to meet you—just for a talk," said Rennie.

"But of course! Why don't you come out here this afternoon? Everyone has gone to Blida for the weekend, to my sister's, but I am not going. It will be splendid to see you."

Rennie didn't know where "here" was or how to get there, but she came to his rescue.

"I'll come for you in the car," she suggested. "Do you know the Hotel Aletti? But of course, you must—it's such a landmark. Meet me opposite the Hotel Aletti at two. I'll pick you up."

It was twenty past two when she finally appeared. Rennie, wearing a lightweight gray suit, a lemon-colored silk shirt and blue-gray-yellow striped tie, felt strangely out of place amongst the hundreds of servicemen in khakis and whites parading aimlessly in the vicinity of the hotel. There was no escape from the post-noon heat of the sun and, in the half hour he waited, Rennie wished a hundred times that he had dressed a little less conventionally and plumped for an open shirt and slacks.

There was little formality in the dress Arlette Mercier had chosen. She was wearing a red sun-top and white beach shorts when she breezed up in an open 1937-vintage Bugatti two-seater. She looked round anxiously, not recognizing Rennie until he ran across and said: "Hello there. It's me, John Rennie."

She flashed him a dazzing smile.

"Sorry I'm late. The traffic! C'est formidable." She seemed oblivious to the group of British sailors who were ogling her without any pretense of subtlety, and to half a dozen GIs who were making far from coy propositions of a distinctly amorous nature. When Rennie climbed into the car, he became the target of comments which were both ribald and envious.

Half an hour later, they were clear of the city and Rennie was luxuriating in the fan of cooling air provided by the Bugatti's fifty-miles-an-hour progress along the coastal plain of the Sahil Mitija. The road was good and there was a fair number of military trucks using it. But, on the highway, the traffic was strung out and seemed thin after the congestion of the city streets.

After an unsuccessful attempt to make himself heard over the city traffic, Rennie had made no conversation. Now, on the open highway, he tried again.

"You'll have to shout," Arlette yelled. "What did you say about Jean-Paul?" The wind was shipping at her hair and, as four three-ton trucks lumbered towards Algiers in a rush of sound, she gave a resigned shrug and smile as if to say: "How can we compete?"

"Have you heard from Jean-Paul?" Rennie shouted. "Is he all right?"

Her look darkened.

"Jean-Paul is a fool. I will tell you about it when we arrive."

"Then he is alive? He is all right?"

"As far as I know."

She put her foot down hard and the speedo needle danced across the dial in response. She stared fiercely at the road ahead.

Rennie was perplexed. Relief flooded through him at her confirmation that Jean-Paul was alive and all right, but the manner of her confirmation bewildered him. They drove for several kilometers in silence. Rennie felt he had to break that silence.

"Are we going far?"

The sideways glance she flung at him was coquettish. "How far would you like us to go?"

He did not know if the *double entendre* in her words was intentional or not. His confusion showed, and it embarrassed him. He hadn't been in her company an hour and, already, she was making him feel juvenile and gauche, unequal to her womanly self-assurance and sheer feminine power.

"I could go on for miles with this breeze about my

face," he said lamely. She smiled, as if the answer secretly amused her. He had sidestepped any question of ambiguity, with the result that he sounded in his own ears exactly what he didn't want to appear: the slightly priggish, strait-laced Englishman who flounders hopelessly when a woman is anything other than demurely coy.

"Am I too fast for you?" she bounced at him, her eyes teasing and bright with challenge. Again the ambiguity. Not am I *going* too fast for you, but the suggestion that she was talking about herself and not her driving. He met the challenge in the sidelong looks she kept throwing him.

"I like to live dangerously," he shouted in her ear.

"Good," she cried. "So do I."

With a laugh, she swung the car out into the middle of the road. A big army truck emblazoned with the white star of the United States Army was coming the other way at a plodding thirty. Arlette eased the Bugatti into the left-hand lane and straight into the path of the oncoming truck. The vehicles closed at something like a hundred miles an hour. The GI at the wheel of the truck jammed a hand on the horn and kept it there. A collision seemed inevitable.

Rennie could feel the hairs stand erect on the back of his neck. He sucked in his breath involuntarily and his arms went back against the sides of his seat in expectation of the impact that seemed only seconds away. The truck driver's nerve went first. The big vehicle veered off the road and bumped over uneven ground which sloped up from the shoulder. It careened crazily before stalling against a bank of ground that was too high to ride. The girl at Rennie's side teased the wheel gently right and returned the Bugatti to the right-hand lane. Her perfect white teeth were bared in a grin of sheer exhilaration.

Rennie sagged in his seat. His heart was hammering.

"For God's sake, slow down!" he shouted through gritted teeth. In that moment he would gladly have wrung Arlette Mercier's neck.

She let the speed of the Bugatti drop. Now, there was laughing mockery in the sideway looks she gave Rennie.

"You said you liked to live dangerously," she taunted him.

"That was a lunatic thing to do," he cried. "You could have killed us both."

She ran the car off the road on to the rough shoulder

and braked it to a stop. She turned round in her seat and stared at him. It was a regal, imperious stare.

"Are you afraid of dying?"

The question was so unexpected that it halted the flood of recrimination that was on the tip of Rennie's tongue. He stared back at her, dumbfounded.

"I asked you if you were afraid of dying?" she said.

"I'm certainly not looking forward to it with the same enthusiasm as you," he replied tartly. "What in heaven's name possessed you to do a crazy thing like that?"

"You said you liked to live dangerously. I thought you meant it."

Rennie sighed.

"There's a difference between living dangerously and dying stupidly. You don't seem to know the difference," he said.

"You don't understand me, do you?" she said vehemently.

"No, I damned well don't!" he replied with equal feeling. "It's bad enough you trying to commit suicide and dragging me along for laughs . . . But why you should think it ought to be followed by a roadside philosophical debate, I certainly don't know. I didn't know that this was what you had in mind for this afternoon."

"I had nothing in mind for this afternoon until you telephoned me this morning." She turned her head away from him almost shyly. "I was curious about you. I wanted to know more about you."

"I'm sorry I've been a disappointment . . . That I don't share your passion for driving cars straight at defenseless army trucks."

She smiled ruefully.

"Maybe it *was* crazy. Maybe I am. I just wanted to show you that I meant it when I said I liked to live dangerously. I really meant it." She looked up at him and her eyes seemed to light up from within. "To live a centimeter's distance from death is to taste life to the full, to extract the maximum essence from living. Have you any idea how dull life can be for a woman? She's expected to stay at home and cook and sew . . . when, in her heart, she may be longing for excitement and stimulation. But what chance do we get to fly a fighter plane or climb the Matterhorn or pilot a submarine into an enemy's harbor?

Why should I be disqualified from taking risks simply because I am a woman?"

He gave a shake of his head.

"We men have all the fun, eh?" He wondered what it was that, only moments before, had made him feel the immature one. Now, he felt many many years her senior.

"I don't envy men," she said. She was still very intense. "But I object to an order of things which says I have to live my life by the rules that men have made. What right has any man to say what woman should do or should not do? I am not to be owned by any man—whether it is a father who tries to tell me how I should think or a husband who wants me for a mattress and assumes that my mind can be kept like butter in an icebox, to be brought out and used sparingly two or three times a day."

"You sound bitter," said Rennie. "You weren't like that the last time we met. I thought you were an angel of mercy, all warmth and compassion . . . A loving and devoted wife risking her life for her husband . . ."

She laughed.

"You thought exactly what I wanted you to think. Men are such children." She shook her head in mock despair.

"Do you mean it was all an act?" asked Rennie.

"No, I didn't say that. We all play parts but I am never aware of consciously—as you say—putting on an act. I am me, whatever I am doing—even if I choose to reveal only a little of my total self. You formed an opinion of me when we last met—but you saw only a fraction of me. You don't know any more about me than you would know of a book after reading a single page."

"So, today, I'm seeing a different page?"

She smiled.

"Yes, today you see a different page. Tomorrow, perhaps another quite different."

"How many pages make up the volume?" Rennie asked with a trace of irony in his voice.

Her face lit up.

"But hundreds, thousands! More than you could read in a year. More than you could ever understand."

She put the car into gear and, with a screech of spinning wheels and revving engine, gunned the car off the shoulder on to the highway in front of a dilapidated bus heading for Cherchell.

Arlette drove the Bugatti into the stable-yard at the

rear of the house, then led the way by a stone-flagged path to the front. Here a broad stone terrace, partially canopied by a balcony running the length of the two-story part of the house, looked out to sea.

They entered the house by a French window. The long terrace room was multi-functional. At one end, a massive mahogany dining-table with chairs to match was capable of seating twenty. The other end was furnished as a lounge and reception area with easy chairs and chaises-longues of varying types and periods. Carved chests sat against the walls amid occasional tables festooned with ebony elephants, cherrywood gazelles and other bric-a-brac of markedly oriental origin. The walls themselves were adorned with assegais, zebra-skin shields and enough ancient musketry to have suitably equipped the Riff chorus in "The Desert Song."

"If you think this place is bad, you should see the family seat at Blida," said Arlette. "It dates back to the time of Napoleon and was once the palace of a Turkish governor. It's like something out of the *Arabian Nights.* My sister stays there all the year round but my father and I prefer to live here near the sea in the summer."

"It must be nice to be people of property," said Rennie. "I was brought up in a two-bedroomed semi-detached and thought I was pretty lucky if I got two weeks at a Scarborough boarding-house in the summer." He looked around, picking up a hand-carved Chinese dragon ornament to examine the detail. "I would have expected to find more of a nautical flavor in an Admiral's house—models of galleons and men o' war, and maybe a three-hundred-year-old sextant."

Arlette laughed.

"My father didn't spend more than six years of his life at sea—and most of that before the nineteen-fourteen war. He came out of the Navy for the Colonial Service two years before I was born."

"Is he still in it, the Colonial Service?"

"Good heavens, no. He retired in 1935 . . . He has various business and political interests."

"So I've heard." Rennie put down the ornament and looked at her. "He has something to do with Delta-Afrique?"

Arlette frowned. She regarded Rennie questioningly.

"You know about Delta-Afrique?"

"I said I've heard about it."

"Then you'll know my father doesn't involve himself all that much in the Company nowadays. I'm running it now."

"You?"

She bridled.

"Do you think a woman isn't capable?"

"No, no, not at all. I'm just surprised. I had no idea . . ."

Her annoyance vanished as quickly as it had been roused. She treated him to a sudden dazzling smile.

"Another page, Captain Rennie. I have given you another page of the volume. Arlette, businesswoman!"

Rennie grinned. "You're quite a book of revelations. Is there anything else I ought to know?"

"No. What you don't know can do you no harm. Besides, isn't a woman more interesting if she reveals a little at a time?"

"I'll take your word for it," said Rennie.

She rang a little brass bell and an Arab houseboy in blue trousers and white tunic materialized from the interior of the house. He brought them iced orange drinks, which they drank on the terrace.

"Are you ready now to tell me about Jean-Paul?" Rennie asked. He had waited with great patience for her to bring up the subject of her husband of her own accord. Now, he didn't intend to be side-tracked.

"Must we talk about him?" she replied. "I know you were on that island with him and he was your friend. But so was that other British officer, the strange one—Commander Bishop—but he couldn't care less about Jean-Paul."

"Commander Bishop doesn't care much about anybody except himself."

"Is that why you attacked him outside his office?" she asked pertly.

Rennie's eyebrows shot up.

"I didn't attack him. We . . . We had a difference of opinion. How come you know about that?"

Her smile was enigmatic.

"There's very little happens in Algiers that I don't know about."

"I want to know about Jean-Paul," said Rennie.

"Why?" she demanded with feeling. "As far as I am concerned, he can rot in hell!"

"If my memory serves me right, that's just what he was doing the last time I saw him—rotting in hell. You went to a lot of trouble to try to get him out, remember?"

"Yes," she snapped, "and he made a mess of that, like everything else he's tried in his life."

"That's hardly fair," said Rennie. "It wasn't his fault that he didn't get away from that island."

"Then whose fault was it? Everything was arranged."

"Someone tipped off Junot about the escape. He was waiting near the beach with his soldiers."

She looked at him with eyes wide.

"Who can have done this?"

"That's what I'd like to find out," said Rennie. He stared grimly out across the terrace, lost for a moment in his own thoughts, which he seemed to speak aloud when he added: "I don't think I'm ever going to have peace of mind until I find out who."

Arlette Mercier watched him through narrowed eyes. She, too, was thoughtful.

"Why is it so important to you?" she asked. "It's not as if you were involved or had any responsibility for Jean-Paul not escaping."

Rennie returned his gaze from distant space. He turned to face her with an air of surprise.

"But I *was* involved. There were three of us. An American and myself as well as Jean-Paul."

It was her turn to register surprise.

"Three of you? But the instructions . . . It was to be Jean-Paul alone." She was staring at him with mounting horror, as if pieces of a puzzle were clicking into place in her mind. "Don't you realize what you did? It was you who betrayed Jean-Paul . . . You and that unbearable Major Junot."

Rennie could not have been more thunderstruck.

"I don't understand," he mumbled. "What you're saying doesn't make sense. Me and Junot?" The thought was so unpalatable to him that he seemed unable even to consider it and remain seated. He got up from the white-topped table with its ornate wrought iron legs, almost upsetting the crystal jug of iced orange and glasses on top, and took three or four agitated steps along the terrace before turning to face her.

"Only four of us on the island knew about the escape plan," he said, making a résumé of the facts in his mind. "There were the three of us who were going to make the break and Commander Bishop. I thought it was maybe Bishop who gave the thing away—but I'm convinced now that he had nothing to do with it. Yet somebody still tipped off Junot. Who? It certainly wasn't Jean-Paul or the American. And it certainly wasn't me."

"Oh, you fools!" she cried. The expression on her face was tortured. "Don't you realize that I had to make a hundred per cent sure Jean-Paul would get away . . . ? That I couldn't take a chance on the schooner captain not going to Junot and telling him everything . . . ? I had to make sure of Junot, too!"

Rennie let the import of her words sink in. He couldn't believe she meant what he thought she meant.

"Junot *knew?*" The words were no more than a whisper from Rennie.

"I bought his co-operation," she said softly, her voice so faint that Rennie could scarcely hear her. "I gave myself to that pig, so that there would be no alarm afterwards. Jean-Paul's disappearance was to be explained away like all the others who had tried to get away from that place . . . Drowned trying to make it to the mainland . . ."

Rennie had an instant image from the past of Junot strutting in front of Jean-Paul, taunting him with innuendo about Arlette. Now this. He felt sick to his soul.

"Oh, my God," he murmured, filled with nausea at the thought of Junot pawing the body of this vital and endlessly surprising woman. He could imagine her shame and her loathing—and for what end? Nothing. It had all gone hideously wrong. No wonder she flirted with death in fast cars; treating life as a joke, a sick game.

Rennie took her hand in his. Her skin was icy cold. She turned questioning eyes up to his.

"Was it I who betrayed Jean-Paul? Was I a fool to think Junot could be trusted?"

"You did what you thought was best. No one can blame you."

"Jean-Paul already has," she said in a flat voice.

"I . . . I don't understand." It occurred to Rennie almost with a sharp sense of shock that he was still none the wiser of Jean-Paul's present whereabouts or what had befallen him after that nightmare night on the island. "You've seen him?" he asked.

Arlette shook her head.

"No. But I got a letter. He made his feelings very plain. I don't know how he found out but he knew about Junot and me. He called me a whore, amongst a whole lot of other things. He never wanted to see me again—and he said he would take immediate steps to have our marriage annulled the moment he got out of prison."

"Prison?"

"He was sentenced to five years. The trial was here in Algiers. Darlan ordered it himself. It only lasted a morning. I don't know all the details because the special tribunals who dealt with that kind of case always met in camera and announced the findings afterwards."

"When was all this?" asked Rennie. "Was it a court-martial?"

"It wasn't a military court, no—although the tribunal was made up of two army officers and a civilian. They were appointed by the Government under *une ordonnance exceptionelle*. Jean-Paul was tried by them as a criminal because the Navy in Dakar had washed their hands of him while he was on that island and declared him discharged as medically unfit."

"But when did all this happen?" persisted Rennie, bewildered and dismayed that such things could happen outside Nazi Germany.

"The trial was just two weeks before the Americans landed here."

"And has he been freed?" Rennie suddenly realized that he was gripping fiercely at her wrist in his agitation to know what had happened to his friend. He let her go with an embarrassed apology.

"The Americans have no power to free him," she said.

"But he's a political prisoner. Surely something can be done."

She shook her head.

"They can't interfere. He wasn't sentenced for a political crime."

"Then what, for God's sake, is he supposed to have done?" cried Rennie.

"The charge against him was attempting to escape from custody and attempted murder."

Rennie snorted his disbelief.

"Attempted murder? You've got to be joking. Who was the intended victim? Darlan?"

"Major Junot," she said. "Jean-Paul tried to murder Major Junot."

Rennie's eyes were like flames. The more he heard, the more obscene the mess seemed to become.

"After what Junot did to him!" he exclaimed. "Are you trying to tell me that Jean-Paul tried to kill Junot . . . That he as much as got the opportunity?"

She was clearly puzzled.

"What did Junot do to Jean-Paul? I don't understand."

"Junot speared Jean-Paul to the ground with a bayonet. That's what he did! Not just once, but twice! First one leg. Then the other. I saw him do it with my own eyes. We were caught on the beach . . . We couldn't run away . . . He had us trapped . . ."

Rennie turned away. He was breathing like an old man, burned almost to emotional exhaustion by the bitterness and anger coursing in him. He clenched and unclenched his fists. God knew that, given half an opportunity, he would gladly have killed Junot with his bare hands. And God knew that if anyone in this world had justification for tearing Junot apart a limb at a time, then Jean-Paul had. But when? Where? How had that circumstance arisen?

He became aware of the ashen face of Jean-Paul's wife and the intense way she was looking at him. Still she showed puzzlement.

"You didn't know that Junot used Jean-Paul for bayonet practice?" he asked softly. Again the little shake of the blond head.

"No. He said nothing in his letter. And from what I've been able to find out, no mention of it was made at the trial."

Rennie gave a snorting grunt. A sound which expressed in its explosive eloquence the cynicism he felt.

"They probably had to carry him to court on a stretcher," he said. "When was he supposed to have tried to kill Junot?"

She shrugged.

"I don't know. I took it to be when he was trying to escape. Junot had tried to arrest him and he had flown at Junot with a knife. Junot would have been killed if his soldiers hadn't rescued him. Four men were needed to overpower Jean-Paul."

"You believed this?" asked Rennie.

"I didn't have any reason not to believe it," Arlette said in a quiet voice. "It's the sort of thing I can imagine Jean-Paul doing in a real fury."

"He was rail-roaded," Rennie said quietly. "It makes me want to vomit when I think of what they did to him. Well, I'm not going to leave it at that. I'm not going to leave him to rot. Where do they have him?"

She was eyeing him anxiously. A little awed, perhaps, at the way he spoke. He had invested his words with all the steely resolution of a Corsican brother vowing vengeance.

"He's not in Algiers," she said. "They have him in a special prison in the desert—a place called Mecharja."

"Well, I'm going to get him out. One way or the other. Even if I have to go there myself and knock a hole in the bloody wall!"

There was no doubting that he meant it—a fact which seemed to increase the anxiety in Arlette's drawn face.

"It could be dangerous to interfere," she said. "Things are not straightforward here. It is not like England."

He smiled.

"Are you afraid I'll do something desperate?"

"It's not that. You are a foreigner. Not all foreigners are liked. I am trying to warn you that some people play very rough . . ."

"Maybe that's what I should have done a long time ago," said Rennie, thoughtfully. It was true. Ever since the start of the war, he'd been taking it on the chin and bouncing straight back for more. Always a victim, never the aggressor. Three times torpedoed. Always on the receiving end, never handing it out. Booted around by the French. Pushed around by armchair wizards in Whitehall. Well, to hell with it, if this war was about anything, it was about people like Jean-Paul. People who saw their country over-run by thugs and taken over by bully boys and, yet, who still had the courage to dig their heels in and say enough's enough.

On 3 September 1939, at 11 a.m., Germany had declared war on Britain and created a situation which, ever since, had placed the life and freedom of John Rennie in a state of perpetual peril. On 24 July 1943, John Rennie made his own private declaration of war. He made it not against any particular nation or group of nations, but against all those enemies, unnamed and as yet unseen, who might try to divert him from his chosen path to get justice for Jean-Paul. He had no doubt that these enemies would reveal themselves by their disdain for truth, reason, tolerance and freedom—because no one with any regard for these commodities was going to stop him.

He recalled Kerslaw's words back in Toronto: "In war, someone's got to get their hands dirtied." The twenty-fourth of July was the day John Rennie took the gloves off.

Chapter Thirteen

THE order that the meeting should take place had come from the very top. It had been endorsed by a committee known as the JCI (Joint Chiefs Intelligence) but referred to irreverently as "The Brotherhood of Cousins." The meeting was to take place in London, with Kerslaw in the chair and two representatives each from the American and British secret intelligence services.

Kerslaw was already seated at the table with a folder of notes in front of him when the British delegation was shown in. He got up and shook hands with Bolsover, the senior of the SIS representatives, whom he had met once previously and knew by repute as a bit of a neat-gin-drinking character.

The Canadian also shook hands with Bolsover's younger colleague. It was his first meeting with Philby, of whom he had had conflicting reports. Most acknowledged that he was an extremely gifted man but not that easy to get along with. His dislike for Americans was well known and equalled only by the antipathy which certain people in the States reserved for him.

The Americans arrived right on time. Their number one man was a giant of eighteen stone. He was moon-faced and bald, with a deep brown tan extending over his shining pate.

He introduced himself to Kerslaw.

"Lew Peterson," he said. He shook hands with Kerslaw, then Bolsover. He hesitated before sticking out a hand in the direction of Philby.

"We've met before," he said. "Trilby, isn't it?"

"Philby, Mr. Peterson. And it was Cairo."

"Yes, that was it. Cairo. Nice to see you again. I'd like you all to meet my colleague." The athletic-looking six-footer who stood a little way behind Peterson moved forward to the table to shake hands all round.

"This is Richard Hobart," said Peterson. Neither Bolsover nor Philby gave the slightest sign that they had heard the name before. Kerslaw allowed himself a quiet smile of satisfaction. Ever since he had heard of Hobart's escape from West Africa, he had wanted to meet this young man. It was appropriate that the Americans had nominated him for this meeting.

"Well, gentlemen," said Kerslaw, "let's get started. I have a small piece to say. I'll say it and then we'll get down to the main business. I'm not going to beat about the bush. Indeed, I'll be quite blunt. Afterwards, I don't want time wasted on recriminations or post-mortems. You will have paid attention to what I've said and you will go back to your respective camps and spread the word that the heads of Government on both sides of the Atlantic really mean business. I assure you that no man, no matter how secure or entrenched he may believe himself to be, will last five minutes if he comes in the way of the harmony we want to achieve between our services. I can promise you that if the desired improvement isn't achieved, heads will roll in the dust. We are all on the same side. We are fighting one war. And nothing is going to stand in the way of winning that war."

Kerslaw paused for a moment and spread his hands on the table in front of him. That was the warning rocket. Now to be specific.

"Gentlemen," he continued, "you are all in your own ways experts on French Africa. That's why you're here. I am here because there is no sorrier mess of co-operated effort than that existing between your respective services in North and West Africa. Lives have been lost as a result."

For perhaps half an hour recriminations, accusations, arguments flowed across the table. Finally, Bolsover cleared his throat.

"May I say something, sir?"

"By all means."

"First of all, I want to thank you for your chairmanship," said Bolsover, for all the world like someone addressing a board meeting. "You have not minced words, sir, but I am sure that what you have said needed to be said. May I, on behalf of the British side of the table, give an assurance to our American friends that—whatever differences we may have had in the past—we shall do everything in our power to ensure that our future relationships will not only be friendly and harmonious but blessed with success."

"Hear, hear," said Philby. Sanctimonious old hypocrite, he thought. There was nothing to ginger up Bolsover's love of Americans like the crack of a whip. Not that Philby was unresponsive to the crack of a whip. He realized that some show of Yankee-loving was on the cards for himself if he wanted to keep his nose clean.

"I go along with Mr. Bolsover's sentiments," Peterson was saying. "Sure, we've not always rubbed along as well as we might but, as far as my guys are concerned, we're ready to call that water under the bridge."

"OK," said Kerslaw, "we've got two items on the agenda 'Emperor' and the 'Barbary Consignment.' We now know they're connected. The question is what we do about it? First, though, I'd like to hear from both sides of the table on what has been snagging both these operations so far. They've both been on the books for a year now and we don't seem to be much further forward than the day we started."

He nodded in the direction of Bolsover, who scratched his head distractedly at being given the task of starting the ball rolling. But when it started it seemed it would never stop. Bolsover's long-winded analysis finally wound to a halt with an up-tempo flurry of words . . .

"So you see, the British can't haul in a suspected hostile without the OK from the Americans and the Americans have to consult the French and, if one lot of French agree, the other lot screams bloody murder and nothing gets done. The whole place is a mad-house, as Peterson here will probably agree because his people are in the same boat. They've got their hands tied behind their backs because when action is needed, they hold their hand until the French Committee of National Liberation is put in the picture and they make sure that we're not going to take the huff. Christ!"

Kerslaw smiled.

"Mr. Peterson?" he said, looking expectantly at the American.

"He's right," said Peterson. "The lack of any one strong authority as back-up is ham-stringing the entire security set-up. Everything is fouled up by protocol. It's OK saying that all French authority is vested in the FCNL, but the FCNL is a toothless two-headed dog which doesn't scare anybody because it's totally preoccupied looking for fleas up its own backside."

"I like your imagery," said Kerslaw with a smile, "but I don't think our French friends would be flattered."

"But it's true," said Peterson. "Whoever heard of a committee with two co-presidents? And when the presidents are de Gaulle and Giraud, the whole goddamned thing is unworkable. If they had to answer a simple question with the word 'yes', they wouldn't be able to agree on the wording."

"OK," said Kerslaw, "all this makes one thing clear. It means that our team for tracking down 'Emperor' and the 'Barbary Consignment' has to be Anglo-American with power to over-ride any local authority on the ground and backed by Eisenhower himself."

"That would be a big help," said Peterson. "On the American side, we've had a hell of a problem in North Africa from our own army people. They don't really understand the role of the OSS. Our guys are trained for deep penetration, but when some general gets a team put on his strength, he uses them for the front line G-two . . . Puts them forward with the infantry for scouting and tactical reconnaissance. We lost a lot of good men in Tunisia fighting as infantry, when that wasn't the job they were trained for at all. These guys should have been in Sicily and Italy and France setting things up for the *next* campaign."

"This operation will be against enemy subversives," Kerslaw pointed out. "So, the circumstances will be rather different."

"Agreed," said Peterson. "All I was getting at was that some local army commanders may not fall over themselves to be helpful if we muscle in on their territory."

That's why I said our team would have special powers. A few toes may have to be stood on."

Kerslaw turned to Bolsover.

"Your people had some theories on why Mr. Hobart was in Dakar?"

Bolsover's florid face reddened with confusion. Hobart looked questioningly at Peterson.

"Go ahead, Dick. Tell them."

"There were two of us," Hobart began, "Clem Ritchie, another geologist, and myself. Our cover was quite genuine. We were hired by a French company, with Vichy Government blessing. It was all done through our legation in Vichy. We were contracted for two years and had carte blanche to go anywhere in the French territories—Algeria, Morocco, the Sahara, right down to the Gambia border."

"Nice work if you can get it," said Bolsover.

"What were you after?" asked Philby.

"We had more than one objective," said Hobart, "but, of course, the guy we were really after was the king-pin, 'Emperor.' We didn't know what he looked like or very much about him at all—but we knew his track record. Three Resistance groups blown from inside, two escape routes from Europe plugged and every way station closed—one was a Marseilles-Oran-Tangier lane for Polish army, the other was a Marseilles-Algiers-Tangier lane for fliers. We weren't even sure if 'Emperor' was one man or several. He certainly covered a hell of a lot of territory and often seemed to be operating in two places at one time. Anyway, he was our number one target. My starting place was Casablanca, Ritchie's was Algiers. I was to go south, then west, then up north again. Ritchie was to cover the territory round Algiers and as far west as the Spanish Moroccan border."

"How were you to justify all this roaming around?" asked Bolsover.

"That was the least of our worries," replied Hobart. "Ritchie and I had both worked for the French Government before the war and knew the territory. We were just carrying on an operation that had been suspended at the outbreak of war. Vichy decided to push on with it last year when they discovered that the financial backers of the program—which just happened to be an American-owned international oil company—still had funds available for the project. The dollar flow to their Colonial Mineral Development Institute would be resumed any time, they were told, that the work was restarted. Roughly speaking, what we had to do was a preliminary mineral survey of the entire area, talk to companies already working the area—whether they were digging out phosphates or exploring for oil—and then make very general recommendations on how the natural resources could be exploited."

"What went wrong?" asked Philby. "I mean, you were arrested, weren't you?"

Hobart sighed.

"Yeah, I'm afraid I was, although I didn't find out the real reason until a couple of weeks ago, when I got back to Washington. The French pulled me in and put me on ice because I was straight, absolutely clean. Ironic, isn't it? They were so damned sure I wasn't working for Uncle Sam on the side that they locked me up and put me on ice!"

"I don't understand," said Bolsover.

"The Germans and the Vichy Secret Police cooked it up between them. At least, that's the way we see it now. The Nazis had a very special agent for sounding out Resistance groups, so what better way than to wander here, there and everywhere pretending to be an American geologist who is really working for the Allies?"

"You mean 'Emperor'?" exclaimed Bolsover.

"Who else?" said Hobart. "The easiest way would have been to bump me off and have supplied 'Emperor' with my papers and a ready-made identity. But, for some reason, they just took me out of circulation. Maybe because they thought the day might come when it might be useful to produce the real Richard Hobart out of a hat. My bet, though, is that 'Emperor' has a dozen different identities he can use, depending where he wants to go—and all of them just as credible as the one he stole from me."

"My God, it's an operational planner's bloody nightmare!" Bolsover said in a shocked voice. "You put a man in the field with a cast-iron bloody cover and he gets jugged, not because his cover's blown but because the opposition want to pinch it! It's diabolical!"

"What reason did they give for jugging you? Or didn't they say?" asked Philby.

Hobart grinned ruefully.

"Oh, they said all right. They said I was contacting people with anti-Vichy sentiments and stirring up rebellion. That had to be a lot of baloney, of course, because I took damned good care to deep well clear of our known friends. If the guys I had anything to do with had been arrested for plotting treason, the jails would have been full of Hitler-lovers. One of the side-lines I was doing for home office was identifying the real out-and-out Nazi types amongst the Vichy French and passing the names back to headquarters. Our guys would fake really compromising letters to them and then make sure the letters were intercepted by the Nazis or the Vichy censors."

Kerslaw took a photograph from the folder in front of him and passed it to Bolsover. He said:

"We're ninety-five per cent certain that this is 'Emperor,' the most wanted man on our files and, without a doubt, the most dangerous. He was interviewed by an American newspaper correspondent after the 'Torch landings. He said he was Richard Hobart."

Bolsover whistled. "The man's got nerve." He passed the photo on to Kim Philby. He, in turn, passed the photo across to Hobart and asked him:

"How did you get away from the French?"

"With the help of a Vichy officer I met before they put me inside," Hobart replied. "On the day of the Casablanca landings, all the people who were guarding us were shipped up north to repel the invader. I was sent to a camp near Dakar where the Commandant turned out to be this creep I knew—a real German-lover. He was convinced Germany was going to win the war but he got sicker every day with the news from the north of what was happening to the Afrika Korps. For some reason, he started seeking me out and using me as a father-confessor. He realized the writing was on the wall for him and the other collaborators, that the Dakar regime wouldn't be able to hold out forever. Anyway, he was running scared. I kept telling him that the best thing to do would be to get out before the end came and offer his services to the Allies. I also planted the idea that things would work out better for him if he had an American citizen to put in a good word for him."

"And he bought it?" asked Philby.

"Von Arnim's surrender in Tunisia did the trick. He and some top brass in Dakar got hold of a Portuguese airline and chartered it to fly them to Brazil. I was taken along as a kind of insurance."

"What about your friend, Ritchie?" asked Philby. "If he was in Algeria, he was probably on a better wicket than you."

"Just what I was thinking," said Bolsover. He looked at Kerslaw. "Might have been a good idea to fly him over and brief us on his part of the operation."

"Ritchie wasn't quite so fortunate as Mr. Hobart," said Kerslaw gravely. "He's dead."

"Oh, I'm sorry," said Bolsover. "I'd no idea. Jolly bad show."

"We think that 'Emperor' got to Ritchie before Ritchie got to 'Emperor'," said Peterson.

"It's the connection," said Kerslaw, "The connection between 'Emperor' and the 'Barbary Consignment.' You'll recall, Mr. Bolsover, that the 'Barbary Consignment' was part of the British contribution to the groundwork for 'Torch.' Your 'Alpha' group in Algiers was to be ready to sabotage communications in the event of the Vichy French committing the large forces at their disposal against our beach-heads."

Bolsover nodded.

"That's correct. Our difficulty was getting the 'Barbary Consignment' from the landing place into Algiers. We asked our American friends if they could help and they kindly agreed to do so. Unfortunately, although the stuff was landed OK and handed over to an American agent, it was never delivered to 'Alpha' in Algiers. It vanished completely."

"But the agent reached Algiers, Mr. Bolsover?"

"Yes, in a manner of speaking. His body was found. He'd had his throat cut."

"The agent was Ritchie," said Kerslaw quietly. After a pause, he said: "What steps have been taken to recover the 'Barbary Consignment,' Mr. Bolsover?"

Bolsover spread his hands in a gesture.

"We've done everything we can think of. 'Alpha' was disbanded after 'Torch,' but we checked out every member of the group and they all came up smelling of roses. The more we looked at it, the more convinced we became . . ." he grimaced apologetically at Peterson . . . "that it was the American agent who had been blown, not one of our people."

Kerslaw threw Peterson a questioning look.

"And what was the American conclusion?"

"We never got to the bottom of Ritchie's death," said Peterson. "But we were pretty certain of one thing. He met his death as a direct result of contacting 'Alpha'." This last emphatic statement was accompanied by a belligerent stare at Bolsover.

"Gentlemen," said Kerslaw, "I have been co-ordinating

certain inquiries ordered by London and Washington—or rather the results of them. The object was to do a trace on suspected German agents we've had in our sights from time to time and see if we could come up with some clues on 'Emperor.' Let's concentrate on what we know and decide what we are going to do. My belief is that, if we find 'Emperor,' we find the 'Barbary Consignment'."

"Can we be sure of that, sir?" said Bolsover. "Admittedly, Ritchie is one possible link, but a rather tenuous one in my opinion."

"If I'm wrong, the responsibility is mine," said Kerslaw. "I got involved in this case more or less by accident but now that I am involved and have been authorized to take certain initiatives, I intend to see it through."

"That sounds like you stuck your neck out, Dr. Kerslaw." Peterson was grinning at him broadly. He grinned back.

"That's precisely what I did, Mr. Peterson. I stuck my neck out. There was even a time when I thought that catching 'Emperor' and relocating the 'Barbary Consignment' wasn't all that important compared with some of the matters requiring my attention. Not any more. Because I believe, gentlemen, that 'Emperor' has now gone over to the offensive. He hasn't been hauled out, now that there are no Resistance groups to penetrate and hand over to the Gestapo . . . He's still in North Africa orchestrating a sabotage campaign against our shipping."

Kerslaw consulted a sheet of paper from his folder before continuing:

"Fact one: a fire on the American liberty ship *Joseph P. Maguire* in Oran harbor on July twelve. Origin of fire —an explosive device fitted with an L-Delay fuse of British manufacture . . ."

"From the 'Barbary Consignment'?" queried Bolsover with alarm.

"From the 'Barbary Consignment'," said Kerslaw, and continued. "Fact two: in Algiers harbor on July sixteen, the Norwegian frieghter *Bjorkhaug* blew up while loading landmines and caused considerable damage and casualties. The ship was a total loss and the master was among the nine crew members missing, presumed killed. The explosion started a fire on the Biitish merchantman, *Fort Confidence,* loaded with petroleum. She was towed out of the harbor and beached as a total loss. She is still burning and may have to be sunk by shell-fire as she constitutes a danger to other shipping. Cause of explosion on *Bjorkhaug*—unknown. Fact three: in Algiers harbor on July twenty-four—that's yesterday—a small explosion occurred in a loadpipe through which the tanker *Orange Glory* was discharging petroleum fuel. The loadpipe fractured and the fuel pouring out of it ignited, setting fire to the tanker and spilling burning fuel into the dock. A major disaster was averted only by prompt and effective action on the ship in containing and bringing under control the shipboard fire. It took fire tugs and naval units several hours to put out burning fuel which was floating on the waters of the docks. The operation was made more difficult by the necessity to evacuate six ships from the harbor while it was in progress . . ."

Kerslaw stopped reading from the sheet of paper and put it down on the table.

"There are more details," he said, "but these are beside the point. The significant thing is that a talent for anti-shipping sabotage is consistent with the identi-profile we've made of 'Emperor.' If our homework is right, we're dealing with a man who in the space of a few weeks, has caused more damage in the Western Mediterranean during that time than all the U-boats and Luftwaffe strength deployed in the area. We've suffered losses we can ill afford. The Combined Chiefs are anxious that our forces don't lose their momentum when the campaign in Sicily ends. The build-up for the next push is already under way and it is being concentrated in the North African ports, from Oran to Bizerta. If it doesn't go ahead as planned, a large Allied army will be tied up inactive in North Africa—and all because of one man, 'Emperor.' We've got to find him and we've got to find him fast!"

"You mentioned an identi-profile, said Bolsover.

Kerslaw drew another sheet of paper from his folder.

"This profile was drawn mainly from information we've extracted from captured enemy agents, also dossiers on suspects and traces in archive material. It points to one man."

Kerslaw outlined the background of the man he believed was 'Emperor'. His name was Franz Dorf, born in Beirut, Lebanon, in 1910, of German parentage. Johann Dorf, his father, ran a successful import—export business.

Marta Dorf, his mother, was the daughter of a wealthy Prussian family.

Dorf's father was in Berlin on business when the 1914 war broke out. He rejoined his old infantry regiment with the rank of Major and was killed at the first battle of the Somme. In the meantime, Marta Dorf and her young son were interned by the French and the family business was confiscated.

In 1920, Marta Dorf remarried. Her second husband was a wealthy Lebanese businessman called Youssef Din. Marta Dorf became a Mohammedan convert in order to marry but the boy, Franz, was not obliged to follow suit. In 1923, at the age of thirteen, he was sent to be educated at the Kurt Klein International School in Geneva, Switzerland, a co-educational establishment which catered for the sons and daughters of rich German, French, Belgian and Swiss nationals in overseas posts.

Young Franz remained there until he was nineteen, when he returned to Beirut to join his stepfather's business. In the next few years, he spent a lot of time travelling in North Africa, Europe and the Middle East on business for his stepfather. He was fluent in five languages. In 1937, he spent most of the year in the United States.

At some stage on his travels, he was recruited to the German Secret Service, and in 1938 he completed a short period of military training in Germany. He also trained at Hamburg and Keil in the art of ship sabotage and was assigned to Abwehr, Section 2, which specialized in sabotage.

He was suspected of being involved in sabotage attempts against British shipping in American ports in 1939. An active ring was broken up but Dorf was never apprehended. He resurfaced in the Lebanon after the fall of France and was believed to be one of two German agents who had talks with the Grand Mufti of Jerusalem on the subject of an Arab Holy War against the British throughout the middle East. It was about this time that he is believed to have fallen out with his Abwehr bosses, but his services weren't lost to Nazi Germany. He was snapped up by Heydrich's SS who, at the time, were rapidly extending their own Intelligence Service, the SD, to territories outside Germany.

The SD used him to penetrate French escape networks operating from Vichy territory in Unoccupied France.

Then a man, almost certainly Dorf, popped up in Lisbon and, later, Malaga. He was believed to be responsible for the still unsolved murders of four British agents in Spain and Portugal.

At this point, the trail on Dorf petered out. But a new one opened up. American agents in Tangier picked up the scent of a Geman agent whose code-name was 'Emperor'. A mass of small details, from modus operandi to the style and variety of aliases used, pointed to Dorf and "Emperor' being one and the same.

"There are still puzzling inconsistencies in the picture of 'Emperor'," Kerslaw told his listeners. "It seems almost impossible for one man to have pulled off all we give him credit for in North Africa. At the same time, it must be remembered that he had the resources of the regime in power to give him all the help he needed. Alternatively, he had a partner whom we know nothing about. Someone powerful. Someone big enough in Vichy circles and well enough informed to mark his card while Dorf stayed in the shadows. We're calling the shots in North Africa now but Dorf, or 'Emperor,' has laid low there for eight and a half months. Mr. Peterson here will confirm that Washington came to the conclusion that the bird had flown. The incidents of the past couple of weeks have changed all that. 'Emperor' has been re-activated in the job for which he was originally trained. And we've got to find him before he does any more damage. The first ship to go, that American freighter in Oran, was set on fire with a five-pound incendiary fitted with one of our very latest delay-action detonator fuses. Think of that. He wrote off ten thousand tons of ship with five pounds of explosive! There was damned near three tons of highly sophisticated sabotage merchandise in the 'Barbary Consignment'! 'Emperor' hasn't even started yet. He could burn North Africa from end to end unless we stop him."

Bolsover wrinkled his brow.

"What do you propose we do, sir? Send in the storm troopers? Roust out every shady character between Gib and Tunis and hope like hell that 'Emperor' doesn't escape the net?"

"Is that what you would recommend?" asked Kerslaw.

Bolsover shook his head.

"Waste of time, if you ask me, sir. We'd need a more subtle approach than that for this artful dodger. He'd do a bunk when he heard the first tramp of heavy boots. Either that or he'd brazen things out—come out with cups of tea for the troops and egg the boys on. My bet is that he has a pretty good cover and a big smoking-out operation won't work."

"I agree," said Peterson.

"What *would* you do?" Kerslaw asked Bolsover.

"Proceed in the manner of the old-fashioned British bobby," Bolsover replied cheerfully. "Not door-to-door enquiries exactly, but I'd go back to square one—Richie's murder . . . 'Alpha' group . . . We've missed something, so we start all over again. At the same time, I'd have a team investigating how the ships were got at. Who was aboard? Who had the opportunity to hide a bomb in the hold? There's no substitute for painstaking inquiry."

"Does that fit in with what you had in mind?" Kerslaw asked Peterson.

The big American nodded.

"I'd like Dick Hobart to fly out there and take charge of the investigation. He knows the score exactly. He knew Rithcie. He knows the French. We can give him an OSS back-up team from Sidi Ferrouch. Maybe he could team up with one of Mr. Bolsover's officers."

"That would get my vote," said Kerslaw. "What do you say, Mr. Bolsover?"

"Well, it's a job for a good field man," said Bolsover. "I don't see any reason for sending someone specially from this country when we've got a first-class chap right there on the spot."

Philby stared hard at his chief.

"You don't mean . . . ?" he began.

"Baldry? Yes, I do," said Bolsover. "I know he's a bit outspoken for your tastes and is a bit apt to tell us Whitehall types to go and get stuffed, but he has all the qualifications for this job. He's a hunter, and bloody good at it."

"He's in Algiers?" asked Kerslaw.

"Yes. Holed up in a brothel, probably. We moved him in from Egypt a couple of months ago to keep tabs on a couple of Arab revolutionary types who need a bit of watching: disciples of Trotsky as well as Mohammed, and trouble has a nasty habit of following them around. Baldry's a bit of a hell-raiser himself, but not when he's kept busy."

"What's his background?" asked Kerslaw.

"Good family background. He was the black sheep. Got kicked out of University and went and joined the Palestine Police. Had a good record there but he got involved with a Jewish girl. Had to leave the service under a cloud. He married his little Jewish girl but she was killed during some trouble with the Arabs. After that he drifted. He'd work for a bit and get a bit of money. Then he'd blow the lot in one terrific blinder in places like Beirut or Cairo. We took him on the strength after he got into a bit of a scrape on the Syrian border. Smuggling. We have been making good use of his abundant talents, ever since."

Peterson was smiling broadly.

"Sounds like some of my best friends," said Hobart with a grin.

Kerslaw then over-ruled some minor reservations expressed by Philby about Bolsover's nomination of Baldry to spearhead the operation with Hobart. Another hour was spent discussing details before the meeting finally broke up. Twenty-four hours later, Hobart was at an airfield in Wiltshire, sitting in a Wing Commander's office waiting to board the aircraft which would take him to Maison Blanche in Algiers.

It was here that a special messenger found him and handed over secret files which he had requested from Bolsover as necessary to the investigation in prospect. These included reports on the operation of shipping the "Barbary Consignment" to North Africa in 1942. There was also a detailed report of investigations to recover the missing arms shipment after North Africa had been invaded. This listed the code-names and real identities of the eighteen members of the Algerian Resistance Group known as "Alpha." Small biographical summaries had been appended to each name on the list, also a brief service record and commentary on their activities since disbandment of the group in January 1943.

One name jumped out at Hobart from the list on his knees. Opposite the cryptonym "Daisy" was the name Arlette Mercier. He had only to read on to learn that this young woman, daughter of an influential figure of the French Empire—albeit one with a reputation for political fence-sitting, and an intimate of Darlan and others, had at great risk secured information of Vichy intentions of value to the Allies, and Hobart knew that she was the wife of the man who had shared a prison hut with him in Senegal.

Hobart had long ago ceased to wonder at the chance ways of Fate which cause the lives of individuals to cross and re-cross almost as if the routes were predestined. A different kind of excitement gripped Hobart. Kerslaw had fired in him a desperate urgency to find "Emperor," and this, in turn, had made him question his adequacy for the task. He was to try to pick up a trail that was nearly nine months cold. The awesome responsibility of finding "Emperor" was daunting. Where did you start looking for a needle in a haystack? Where indeed? And then, here, suddenly, on a piece of paper spread across his lap—one name which was more than just ink on paper. It had personal meaning.

He knew now where to begin. He would begin with Arlette Mercier.

Chapter Fourteen

RENNIE was in a foul temper. Two days had passed since he had made his private vow to get Jean-Paul Mercier out of prison, even if he had to move heaven and earth to do it.

In the course of those two days, Rennie had discovered that heaven and earth were minor obstacles compared with the civil and military bureaucrats of Algiers. With Blom as guide and mentor, he had first sought out a member of the Faculté de Droit with the idea of getting the lowdown on the correct legal procedure for obtaining Jean-Paul's release.

This man had not taken too kindly to being disturbed on a Sunday. However, out of courtesy to a foreigner, he had spent an hour telling Rennie how low his estimate was of the success of his venture. Rennie, in turn, came away from the meeting feeling he knew a great deal more about French Colonial government but next to nothing about the next step to take.

His next step was the home in Mont Hydra of a lawyer friend of Blom's who had tried to fight Vichy's mass internment of dissidents until he, himself, had been imprisoned in Maison Carrée. He advised petitioning against the findings of the original court on the grounds that the *Ordonnance Exceptionelle* under which the court had been constituted would no longer be law when the powers of territorial government passed finally from the old Vichy-appointed authority to the French Committee of National Liberation.

There was a snag. The FCNL would have no teeth to implement its powers until it was accepted as the governing body by the Colonial Administration and officially recognized by the Governments of Britain, the United States, China and the USSR. The lawyer did not think this would happen soon, although de Gaulle was taking advantage of Giraud's absence in the USA to get things moving in the right direction.

There was little more that Rennie could do that day. Early the following morning, he was doing the rounds once more. This time, he concentrated his quest for help on the Allied military establishment. Without being given access to anyone more senior than a lieutenant, he spoke to five officers—two American and three British—whose jobs were in Civil and Military Liaison.

They all sang the same song. They could not interfere in the case of a French national. The initiative would have to come from the man's next of kin. They could take up with the French, perhaps a matter which had been brought to them by a French citizen about another French citizen, but they could not intervene on behalf of a non-French citizen in a purely French matter.

Angry and frustrated, Rennie returned to Blom's office in need of advice and consolation. Blom, who was sympathetic to the cause which Rennie had espoused, supplied both.

"The military are still your best bet, my friend," he told Rennie. "The French administration will happily let you dash your head against their intransigence until you are an old, old man. You will get nowhere with them. Get hold of Mercier's wife and parade her before those British officers you've been talking to. She'll have them falling over themselves to help. You'll see. The trouble with you is that you are just not pretty enough."

Blom even loaned Rennie his van to go and see Arlette. Thus, for the second time in just over two days, Rennie found himself speeding along the Oran highway heading for the Bousquet villa. This time, the risks he took in the inevitable military traffic were calculated, or imposed by the fact that he had not driven in over two years and was a little out of practice.

Darkness had fallen by the time he left the highway and was bumping along the dusty dirt sideroad through Bousquet's vineyards. He left the van in the stable-yard and, as before, followed the flagged path to the front of the house. He halted before the open French windows.

Inside, four people were sitting at one end of the long dining-table. There were Arlette, her sister Geraldine, and two men. The man at the head of the table was unmistakably the father of the two girls, the Admiral

Bousquet of whom Rennie had heard so much. Although Rennie knew he must be older, Bousquet would have passed for fifty. He had a head of luxuriant white hair, neatly parted and with natural waves. As a young man, he would have been blond and quite an Adonis. The looks were still there, engraved now with the furrows of age and harshened by the sun, but there nevertheless. Bousquet had been and still was a handsome man. Only the tight line of his lips and the cold severity of his gray-blue eyes robbed his face of benignity.

The fourth member of the dinner party was nondescript by comparison. His eyes hid behind thinly tinted glasses in horn frames. A pencil moustache adorned his upper lip. His shortish, dark hair was oiled and combed with not a strand out of place. Like Bousquet, he wore a white dinner suit and hand-tied bow. He was a lot younger than Bousquet, perhaps thirtyish.

It was Arlette who saw Rennie standing, hesitant, on the terrace. She got up from the table and came towards him. She was wearing a plain white satin evening gown which clung voluptuously to her figure.

"Captain Rennie, what a pleasant surprise. Won't you come in? We were just finishing dinner."

"Yes, do," said a voice from the table. It was Geraldine's. "We were having quite an interesting discussion . . . About the Americans and the English . . . We were trying to decide who were the most obnoxious!"

"Geraldine!" snapped the white-haired man at the head of the table. "Taisez-vous!" He rose and came to meet Rennie. The gray-blue eyes were neither hostile nor friendly. They inspected Rennie dispassionately, with the detached kind of interest a butcher might display when inspecting beef on the hoof. His English, when he spoke, seemed as effortless as the rest of the family's.

"So, you are the Captain Rennie? I have heard much about you."

Rennie inclined his head.

"I have heard a lot about you, too, sir. You must be Admiral Bousquet."

Arlette leapt in with an apology to make belated introductions.

"We have had the misfortune to meet already," Geraldine called from the table, earning another reproachful glare from her father. The man at the table was introduced as Jacques Previn, "who looks after some of our business interests in the port."

"I didn't mean to interrupt your dinner," Rennie apologized.

"We were just about to have coffee," said Bousquet. "Perhaps you would like to join us?"

"I just wanted a word with Arlette. I don't want to intrude."

Bousquet seemed not to hear him, however. He was already giving instructions to the Arab houseboy by the door to bring coffee for five. They would have it on the terrace.

Geraldine pointedly took a seat some distance away from the white-topped table on which the houseboy set the coffee things. She sat on her own in a wicker chair as if deliberately placing as much distance as possible between herself and Rennie.

"Aren't you being a little silly?" Arlette reproached her, speaking rapidly in French and in a low voice.

"I am not going to be a hypocrite like the rest of you. English, Germans, Americans, traitors—they are all the same to you and Papa. I am made differently. What I despise in private, I despise in public."

"There is such a thing as civilized manners!" Arlette flung at her.

"You must forgive my daughters," Bousquet said to Rennie. "Leave her, Arlette. She was like that all weekend in Blida. Why she didn't stay there, I don't know." He turned again to Rennie.

"Why did you want to see Arlette, Captain?"

"I need her help," said Rennie. He flashed her a smile as she sat down next to him. There was silent appeal in the look.

"How can I help you?" she asked.

"I've been chasing all over Algiers trying to get something done about Jean-Paul. I would make more headway—or so I'm told—if I had his wife along with me to put the pressure on."

Arlette's face fell.

"Oh," she murmured.

Bousquet, who had a coffee cup raised half way to his lips, put it down again abruptly.

"It is out of the question," he said. He looked sternly at Rennie. "You took advantage of my absence on Saturday,

Captain, to tell my daughter a lot of nonsense about that worthless wretch she got herself married to. I would consider it a favor if you were to refrain from even mentioning his name while you are under my roof."

Rennie stared back at Bousquet steadily, refusing to be intimidated by the other's fierce expression. He replied calmly, choosing his words carefully.

"I have no wish to abuse your hospitality, Admiral, but I'm not going to do anybody the favor of pretending Jean-Paul doesn't have a name. But I will do you a favor. I'll put you right on three things you've just said which just aren't true. I didn't take advantage of your absence. I didn't tell Arlette any nonsense. And Jean-Paul isn't, in my humble estimation, a worthless wretch . . . Which is maybe more than I would say for anyone who'd talk about him that way."

Bousquet's unsmiling stare never wavered. With an air of condescension, he said:

"Be impertinent, if it pleases you. Contradict me, if it pleases you, but do not make the mistake of doubting me when I give you a friendly warning. Forget you ever met Jean-Paul Mercier. He is not worth your concern. He betrayed the uniform he wore. He betrayed the wife who stood by him. He dishonored the house and the family into which he was welcomed as a son. He deserved neither my mercy nor my help in saving him from the folly of his own actions—but, against my conscience, he got both. As a consequence, he has his life—which is more than he deserves—but, as far as this family is concerned, he is dead. I will not have his name mentioned."

Rennie glanced at Arlette.

"Did you tell your father what Junot did to Jean-Paul?"

"I tried . . . He does not believe a French officer would use a bayonet on a brother officer."

"Perhaps if Junot could be produced," said Rennie. "The Admiral doesn't need to take my word for it alone. There were other witnesses . . . He has influence in Dakar. They might hand Junot over to him . . . By God, I'd get the truth out of him."

Bousquet interrupted coldly:

"Do I take it you are referring to the officer Mercier tried to murder?"

"Junot, yes," said Rennie. "But it was the other way

round. He attacked Jean-Paul with a bayonet while four soldiers held him helpless."

Bousquet regarded Rennie with contempt.

"How can you malign the memory of a gallant officer with such lies?" he asked angrily.

Rennie stared at him.

"What do you mean 'malign the memory'?"

"Just what I say," replied Bousquet. "You only dare to slander this Major Junot because you know he cannot defend himself from the grave."

Rennie looked from Arlette to Bousquet and back to Arlette again.

"He's dead? Junot's dead?"

"I didn't know," said Arlette.

"Then your memory's failing you, my dear," said Bousquet. "We talked about it here on this terrace. It was only two weeks after Mercier had been sent to prison, a day or two after the Americans landed . . . It was Gaston Dorange who told me—he'd been in Indo-China with Junot. Said what a pity it was that the poor fellow should get killed thirty minutes before the cease-fire."

"I don't remember it," said Arlette. "It must have been Geraldine you talked to about it."

"What does it matter?" snorted her father. "The fact is that the poor fellow's gone."

"Unmourned as far as I'm concerned," said Rennie. "If he's dead, I can't say I'm sorry—except that getting him to confess to the truth would have been one way of clearing Jean-Paul."

Bousquet stared at Rennie contemptuously.

"Let him rest in peace, Captain. Do not persist with your lies. It will do no good. No French court would accept your word and Mercier's before the honor of an officer who gave his life under the flag of France."

Rennie ignored the accusation of lying.

"How did Junot die?" he asked. "I thought he had a nice safe little billet where the only fighting he had to do was against unarmed prisoners."

"He died facing the Americans in Morocco, Captain. Not perhaps the enemy he would have chosen, but he was a soldier who obeyed orders. We did not invite the American army to Africa, Captain. They came with their guns and their tanks and their bombs. It was every Frenchman's duty to resist. All who serve know this. One's country right or wrong."

"Sure, Admiral, there's no fool like a patriotic fool," said Rennie bitterly. "I wasn't really interested in the questionable ethics you choose to justify Junot having to get killed. I personally prefer to admire people like Jean-Paul who have the guts to disobey orders that are morally indefensible. All I was wondering was how Junot managed to get himself out of his funk-hole in Dakar and near enough anyone who was likely to shoot at him."

"You insult a brave man!" Bousquet cried with outrage. "Major Junot volunteered for action within hours of the Americans landing. He was in the first wave of reinforcements flown from Dakar to Port Lyautey. He died defending the airfield there."

Rennie did not attempt to answer. Arguing with the old man was pointless. It certainly wasn't going to do Jean-Paul any good. He looked despairingly at Arlette.

"Are you going to help me get Jean-Paul out of that prison?"

"I don't know." She seemed unable to look him in the eyes. "Can't you see how difficult . . .?" She trailed into silence.

Rennie stood up.

"Looks like my coming here was a waste of time. I'm sorry I disturbed your evening."

The corner of Bousquet's mouth trembled slightly. It was the nearest approach to a smile he had shown since Rennie's arrival.

"You would be welcome to stay longer but, if you have to return to Algiers tonight, it would be wrong of us to detain you. Good-bye, Captain." He stood up and glanced round at Previn, who had sat expressionless and never opened his mouth. "Come, Jacques."

Bousquet strode into the house, followed by the silent Previn. Rennie, feeling that he was being stared at from behind, turned to find that Geraldine Bousquet was covertly studying him with a strange intense expression on her face. She rose, embarrassed that he had noticed her.

"Good night," she said and walked away from the terrace, taking a path that wound down through neat gardens towards a distant grove of trees. Like Arlette, she was wearing a long evening gown, but hers was dark blue and high-necked: quite different in character from the clinging white creation with plunging neckline which her sister wore. Rennie watched her go until she was ghost-like and indistinct amongst the trees.

"You are disappointed in me," a voice said behind him. He turned to look down at Arlette. Tears glistened her eyes. "I have let you down, yes?"

"It's not me you're letting down. It's Jean-Paul."

"Is that what you believe?"

"What else can I believe?"

She walked a little ahead of him.

"Has it not occurred to you that I might have reasons for not wanting to help Jean-Paul any more . . . And that they are stronger than any reason there is for helping him?" She had stopped and was looking back at him. She let him catch up. "Well?"

"There's a damned good reason why you should help him," he said fiercely. "He's still your husband—and no matter how badly he may think of you, he doesn't deserve to be left to rot. Have you any idea what he has suffered? Can you blame him for maybe not thinking straight? Does the injustice of what happened to him not matter to you?"

She did not flinch before the passion in his voice. She met it with passion in her own.

"What about his injustice to *me*? I would have gone to the ends of the earth for him. I risked my life for him. I debased myself for him. And for what? Nothing. Not a word of thanks. Not for the slightest sign of gratitude. No—instead I get his abuse, his loathing. I am told that my name stinks in his nostrils . . . That I am a whore . . . Why should I bend one little finger to help him?"

Rennie was silent.

She turned and began walking slowly towards the grove of trees where Geraldine had disappeared. He followed and walked beside her.

"Arlette, I know it's hard, but can't you make allowances for what he has been through?"

"Why should I?"

"For me, if for no one else."

She glanced up at his intense face.

"I would like to please you but I don't think anything I can do is going to make any difference. And you heard my father. There's no saying what lengths he might go to. He could even make things more difficult for Jean-Paul."

"Perhaps if you gave him a more accurate picture of what kind of man Junot was . . . He obviously doesn't know that you . . . About what really happened on the island."

"No!" The word burst from her. She stopped and stared up at him with a passionate intensity. "My father must never know that I tried to make . . . an . . . an arrangement with that major. He doesn't know that I used him, and his friends . . . I traded on my father's name to get to Dakar and to try to help Jean-Paul escape. He would never forgive me if he knew the truth."

She started walking again.

"There's a lot I don't understand about your father," said Rennie. "I've heard a lot about him, one way or another, and none of it is very complimentary. Jean-Paul thought he was out-and-out for Vichy . . . And if that propaganda idea you had to spell out to Jean-Paul was a sample of the kind of thing your father went along with, I don't blame him."

Arlette kept walking in silence, so Rennie went on:

"I'm puzzled, too, about you and your father. He seems to have been a pillar of the Pétain brigade and yet you were in the Resistance. That puts you on opposite sides of the fence, yet you all get along famously under one roof. I just don't get it."

She smiled at him and put out a hand for his support as she guided him down stone steps hewn roughly out of

"This leads to our beach," she said, before replying to what he had said. The waters of the Mediterranean glistened before them and sighed in a gentle surge against a stretch of golden beach.

"I wouldn't expect a foreigner to begin to understand the Bousquet family," she said. "Especially to understand my father. Power is like oxygen to him. He has been used to it all his life. In the Navy. In the Colonial Service. In business. In his home. I know he is autocratic and difficult. But he is ruled by a kind of divine assurance of what is right. That is why he is respected, and feared, throughout the Empire. And he's consistent. He doesn't change with every political wind that blows. He deliberates, then he decides, and he sticks to what he decides. That's why Vichy and the Germans were so anxious to have him appear their friend. That's why the British have been courting him since the death of Darlan. That's why the

Americans—who don't really like him—take care not to offend him. They don't like the influence he has but they know he can't stand de Gaulle any more than they can. The ironic thing is that while he believes the future of this country will depend on the American dollar, he won't commit himself for Giraud—which would please the Americans. But he thinks Giraud is a weakling and has no more time for him than he does for de Gaulle."

"Maybe he's waiting for de Gaulle and Giraud to cancel each other out," said Rennie thoughtfully. "Maybe he's sitting it out like Napoleon at Elba, waiting for the call."

She gave him a searching look.

"What made you say that?"

"I don't know. Maybe it's after hearing so much about him, and then meeting him tonight."

"You didn't like him, did you."

"If you want the truth, no. I think men like your father are dangerous."

"That's a sweeping thing to say after only five minutes in his company."

Rennie smiled.

"It's the animal in me. I go by my instincts."

"What do your instincts tell you about me?" she asked.

His smile broadened.

"I *know* your're dangerous," he said. She made no reply, not sure whether he was teasing her or really meant it.

"Did your father know you were in the Resistance?" he asked.

"Good heavens, no!" she exclaimed. "He would have had me arrested."

It was Rennie's turn to look at her askance.

"You're not serious?"

"I'm serious all right," she replied with feeling. "I told you that you couldn't begin to understand my family. Papa would have gone through the roof if he'd known that I was passing on information eavesdropped at his dinner-table. He's an old Roman with his own very particular code and ideas about honor. That's what I've been trying to explain to you. He really meant it when he said that he acted against his conscience in trying to get Jean-Paul off the hook. When Jean-Paul disobeyed his captain, Papa would have gone along with him being court-martialled and shot. Jean-Paul broke the officers' code. That is a capital offense in my father's eyes."

"And you approve?" asked Rennie.

"I understand it," said Arlette. "And I respect my father for the way he sticks to his principles—which is more than I can say for Jean-Paul. He was a fool to behave the way he did. He must have known that, alone, he could achieve nothing . . . That, in the end, nothing would be changed."

Rennie looked at her sideways.

"Are you saying that what you can't forgive has less to do with what Jean-Paul did than the fact that he had no hope of winning?"

They had come to what Rennie took to be a changing hut for swimmers using the beach. A couple of deck-chairs were propped against the short veranda. Arlette stopped and, leaning against the veranda, kicked off her shoes one at a time. She considered what Rennie had said.

"Yes, you're right," she said. "I find it very hard to forgive a gesture that is an exercise in futility. Why do anything if there is not going to be a prize? Why run terrible risks aganst fearful odds if you know you're going to lose? There's no point. Winning is all that matters. That's what makes all the risks worthwhile."

Rennie smiled.

"How do you reconcile that philosophy with a young lady who drives cars straight at army trucks just for the hell of it?"

She smiled back.

"I wasn't afraid of losing. You were! I knew the other driver's nerve would give before mine did."

"There are cemeteries full of people who think that way," said Rennie soberly. She gave a soft laugh, a mere tinkle of sound.

"You know, you're a very, very serious man," she said. "Don't you ever relax?"

"I haven't had a lot of laughs lately," he agreed. "Maybe because there aren't many around when half the population of the world is hell-bent on wiping humanity off the face of the earth."

"It all seems very far away from here,' she said. "Look at the sea, how calm it is—and inviting. Let's go for a swim!"

"You're wearing just the gear," he said. "That long

dress was just made for the beach. Even if you were serious, it's a bit soon after your dinner. You could take stomach cramps."

She tripped lightly past him in her bare feet, padded up the wooden steps to the veranda, and disappeared into the hut. She was gone for less than two minutes. When she emerged, she was wearing a black one-piece swimming suit and carrying a big white towel.

"There are trunks and plenty of towels inside, if you want to borrow them. I'm off," she said. With that, she raced off down the beach towards the water's edge.

He debated with himself for a moment. A swim in the sea was nowhere on his list of priorities. The whole idea was crazy. He should be getting back to Algiers. But the night was warm, and the sea *did* look inviting. He tried to expel the thought that she looked inviting, too. Those long brown legs and the eager body bursting out of the black swimsuit.

"What the hell," he muttered and strode into the hut to search for a pair of trunks in the lightless interior.

She had waded out through the surf and swum out for more than a hundred yards. At first, he couldn't see her as he waded through the breakers, but she shouted to him and he swam towards her voice in long lazy strokes.

"You're out of your depth," he called, as he came up with her.

"So are you," came the reply. "Let's go further out." She began to cleave through the water with graceful strokes. Rennie followed, contenting himself with a slow easy crawl. He began to enjoy the cool clean luxury of it. The sea was calm with only a gentle suggestion of swell.

Stopping to tread water, the dim outline of the shore made him realize that they had swum out half a mile. With a backward paddling motion, he splashed round through a complete circle, and felt a cold touch of panic when her bobbing head was nowhere visible throughout the completion of the turn.

Then a hand touched his ankle and slid groping up his body until she surfaced, her face only inches from his. She shook spray from her hair, and blew water from her mouth in a literal gurgle of laughter.

"Oh, that's tiring," she cried, breathing huge gasps of air. "You'll have to let me lean on you." She kept her arms on his shoulders and her body drifted against him.

The sensation was deliciously electrifying. But the surge of pleasure it provoked in Rennie also had the effect of slowing his paddling hands and legs and they sank, bodies wrapped against one another's. They broke apart and splashed to the surface independently.

"You'll have us both drowned," cried Rennie, but his voice was laughing. The lingering sensuality of the encounter was still making his pulse race.

She struck out for the shore and he followed, finding that he had to increase his rate of stroke to stay close behind her. In the shallows, she got to her feet, breathless and laughing, and turned and sent a cascade of water over him with the flat of her hand. Then, scampering like a child, she ducked him: two hands on his back and pushing him down until his face encountered sand and gravelly shingle.

When he surfaced, spluttering water, she was already running up the beach, laughter tinkling from her. He went after her, sprinting as fast as he could go, threatening vengeance between rapid gulps of air.

He caught her ten yards from the hut, catching her by the arm and propelling her up into his own arms. He carried her, struggling, back towards the sea.

"What are you going to do to me?"

"Give you a taste of your own medicine," he said.

"You're a bully," she cried, without any indication that she really meant it. There was laughter in her protest and no real determination to free herself as she continued to wriggle and struggle.

"Stop wriggling," he said. "You're losing your swimsuit." The straps had come loose from her shoulders, exposing one breast. He could feel the hard button of her nipple against his skin as she continued to twist.

He waded out through the surf and the struggles stopped. Her smile, as she looked up at him, was challenging and provocative, but her words conceded defeat.

"You are too strong," she said.

"And you're going to get wet," he said. Holding her out from his body, he dropped her unceremoniously into three feet of water. She gave a little shriek as she hit the water with a splash. She stood up, water streaming from her hair and shoulders and faced him, grinning.

"Brute!"

The other strap had fallen from her shoulder and the

suit had slipped, leaving her naked to the waist. Rennie stood, staring. She made no show of modesty. She put her hands on her hips and posed for him.

"Do you think I have a good body?" she asked impishly.

"You're very beautiful."

"There's more of me," she said, and wriggled the wet bathing suit down over her hips. The flesh at the confluence of torso and thighs was a white band against the golden tan of the rest of her body. With a deft movement, she pulled her swimsuit off. Deliberately, she wrung the water from the garment and then threw it to Rennie, who caught it.

He was still staring at it, startled momentarily, when she waded towards him and took it back out of his hands. She rolled it in a ball and threw it up the beach. Then she slid her arms round his neck and pulled his head down until their lips met. The salty taste of that first contact was both bitter and honeyed as her mouth opened and her firm probing tongue sought his. Arrows of quivering desire pulsed through him and he pulled her body to his, his hands pressing on the cool wetness of her hips. They locked in a fierce body-pressing embrace until shortage of breath made them break apart, trembling and gasping.

Teeth bared in the merest murmur of a laugh, Arlette broke free and went scampering up the beach. She waited for him where they had left their towels side by side. She handed him a towel.

"Dry me," she commanded.

He took the towel and she stood, head thrown back, as he dabbed it in short rubbing caresses over her out-thrust breasts, across the hard flat of her belly and into the crevice of her thighs. She breathed sighs of delight, then pushing the towel away, she pulled his face towards her again: her fingers twined tightly in the short hair at the back of his head, compelling his head downwards. Her kiss was urgent, transmitting desire in currents.

"Oh, John Rennie," she murmured, "take me."

He wavered momentarily, just a trembling hesitation, but she sensed it and knew the reason.

"Forget Jean-Paul," she whispered. "There is only us."

Just the mention of Jean-Paul's name was enough to make Rennie draw back. Shame fought with the desire his body felt. It started as no more than a rainspot against the prairie fire of his sexual arousal. In no time, it was a torrent; quenching the fires and damping them down to a flicker.

The flames spluttered out altogether when she almost screamed at him:

"Forget Jean-Paul! I'm free of him now! Don't you see? I'm free of him. If we leave him where he is, he can never come between us!"

Rennie dropped his hands to his sides.

"I thought you were a *man!*" she cried.

He felt an indescribable sadness.

"You feel nothing for me. You just want me to give up on Jean-Paul, the same as your father—only you're going to make it worth my while. Why, Arlette? Why, for God's sake?"

"You! You are the reason!"

"I . . . I wish I could believe you. I . . . I'm sorry."

"Sorry! Is that all you can say? Sorry! Get out of my sight, John Rennie! Get out of my sight! We'll see who's going to be sorry!"

Even in her fury, she was beautiful. Rennie put out a hand to touch her shoulder. His intention was to console, to express further regret. She recoiled from his touch.

"Don't touch me!" she spat at him. "Just get out of my sight!"

Rennie padded into the hut, gathered his clothes together and took them outside. When he came out, he saw that she had gone down to the water's edge, where she stood, looking towards the hut. When she saw him, she turned and walked away along the beach, a sulky Aphrodite unconcerned by her nakedness.

Rennie only half dried himself, hurrying into his clothes and ignoring how sandy his feet were as he thrust them into unyielding socks. He tossed the towel on to the veranda of the hut and turned away, only one thought in his mind: to get away as quickly as he could. He halted, his breath catching in his throat, when he realized that someone was standing motionless at one side of the hut, all but concealed in shadow. He recognized Geraldine Bousquet.

She remained there, silent, unmoving. How long she had been there, there was no way of telling. Briefly, the eyes glinting in the shadows met his. Then he strode along the beach towards the steps to the garden above the rocks. He did not look back.

Chapter Fifteen

It was apparent at breakfast in the saloon of the *Fort Daring* that the Old Man was not quite himself. Rennie's officers suspected that their Captain's surly mood was born of a monumental hangover. In a sense, it was. His encounter with Arlette Mercier the night before had left him with a bitter depression as chronic as any that was derivative from alcoholic excess. He felt overwhelmed by his apparent helplessness to bring the day of Jean-Paul's release any nearer. He had no thought of giving up. Indeed, the more he was devoured by frustration, the more obsessional he became that his French comrade's salvation depended on him alone. Only he, in the entire world, seemed to care that a massive injustice had been perpetrated. And only he seemed to have the inclination and will to put it right. To abandon the task would be to abandon any right he had to hold his head up as a member of the human race.

It was the aloneness, Jean-Paul's total isolation from hope, that affected Rennie most profoundly. He could identify with the despair that Jean-Paul must feel. Rennie could well imagine what it would be like to be in his shoes: the friendlessness, the feeling of being rejected by humanity for no crime greater than having tried to serve it. Rennie could commit no greater crime in his own eyes than to do nothing. *He had to do something*. As long as he had breath in his body, *he had to do something*. It was more important than his ship, his job, or anything else.

On that morning, he found himself resenting the shipboard responsibilities that required his attention. It was as if every task was an obstacle standing in the way of the one on which his mind was set, although he had no clear action in mind. It seemed that he had exhausted orthodox lines of action. Now, something fresh was required. Something *effective*. But what?

A naval officer came aboard to confirm that arrangements to fit the *Fort Daring* with a new propeller would have to be forgotten as far as the immediate future was concerned. Even the preliminary repairs to the ship's stern were being abandoned for the time being. The initial survey had revealed that there was no danger of the vessel sinking. Indeed, the naval authorities had decided to employ the disabled ship usefully while she was laid up in Algiers. The explosion on the *Bjorkhaug* had destroyed premises used to store war materials and deprived the port of valuable storage facilities. The *Fort Daring* was to ease the strain by being pressed into service as a floating warehouse.

A start had to be made right away to prepare the ship for the first consignment of these stores which would be loaded from another merchantman tying up to the *Fort Daring*. The holds had to be made ready for the reception of several hundred tons of smoke floats and AA ammunition.

"Just what we need," complained First Officer Cole. "Not content with turning us into a bloody store, they're going to load us to the gunwales with pom-pom shells. Now, if it had been booze and baccy, we could have run up the NAAFI flag and re-named the ship the SS *Fleet Canteen!"*

The new situation made it impossible for Rennie to leave the ship until late afternoon. By then, a sister "Fort" ship was made fast alongside the *Fort Daring* and all was in readiness for a transfer of cargo to begin with first light the following morning.

Blom had made a brief appearance at the ship during the morning. Sensing Rennie's troubled state over Jean-Paul Mercier and guessing that something had gone wrong at the Bousquet villa, he had not taxed Rennie for details. Instead, he had offered to be available for a council of war later in the day when Rennie was free of his shipboard duties.

Rennie found him sipping wine on the terrace of the Coq Hardy. The brasserie was crowded at that hour of aperitif, as were the streets, and Rennie sat down beside the agent as he watched the passing parade with his sad face.

Blom ordered a glass of wine for Rennie and used the time until its appearance to tell about the Coq Hardy. It had been a favorite haunt of the Resistance during Vichy times, and it was still patronized by them as a kind of special rendezvous for old comrades.

He raised his glass to Rennie.

"I admire you, Captain, for what you are trying to do for Mercier. I envy him the friendship and the loyalty he commands. You have between you what we had, as *résistants:* the bond which can only be forged in dangers shared and hardships endured. I salute you."

Blom's words sent a warm glow through Rennie. What had made him think that he alone cared what happened to Jean-Paul? As long as there were people around like Blom, the battle would never be lost. He tried to tell the agent that *his* friendship had already come to mean much to him, but Blom waved aside his gratitude, discounting the value of his help.

"Your friend is still in prison. What help have I been?" asked Blom.

"You've already done more than I can repay," said Rennie. "I appreciate it."

Blom snorted.

"There is no question of repayment. I am with you all the way. What those Vichy bastards have done is not your responsibility. But it is mine. It is my affair that they have shamed the name of France. I could tell you stories of what they did in this city, Frenchmen to Frenchmen. Your Jean-Paul has not suffered more at the hands of his own people than many who are sitting in this café at this very minute." He pointed at a man sitting two tables away. "That is Georges, a friend of mine. He spent two years in the concentration camp at Hadjerat M'Guil. He was beaten and tortured. They broke both his hands and blinded him in one eye. He is only one. The stinking Vichyists had fifty thousand like him imprisoned in their camps in *Algérie de Sud*. Most of them have been liberated since February of the year, but no Frenchman worthy of the name can stand by idle while one single anti-Vichyist such as your friend Mercier is still behind bars!"

"OK, so we're both in it," said Rennie. "But what do we do? I'm at the stage of going off at half-cock, doing something really desperate."

"Such as?"

"Well, this afternoon, I thought about getting all the

crew together, telling them what happened to Jean-Paul, and then asking for volunteers to go on an expedition and getting him out by force. On board the ship, I have two portable machine-guns, a dozen rifles, two revolvers . . ."

"But now . . . You don't think it's such a good idea?" said Blom.

"No," admitted Rennie. "Apart from the fact that it would probably cause an international incident and some innocent people might get hurt, I don't really have the right to involve the lads on the ship. It's not their fight. It's mine—and it's personal."

Blom nodded his head.

"You are wise not to try anything like that, my friend. I understand how you feel—but you would have no chance against a company or more of regular soldiers, and that's what you would have to face."

He pondered a moment.

"I could get my old Resistance group together, those who haven't already joined up with de Gaulle. We could dress them up in uniforms, bluff our way into the prison and perhaps use force if we have to . . ." He shook his head. "No, there must be simpler ways."

He snapped his fingers, as if he'd just had a bright idea.

"Let me try something first," he suggested. "I have an old Resistance friend who might help, René Capitant. He will be sympathetic and he has friends on the Committee of National Liberation. Perhaps he could get Mercier's case drawn to the attention of the politicians who are most determined to wipe out the traces of Vichy—even de Gaulle . . . Or Murphy, the American envoy . . ."

"I met de Gaulle in London. He knows something about the case already," said Rennie. "And he was sympathetic."

"You've met de Gaulle?"

"One of his press people introduced us. I told him what happened in Senegal."

Blom was delighted.

"Your knowing him could be half the battle. He hates the Vichyists. With him on our side, we could really get some action."

So that was the next step settled. Rennie promised to make himself available to anyone whom Blom could persuade to see him. Blom made out a list of every influential person he could think of who might take up the cudgels on behalf of Jean-Paul Mercier. Rennie made a copy. By the time he had finished, his low spirits of earlier in the day had vanished and had been replaced by a mood of optimism.

A look of horror suddenly crossed Blom's face as he turned over the piece of paper on which he had written the names.

"Oh, merde!" he cried.

Rennie looked at him in puzzlement.

"What is it? Something wrong?"

"I forgot to give you a message," Blom confessed. "I have it written down here to remind me, but it went clean out of my mind until I saw it just now. And the caller said it was urgent."

"Someone phoned you?"

Blom grinned apologetically.

"Your—er—friend, the Commander Bishop. It wasn't him who phoned but someone from his office. They thought it easier to reach you through my office than go trailing away down to your ship at the end of the breakwater."

"What was the message?" asked Rennie.

"Only that he had to speak to you on a matter of great urgency. He had to go to Sidi Ferrouch this afternoon, but he would be at his bungalow tonight after eight o'clock. The person who phoned left instructions on how to get there."

"He has a place somewhere on the Bousquet estate."

"One of the bungalows by the shore. They were built as holiday chalets. Bousquet made a clever investment there. Before the war, he used to invite people over from Paris for vacations on his estate—usually government officials. There was nothing like a free holiday in the Algerian sun for smoothing the way to a Government contract, or getting this franchise or the next. His wine contracts for the French Army, on their own, must have made him millions."

Rennie told Blom about his encounter with Bousquet. The agent guessed that he was in no hurry to meet the Admiral a second time, or any of his family.

"It's all right, my friend, you can reach the bungalows without going near the villa. You keep straight on through the vineyards instead of taking the driveway up to the house. Near the shore, you come to a track which goes past all the bungalows. There must be six in all and, according to the message I got, your naval friend stays in the first."

Rennie was far from sure that he shouldn't just ignore the message from Bishop. He had no desire to make yet another trip along the Oran road on a journey that was likely to turn out a waste of time. Nor was he anxious to presume on Blom's generosity for transport. It was the agent, himself, however, who pressed Rennie to keep the rendezvous and to take his truck.

"Who knows?" he said. "Perhaps the mad Commander has had a relapse of conscience over Mercier and wants to help. At least, even if he is wasting your time, your own conscience will be clear that you neglected no opportunity to follow up everything that might conceivably help your friend."

He was right, of course, Rennie had to admit to himself. And so it was that, just before eight, he was heading west on the Oran highway yet again, flashing past landmarks which were rapidly becoming familiar.

Before, when he had visited the Bousquet villa, the side-road through the vineyards had been deserted. Tonight, there was a difference. Rennie experienced a vague feeling of unease when he left the highway and noticed that a long-nosed black Citroën was parked in the trees beside the entry to the side-road. Two shadowy figures lounged beside the car, the glow from their cigarettes flaring in the darkness and then dying again to tiny beads of light. They were stationed beside a wooden box mounted on a pillar which, Rennie surmised, was some kind of emergency call-box for vehicles using the highway.

Rennie's vague disquiet might have increased had he known that the moment he had gone past, one of the men opened the door of the box, lifted the telephone receiver and rotated the calling handle. There was no dial on the instrument. His conversation was brief.

"C'est lui. Oui Il est arrivé." There was a short interval while he listened, then he added: "Oui, le camion de Blom."

Rennie could not subdue a feeling of furtiveness as he drove on past the driveway entry to the Bousquet villa. He recalled his unattended and somewhat shame-faced departure the previous evening and was pained at the memory. Now he sneaked past the villa like a thief in the night —but not unobserved. The inevitable glow of cigarettes at the gateway betrayed the presence of two more shadowy figures. Had Bousquet posted guards to keep him out? The thought amused Rennie. More likely, Arlette, whom he had scorned, had posted the men there, with orders to shoot Rennie on sight. She had certainly been angry enough last night to have had him boiled in oil. Not many men, he reckoned, could have resisted that body—although he felt no special pride in having done so himself. A bucket of icy water could not have cooled his ardor more quickly than the horror with which he had reacted to her readiness, no, her eagerness to abandon Jean-Paul and have him do likewise.

The road gave way to a track of hard-packed sand which ran parallel to the shore, just above the beach. Six timber-frame bungalows were spaced along the south side of the track at intervals of about two hundred yards. Light burned in the first and the third. The rest were in darkness.

A gray jeep with "RN" emblazoned on it was parked at the side of the first bungalow, an indication that Bishop was at home. Rennie drove Blom's truck in behind the jeep and switched off the engine. He steeled himself. He wasn't particularly looking forward to meeting Bishop. The man was quite unpredictable. Rennie resolved that, whatever happened, he would play it cool and polite.

Rennie ducked under the rail of the veranda at the side of the house and walked along the wooden boarding to the front door. His steps echoed on the timber. The front door was ajar, swinging gently with a creaking sound in the light breeze coming off the sea. Holding the door, he knocked loudly on the wooden frame. The sound echoed through the house. Nothing moved. Rennie waited in the silence.

He knocked again. Still, there was no response. Only that eerie silence. He pushed open the door and called out: "Are you there, Commander?"

This time, he was sure there was a movement, a slight noise. It came from somewhere at the back of the bungalow. Rennie went inside. The front door opened into a short passageway with three doors leading off. The door on his left was open and light streamed from the room beyond into the passageway.

"Are you there, Commander?" Rennie called again.

He pushed into the brightly lit room. He started with a quiver of shock as his foot trod on glass, which gave way beneath his weight with a crunching sound. He stepped gingerly out of he remains of a long-stemmed wine glass and kicked slivers of glass from the sole of his shoe. A pool of pale liquid glistened on the floor beside the broken glass.

Then Rennie saw Bishop. His eyes had been on the splintered glass and the tiny pool of liquid when, from the corner of his vision, he had glimpsed something on the floor. Turning his head slowly right, his gaze still on the floor, he saw first the outstretched hand: quite still, and fingers half-clenched. Then the bare arm stretching into the short white sleeve of a shirt and, beyond, Bishop's face: mouth strangely twisted and eyes staring wide. He was lying on his back, the lower half of his body hidden behind the table beside which he had fallen.

A chill of horror seeped icily into Rennie's bones. For a moment, he could only stare. Then he crossed and stooped down on one knee. Conquering his revulsion, he felt for a heart-beat amid the glutinous red stain on Bishop's shirt-front. There was none. Bishop was dead.

Rennie stood up, the palm of his right hand sticky with blood. There was no sign of a weapon, no telling how he had died. Shooting? Rennie had heard no shot. A knife? Perhaps. It had certainly happened not very long ago. He was still quite warm, the blood barely congealing.

Rennie looked around for a telephone. There was none. The thought crossed his mind that he should clear out, go straight to Naval Headquarters in Algiers and report what he had found. But that didn't seem right. He could go up to the Bousquet villa—there was a phone there—but that was the last place he wanted to go. Then he remembered the light in the other bungalow.

He ran out of the house and along the sandy track. As he neared the other bungalow, he could hear the sound of a man's voice, singing—or, more accurately, da-daing his way through the Italian melody, "Santa Lucia." Rennie paused at the door, breathing hard. From inside, in addition to the wobbly tenor attempt at singing, came the sound of running water. The occupant was having a shower by the sound of it.

In answer to Rennie's shouts and knocking on the door, the singing stopped and the door was opened by a tall, athletically built man whose dripping black hair was plastered close to his scalp. Rivulets of water ran down his cheeks onto his naked shoulders. He had a towel wound round his middle.

"Hi, there," he greeted Rennie. "Is something up?" His words were delivered with a pronounced American twang.

Rennie blurted out the news that he had called on the naval commander in the end bungalow and had found him dead. "I think he's been stabbed," he added.

The man in the bath towel seemed momentarily shocked.

"I'll get dressed right away," he said. "Gee, stabbed you say?"

"I think so. Have you got a phone? We'll need an ambulance, and the police."

"Leave that to me," said the other. "Look, shouldn't you get back there and keep an eye on things? I'll be along just as soon as I can get some clothes on." He paused. "Terry Sullivan's the name, by the way. Chaplain, United States Navy." He looked down at his dripping body and smiled. "Not that anybody would know."

Rennie left him to get dressed and returned to Bishop's bungalow. Some compulsion made him go again into the room and look down at the body. It was as if an inner hope fortified the belief that he had perhaps made a mistake: that Bishop was not, after all, dead. But one look at the glassy staring eyes confirmed the grim reality. Bishop was quite dead.

Rennie turned away and fumbled in his pocket for cigarettes. He lit one and stared out of the window. He could almost feel the stare of those glazed eyes behind him.

He finished the cigarette and walked out to the veranda to throw the stub into the sand. The padre from the other bungalow was taking a hell of a long time to get dressed. Rennie wished the man would hurry. The waiting wouldn't be so bad with someone to talk to—anyone to talk to. Poor Bishop. He had not been one of Rennie's favorite people; strangely humorless compared with other Navy officers he had known. But going like that. Not the glorious end a would-be Lord Nelson imagines for himself. Poor devil.

Rennie glanced at his watch. Fifteen minutes had now passed since he had called the padre out of his shower. Rennie walked down on to the sandy track and looked along at the padre's bungalow. Odd, there was now no light burning there.

His first thought was that the American chaplain would appear down the steps from the far bungalow at that moment, having just switched out the lights as he left. But he did not appear.

Rennie tried to fight down a growing disquiet. What the hell was the man playing at? He whirled suddenly at the sound of an approaching car. A black Citroën lurched at speed round the bend at the point where the track curved round to run parallel with the beach. It skidded to a dusty stop only yards from where he stood.

Two men got out and approached Rennie from either side of the car. One of them was pointing an automatic pistol at him. Two more people got out of the rear of the car. One was a uniformed policeman. The other was Arlette.

"En haut les bras!" barked the man with the gun. Rennie recognized the two men as Bishop's companions on the last occasion he had seen him alive.

"You!" cried Arlette. "What are you doing here?"

Rennie did not reply. He had little opportunity. As soon as he had raised his arms under the threat of the gun, the gunman's companion had whirled him round and searched him roughly from head to toe. Satisfied that Rennie was unarmed, the searcher nodded wordlessly to his companion.

"What are you doing here?" Arlette repeated.

"Commander Bishop invited me. He wanted to see me urgently." Rennie gave a flick of his head towards the two men Blom had described as ex-Deuxième Bureau. "If these two are friends of yours, will you call them off?" He made to lower his arms but the man with the gun said: "Non!" Rennie kept his arms high.

"Where is Commander Bishop?" Arlette asked.

Rennie nodded towards the bungalow.

"He's in there. But don't go in. He's dead. I think he has been stabbed."

Arlette began to speak volubly in French to the uniformed policeman. The other two men listened with apparent interest. The policeman, with a questioning glance at Rennie, turned and went into the bungalow. He returned moments later and went into a huddle with Arlette, talking fast and low but just too far away for Rennie to make out what was being said. He called across to Arlette.

"For heaven's sake, tell him I had nothing to do with it. I was the one who discovered the body and reported it."

Arlette came across to face Rennie. The policeman followed her.

"No one reported the body. That isn't why we came down here," she said.

"Just taking the air, were you? These will be your personal bodyguard, are they?" Rennie could not keep the bitterness from his voice. And his tone obviously nettled her.

"My father received another threat against his life today. It was the third in the last month. These men have been guarding the villa."

"Well, call them off, will you? I haven't done anything."

"I have no control over them. You will have to explain to them what you were doing here. All this land here is private property."

"I've already told you why I was here," Rennie said impatiently.

"You also said you reported finding the dead man in that house. Where did you report it?"

"To the American chaplain in the next bungalow but one. I left him to phone for an ambulance and the police."

"Oh," she said, eyebrows arched in disbelief, "do you arrange other miracles, like walking on water or turning water into wine?"

"What do you mean?"

"I mean that it would be very difficult to telephone from any of these bungalows since none of them ever had a telephone. As for the American chaplain, I know for a fact that he will be away in Casablanca until August. I drove him personally to the airfield at Maison Blanche last week."

The man with the gun gesticulated with the weapon in Rennie's direction.

"Regardez-là," he was saying, pointing at Rennie's shirt front and then at his raised hands. "Et là aussi, les mains. Le sang."

Even the policeman came forward to stare with horror at the blood on Rennie's shirt. There was also a smear on the palm of his hand and his wrist, although he had wiped his hands with his handkerchief. That wouldn't look too good either if they got him to empty his pockets—his bloody handkerchief. A trickle of real fear ran down his spine.

Now the man with the gun was talking volubly. A strange dialect and a delivery like a hiccoughing sausage machine made his words difficult to follow, but Rennie had no trouble getting the drift of his discourse. He was telling the policeman how this *Anglais* was the same one who had been involved in a fist fight down near the docks with the English officer who now lay dead. He personally had heard this Anglais with the blood on his hands threaten to kill the dead officer.

"Now . . . I . . . go . . . Kill . . . you," the man said, carefully mimicking Rennie's English. Then he lapsed into French to recount how Rennie had screamed threats at Bishop and said he was going to make him talk and confess about some betrayal. More, how Rennie had thrown an ultimatum at Bishop and threatened to come looking for him if the dead officer did not respond within four days.

Arlette was looking at Rennie with a pleasure in her eyes that was born of sheer, unconcealed malice.

"It seems that these officers do not believe your story any more than I do," she said in a honeyed voice. "They are going to arrest you for murder."

He faced her with a calm he did not feel.

"Now I've seen all the pages in the book," he said quietly. "You were right. You can't tell from the covers. You should have warned me that the book was obscene."

The malicious delight vanished from her eyes and the smiling lips curled into a cruel snarling slit. The name she called him was a word he did not know, but it was not complimentary. With a full sweep of her arm she slapped him hard across the face with her open palm. His cheek stinging, he stared at her without blinking.

"Thanks," he said. "That makes me feel better about last night."

"Assassin!" she cried at him. "Assassin!"

The policeman stepped forward and made Rennie lower his hands behind his back. He felt the bite of steel as handcuffs were snapped on his wrists. His eyes never left Arlette.

"You still haven't told me what brought you down here," he said. "Did you set this up? Just like Jean-Paul was set up?"

She glared at him angrily.

"Don't dare accuse me, assassin!" she hurled at him. "There is what caused the alarm!" She pointed at the truck with Blom's name painted on it. "The Jews are all Gaullists. They are the ones who want my father's life. The alarm was given when the truck was seen near the house. You should choose your friends with greater care, Captain Rennie!"

He looked at her steadily.

"Before I met you, I did," he said.

The debate seemed interminable. It had started as soon as Arlette Mercier had gone. With a word to the policeman that she would be at the villa if required for anything, she had gone off on foot without a second glance at Rennie. The debate was between the policeman and the other two men. The subject was Rennie.

The policeman insisted that, as the crime had taken place within his area of jurisdiction, Rennie was his prisoner and should be taken to headquarters in Sidi Ferrouch. The tough with the gun disagreed. He and his companion were agents in the secret branch of French Naval Security in Algiers. The dead man was from British Port Security and, to all intents and purposes, a colleague. The investigation was their responsibility and, consequently, they wished to take the prisoner to the cells of *L'Amiraute* in Algiers. Mention of the Admiralty seemed to enflame the uniformed man, who began to argue violently that no prisoner of his was to be taken to that nest of Vichyists. One of his best friends had been murdered there while a prisoner of the Maritime Police on the day after the American landings and while a cease-fire was in effect. No, whether his prisoner was guilty as hell or not, he wasn't being taken to that hell-hole of Vichy scum.

So heated did the argument become that Rennie thought the three men would come to blows. But a compromise was reached. Rennie was to remain at the bungalow in the custody of the two naval security agents while the uniformed policeman went to summon his chief.

Thus, Rennie found the handcuffs being removed by the policeman, who advised the two hoods from Algiers that, as Rennie was now temporarily in their custody, they could use their own handcuffs, if they had any. They did not, but the man with the Hitler moustache waved his gun menacingly and said that if the prisoner escaped, he would not get far.

The policemen then asked the other two if they expected him to walk all the way up to the villa while they had a car which could be used. The two from Algiers agreed with smiles that, yes, they did expect him to walk. He set off muttering under his breath.

The pair, whom Rennie had mentally dubbed Abbott and Costello, seemed to find great hilarity in the way things had worked out. Rennie, however, was far from being sure that the arrangement was going to be benefical to him. If he had any doubt at all, it was soon removed.

After a conspiratorial huddle, "Costello" was delegated to the car. The Hitlerian one approached Rennie and, by prodding him with the gun, herded him down on to the beach. The car followed them at a crawl, down the slight embankment from the track and onto the beach. Rennie could not, at first, understand what the men were up to but, intuitively, he liked none of it.

The Citroën stopped, engine still running, its nose pointing along the beach in the general direction of Algiers. The glow of the city lights could be seen clearly reflected against the night sky to the east.

The man with the gun leaned against the wing of the car while his companion revved the engine menacingly like a racing driver on the grid. Rennie, a few yards in front of the car, wondered what the gunman found so amusing about the situation.

"What's so damned funny?" he shouted at the grinning face.

The man's English was labored and hideously accented.

"You . . . are . . . liberated. Ha, ha, ha, You . . . are free. Go. Allez!"

Rennie regarded him suspiciously. The man waved with his gun.

"Allez!" he repeated.

Beads of sweat stood out on Rennie's forehead. Their intention was now clear. He was being invited to escape. How far would they let him go? Five paces? Ten? Just far enough to be able to point out that he hadn't been shot at point-blank range? Just far enough to look convincing?

Still facing the man with the gun, Rennie began to take a few hesitant steps backwards. Suddenly, the driver of the car switched the lights to full flood. Rennie was caught in the full glare of the headlights. An arm went up automatically to shield his eyes. It was now or never.

He turned and ran, weaving from side to side. But there was no escape from those lights. The car was moving along the beach after him. The gunman had climbed on to the running-board of the car and was aiming carefully.

The first shot went singing past Rennie's head. The second grazed his temple and he felt warm blood running down the side of his face. In that instant, he knew that he had no hope of outpacing the car or a bullet.

A third shot rang out and, with a cry, Rennie threw up his arms and fell. He lay face, down, unmoving. For the second time in his life, he tasted blood and sand in his mouth and, from the corner of his half-shut eye, he could see a beach bathed in a glare of light.

But this time, it was to be different. No waiting for the coup de grace. This time he was going to bloody well fight. He wasn't going to make it easy for the bastards.

He lay completely still as the car became stationary a short distance away. He heard the shuffle in the sand of the gunman's footsteps, knowing that the gun would be pointed warily at his head.

"Est-il mort?" asked a voice from the car.

The gunman made no answer. He had stopped and was looking down at Rennie, his toe-cap only inches from Rennie's nose.

Rennie made his move with the speed of a striking cobra. Toes coiled, he pushed himself forward. His arms went round the ankle of the foot that was just inches from his nose and he thrust his forehead hard against the shinbone at a point just below the knee. The man went over backwards. He fired as he fell, the bullet flying harmlessly in the air. The gun flew out of his hand, crashed against the windscreen of the car, and rattled down the wing before falling in the sand. Rennie, with the initiative of having completely surprised his opponent, was first to his feet. As the other rose, Rennie was already moving forward and aiming a kick at the other man's face. It caught him on the point of the jaw with a crack like a pistol shot. The man fell back and didn't get up.

The door of the car was opening as Rennie reached it. He sailed into the door with shoulder down. There was the hideous sound of flesh and bone being ground against metal and a piercing scream as "Costello" fell back inside the car. His head and, lower down, his knee-cap had been caught between car door and the post against which it closed. He was out of the game.

The gunman was stirring and trying to rise as Rennie turned away from the car. Rennie, his blood raging, hammered a fist into his face as the man tried to sit. Then he punched again and again. His opponent sank back on the sand, moaning and choking in his own blood. The battle was over.

For a moment he stood there, gasping air into his lungs and looking without pity at his vanquished enemies. The short, sharp battle had expurgated some of the frustration that had eaten at him for so long. But more and more questions needed to be answered now.

For the first time, the significance of all that had happened since he had left Blom began to filter into his mind. The discovery of Bishop, the mysterious disappearance of the priest who was obviously not a priest, the advent of the two thugs who had opted to have him taken in dead in preference to alive . . . It all wasn't unlucky coincidence. It wasn't just John Rennie's bad luck. And where did it all tie in with the unlovable Admiral Bousquet and his equally unlovable family? And what was it that Bishop had wanted to see him about so urgently? Was it possible the message hadn't originated from him at all but was simply a ruse to bring a sacrificial scapegoat to the scene of the crime? *Why* had Bishop been killed? Had it something to do with Jean-Paul? Or was it quite unconnected?

The firm conviction grew in Rennie that his quest to free Jean-Paul was incidental to the events of the night. His instincts told him that, somehow, because of his interest in Jean-Paul, he had stumbled into something that was altogether much bigger and much more sinister. *But what?* An elaborate conspiracy? The two hoodlums on the beach were not the kind of toughs who would shoot a prisoner down in cold blood on their own initiative. Someone had carefully arranged for John Rennie to step into a trap, and the same person had told the toughies to make sure that John Rennie didn't live to plead his innocence.

The thought occurred to Rennie that he should beat some answers out of the two men. But he had already done too good a job on them. Neither would be talking very much in the next month.

He turned away. The sooner he got away from this place, the better. His heart nearly stopped beating in his first stride up the beach. The shock of seeing someone standing only five yards away, and whose silent approach he had not heard, brought a cry from his lips. Nerves stretched to breaking point and momentarily frozen with fright, it took him several heart-stopping seconds to recognize Geraldine Bousquet.

He gave a shuddering kind of sigh; partly relief that one woman did not present formidable opposition, partly some relaxation of taut nerves, but mainly the emotional application of the braking system which had stopped him automatically recovering from his surprise with extreme violence.

"I saw what happened," she said. "I thought they had killed you."

"I hope you're not too disappointed I'm still in one piece." His voice was angry with scorn. She ignored his tone.

"Your face is hurt."

He wiped blood from his cheek.

"It's nothing, just a scratch."

"What are you going to do? They said you killed a man."

"I haven't killed anybody . . . yet."

"What are you going to do?" she repeated.

"Get the hell out of here: that's what I'm going to do!"

He thrust past her, but had only gone a few paces when she cried out: "Wait!"

He stopped and half-turned.

"Let's discuss it some other time, eh?" he said.

"I want to help you."

He gave an impatient snort.

"Thanks, but I've had all the help from the Bousquet family that I can use." He turned on his heel. She came running after him.

"They have guards everywhere. You'll never get away."

"I'll take my chances."

"I can get you into Algiers—if you'll let me help you."

He stopped and faced her.

"Why? Why should you help me?"

"Because of them! My father. My sister. Because of what they have done to Jean-Paul. Because they don't care what happens to you." Her voice trembled with passion. "I can't stand by any more and make excuses to myself for them and for me. They are not the same as me. They do not *feel* as I do. They are *without* feelings."

"How do you propose to get me to Algiers?" He found he was wanting to trust her.

"My car is in the trees over there. I will hide you in the back. They will let me through." She led the way up the beach. "You must trust me."

Chapter Sixteen

THE two-roomed apartment was simply furnished but wholly feminine. It was on the third floor and, from the small balcony, it was possible to look down on the office blocks of the commercial quarter and beyond to the harbor.

"I usually stay here when I am in town and work late," said Geraldine Bousquet. "What with the gasoline shortage and other restrictions we used to have, I couldn't keep running in and out to Blida. Have you been to Blida?"

"No," said Rennie.

"It's a lovely place. 'The Little Rose' they call it, because of the flowers and the setting. You should see it when the fruit trees are in bloom. And there are mimosas everywhere. I live most of the time at Blida."

Rennie stood just inside the door, uncertainly.

"Is there somewhere I could wash?" He explored one cheek with his hand and little flakes of dried blood fell away at his touch.

"Of course," she said, and showed him the tiny bathroom. While he cleaned himself up, she got out a bottle and glasses and poured out cognac for both of them.

Her little black Peugeot runabout had been stopped twice before they had got clear of the Bousquet estate, once by *marins* who had been draughted in from Algiers to guard her father, and a second time by the *gendarmerie*. On both occasions, she had identified herself as Admiral Bousquet's daughter and the car had been waved on its way with much saluting. They had had no difficulties once they had reached the highway. It had been her idea to go to the apartment in Algiers. Rennie had made no argument. He needed time to figure what he should do. Her apartment was probably the last place the French police would look.

He raised his glass in salute to her and drained the contents.

"Thank you. I needed that," he said. "It has been quite a night.

"You are a strange man," she said.

He looked at her expectantly, waiting for her to elaborate. She was standing, studying him, her eyes thoughtful as she gently rotated the hand holding her glass so that the amber liquid inside slopped round and round.

"I was very rude to you before. Did you think very badly of me?" she asked.

"I was saddened. The first time we met—when I was with Blom. He told me there were reasons for the way you felt about the British."

"Blom doesn't like me," she said. "Not that I know him or have ever caused him any offence that I know."

"He blames your family for trying to put him out of business, that he has been persecuted because he is a Jew."

She turned away angrily.

"There, you see! Always I am blamed for something that is not my fault." She paced nervously before facing him again. Her expression was tense with the need for understanding. "I have nothing against Jews. I swear it," she declared passionately. "I neither like nor dislike Blom. I don't know him well enough. *He* doesn't like me because of my father."

"You didn't like me because I was British," he reminded her gently. "I have never wished you any harm. Please . . ." He stretched out an arm as she opened her mouth to say something. She let him continue. "I know you were close to your brother . . . That he was killed by our ships at Mers-el-Kebir . . ." He paused, searching for the right words. "What I am trying to say is that I understand why you should feel the way you do about the British. I can even understand that this was a reason for you hating me. British sailors killed your brother, therefore you must hate all British sailors. It's an understandable human reaction—but because it's understandable, that doesn't make it right. I am convicted and branded as an enemy, not because of the way I feel or think or act or because of what I believe, but because of the clothes I wear. Not because of what I say but because of the language I say it in . . ."

"Please, please," she interrupted him. "I know this now. I know that what you are saying is true. I was wrong. I was wrong about a lot of things until tonight."

She stood, head bowed, before him. He placed his hands gently upon her shoulders and willed her to look up at him.

"I'm sorry," he said. "I was lecturing you. I had no right. Especially after what you did for me tonight. I'm grateful."

She did not reply. She looked down again, as if scared to let him read in her face the uninvited tenderness which his gentleness provoked. She broke away and, to hide her embarrassment, invited him to sit down while she refilled his glass.

Rennie took the glass and opted to sit on a studio couch which had a floral-design cover to match the gaily colored window curtains. He lounged back against the wall, watching her over the top of his glass. She didn't have Arlette's striking beauty—a beauty which, to Rennie, now seemed mask-like and false in the way that it totally concealed unsuspected ugliness. Geraldine was plainer but not unattractive. Hers was a face that did not slip into an emotional register at the calculated command from the ice-cool brain of its owner: showing invitation, distaste, enthusiasm, anger, concern, happiness, sadness, whatever the desired projection, as if at the touch of a switch. Hers was a face controlled by the heart, incapable of portraying what was not deeply felt. It was a face that could not keep a secret or support a lie.

Even from the little Blom had told him, Rennie could guess at the gaps in his knowledge of her. A girl brought up in the shadow of a spoiled and prettier sister, unloved by a father and yet still dutiful and obedient to him. Close to a brother who, perhaps, gave her the time and love that the rest of the family never accorded her. A girl who was heart-broken and bitter when she was robbed of the one member of the family for whom she really cared.

Rennie had felt the edge of her bitterness in two short encounters so far. But tonight the bitterness to him was no longer there. What had caused the change of heart? Why had she risked the anger of her father and sister and, possibly, the retribution of the law in order to aid him? Rennie decided to ask her. He said:

"You said you were wrong about a lot of things until

tonight. What made you say that? Why are things suddenly different?"

She answered with no trace of guile.

"Because of you."

"I don't understand. Yesterday, I was like something objectionable that the dog had brought in. Today, with the *gendarmerie,* your sister, and a couple of bully boys from the Admiralty all ready to string me up for murder, you appear like the good fairy and snatch me out of the fire. Why? For all you know, I'm a murdering maniac. You saw what I did to the two bully boys."

"I saw what *they* did to you. They were going to kill you in cold blood." Her voice shook. "I thought they *had.*"

"Shot while trying to escape," said Rennie. "That is what they wanted it to look like."

"I know," said Geraldine Bousquet, her voice little more than a whisper. "That's when I realized I had to make a choice, that I had to choose there and then . . . All my life I have been loyal to a father who has never shown me any love. I've been blind to things and pretended they never happened, although they have revolted me. I have never gone openly against my father because I have always believed that a family is a family and its unity must be preserved at all costs. At least, so I've told myself. Sometimes I've wondered if even that wasn't just an excuse . . . That what really inspired my loyalty was fear—fear of being labelled spiteful and mean, fear that my rebellion on my part would be put down as the ugly duckling's revenge for not being shown enough love."

She moved her arms in a limp gesture.

"Anyway, I didn't rebel in the past. I didn't rebel when I suspected my father was persecuting people like your friend Blom for no other reason than a hatred for their race. He used to rant on about the Jewish financiers and their conspiracy to control the world. I pretended to myself that his bigotry was harmless, that everyone was entitled to some prejudices. Yet, he couldn't hide from me that he was obsessed with a lust for power that was far uglier and twice as Machiavellian as any he accused the Jews of. Power is all he ever thinks about or has cared about. Even now, he and his friends are hatching something up. Intrigue, intrigue. Nothing but intrigue. For the glory of France, of course. Oh, what crimes have been committed for the glory of France!"

She said the last in a way that was a cry of sadness rather than contempt. Rennie did not try to interrupt her flow. It had all been bottled up inside her for so long that her outpouring now had all the therapy of a confessional for her as much as it was an explanation to Rennie.

"As for my dear sister," she went on, "I have tried—God knows I have tried—to love her. Even when she poisoned my friends against me, lied to my father about me, stole away the boys who were interested in me, I kept forgiving her. I lied to myself about her, made excuses for her, said it was not her fault that she had become accustomed to always getting her own way. Even when she took Jean-Paul away from me, I forgave her. It upset father, though. Jean-Paul was good enough for me—but not for Arlette."

"Jean-Paul was *your* boy-friend first?" said Rennie, surprised.

"You didn't know? Oh, it was not a great love affair or anything like that. We went out a few times together. Then, one day, Arlette clapped eyes on him and that was that. Not that I dreamt that they would get married in the end. Usually, when Arlette pinched one of my boyfriends, she had a fling with him and then dumped him. With Jean-Paul it was different. She went after him like a ferret after a rabbit—and that's a fair description of the way it was. Jean-Paul wasn't her usual type at all, an old-fashioned kind of boy and very shy with women. I was really surprised that they made a go of it. She doesn't give a damn about him now, of course, and Father never did. I think they've treated him shamefully—especially now. The lies they've told me about him!"

"Lies?" asked Rennie.

"Oh, I had my suspicions that the things they told me about him were distorted," said Geraldine, "but, as usual, I gave them the benefit of the doubt. Until you came to the villa last night and stuck up for Jean-Paul, I honestly knew nothing about that dreadful business of an officer bayoneting him. God forgive me, I didn't even think he might be innocent of the thing they accused him of."

"Your father didn't believe me about the bayoneting," said Rennie.

"He wouldn't have believed you if you had shown him

a color film of it actually being done. He believes only what it suits him to believe. But I believed you. I didn't want to believe you but I did. Now do you see the choice you forced me to make? I hated you and wanted not to believe you but I *knew* that you were speaking the truth. Then, when I saw you and Arlette on the beach . . . You must forgive me for that . . . I don't make a habit of spying on people . . ."

"How much did you see?" asked Rennie quietly.

"All of it. I knew what she was up to. I should have gone away but I couldn't. I wanted her to prove me wrong about you. I wanted her to reveal how weak you were so that I could go on hating you. Instead . . ."

"She wanted me to forget about Jean-Paul."

"I know," she whispered, "I know." She looked at him with wide, sad eyes. "If you had done as she wanted, I could have gone on being an ostrich with my head in the sand. But you didn't. That was my moment of truth. It was a very humbling experience—to be made to face the truth by someone you hate. I wanted only to loathe you but you can't go on loathing someone you begin, against your will, to respect and then to admire. You made me face the truth about myself and about my family. And the truth wasn't pleasant. I've been wrong about many things. I've deluded myself about many things. I thought that blood was thicker than water. But it isn't. The blood in my veins is the only thing I have in common with my father and my sister. That isn't strong enough to make me deny the way I think and the way I feel. In that respect, they are alien to me. I have more in common with you, a stranger and a foreigner, than I do with them. I cannot love them, I cannot respect them. You made me see this. It wasn't I who helped you escape tonight. It was the other way round. It was you who set *me* free."

She got up and walked across to the window and stood there, looking out. Rennie put down his glass and followed her. He stood behind her and put his hands gently on her shoulders.

"You make me out to be quite a fellow," he said. "I just hope I'm worth it. You know, I keep thinking I'm all alone in this world, that nobody else really cares about the things I care about. I'm always being proved wrong. Someone always comes along to make me change my ideas. It makes me pretty humble, too, when it happens. I feel that way now. Humble. And grateful."

She turned to look up at him.

"It is strange that you should say that—about being alone. I have always felt alone. Jacques understood it, my brother. He was the only one who understood it. He was the only one who knew about my lonely little world and tried to share it with me, tried to make me happy and smile. Since . . . since his death . . . there has been no one. No one who really cared. I locked myself away in my own little prison . . . And that's where I've been ever since."

She smiled up at Rennie.

"Why am I telling you this? It will make you think that I am strange and neurotic—and I don't want you to think that at all."

He laughed.

"I wasn't thinking it. What do you want me to think?"

"That there's some hope for me yet."

"I think you're rather wonderful," he said.

"Do you want to kiss me?" she asked with tentative innocence.

"You know I do. I've been trying to pluck up the courage for the last two minutes."

"So!" she exclaimed, eyes sparkling. "So! Is it so bad that it requires an act of bravery!"

He needed no further invitation.

The ardor of their first embrace was not the aperitif, the opening gambit, to sexual coupling, more a climax to the emotional tensions of the evening's events. They both needed someone to hold, if only briefly, in the way that dreamers emerging from a nightmare need to reach for reality and reassurance. It seemed natural to both that their kisses were exchanged in reaction to all that had gone before rather than as a prelude to anything to come. Neither desired to hasten their relationship beyond a certain point. It was an achievement to have had it journey thus far and no further. So, they were content to hold each other and draw comfort from the fact that they had found something and that it was worth finding. It was much too early to define it as love. Too early even to say it was something from which love could grow, but the possibility was there. And, for the moment, it was enough.

The interlude provided only a short postponement of

facing up to the question which loomed overall. Where did Rennie go from here? The police would be looking for him. The consequences of his battle with the two Admiralty agents would still have to be faced, no matter how strongly he might argue that his actions were justified.

Rennie did not want to implicate Geraldine Bousquet any further; a course which she refused even to contemplate. What was the point of him going to the British Military Authorities and placing himself at their mercy—as he intended—if he had no one to corroborate at least part of his story? He reluctantly gave way to her.

Before making any move, however, he wanted to contact Blom and put him in the picture. The agent's truck was still at the bungalow.

Over the telephone, Rennie told Blom the whole story. It was punctuated only by Blom's periodic exclamations as each development was revealed.

The outcome was that Blom insisted that Rennie do nothing and go nowhere until he got to Geraldine's apartment. It took him only fifteen minutes. The agent agreed wholeheartedly that Rennie's first step should be to seek the protection of the British authorities.

Thus, when Rennie presented himself at the headquarters of a surprised Provost-Marshal just before midnight, with Blom and Geraldine Bousquet in tow, a step was taken which was to have consequences far beyond Rennie's imagining. Major Kemp was a ginger-haired thirty-five-year-old who had been with the Railway Police in Glasgow before enlisting as a Scots Guardsman. He had been a sergeant in the Guards before being commissioned with an infantry regiment, the Argyle and Sutherland Highlanders. There, his stay had been comparatively brief. He had transferred to the Military Police as an SIB officer before arriving at his present position of responsibility, a post which proved both arduous and dangerous.

The story which Rennie told him was, however, something quite new and unusual even for his experience. The more Kemp heard, the more he became convinced that the case had ramifications reaching much further and wider than the run-of-the-mill stabbing cases which he dealt with almost daily. The fact that the victim was no less a personage than the Port Security officer was sinister enough for a start. The fact that his informant—already a prime suspect by circumstance and his own admission—was a ship's captain, bordered on the incredible. And that was only for starters. How the hell did two ginks from French Naval Security get in on the act? And why should they want to bump off the ship's captain? The French Admiral's daughter made a very convincing witness of what had happened out on that beach. Also, the fellow with the face like a mourning bloodhound seemed to be telling the truth ready to swear about getting the message which took the captain out to that bungalow. He said he passed the message on only about an hour before the PSO got stabbed. It would have had to be a pretty impulse killing if the captain did it. No, the thing stank. And how about the phony padre? If the ship's captain had invented that, why the bloody hell had he taken the trouble to invent it? It just didn't make sense.

There was more, of course. The whole thing happened on the doorstep of some great Pooh-Bah of a French Admiral, the girl's father. Some guy who thinks the Gaullists are after his blood and has the place crawling with guards and police. This was the element which Kemp liked least about the whole bewildering business—the French connection. That smelled very strongly of politics. And the mess of politics in Algiers was a morass from which Kemp recoiled holding his nose. He neither understood nor wanted any part of it.

Kemp took signed statements from Geraldine Bousquet and Gerard Blom and politely suggested that they go home to their respective beds. He wanted Captain Rennie to stay on as there were still some questions he wanted to ask him.

After Blom and Geraldine had gone, Rennie was taken to a room where a friendly military policeman from Llanelli plied him with tea and bully beef sandwiches and regaled him with stories of legendary Welsh rugby players. Kemp, meantime, was making a lengthy telephone call, quite unsympathetic to the complaints it provoked from the man at the other end on the lateness of the hour.

"It's delicate and it's political," Kemp repeated several times, "and your people had better get down here fast. I tell you I have a nose that can smell dog shit five miles away upwind—and this doesn't just smell, it reeks to high heaven!"

* * *

* * *

It was ten in the morning when Rennie was finally allowed to go back to his ship. He was red-eyed from lack of sleep and tired of having told the same story over and over again. He had told it to the two officers from Army Intelligence. He had told it again to the man from the Foreign Office. Then there had been the Lieutenant-Commander from Naval Security and, finally, the French Director of Police.

Offstage, there had been intense wrangling and debate and a great deal of coming and going from the Provost-Marshal's HQ. Rennie escaped it although he was aware of distant activity by the number of times Kemp was called away from the various interviews.

It transpired that the British authorities had gone all out to bat for Rennie. They had received every co-operation from the French Director of Police who had agreed, subject to certain conditions, that since Bishop was a member of the Allied Forces the investigations into his death should be carried out by the Military Authorities. His proviso was that should the inquiries reveal that French nationals were involved, his own officers should be brought in. In such an eventuality, he hoped that his forces and those of the Allied Command would co-operate in harmony in the interests of justice and without prejudice. He was given the necessary assurances.

In the meantime, he was to conduct his own inquiry into the activities of the two alleged agents of French Naval Security. These men, he said, had no authority whatsoever to represent themselves as law enforcement officers, which thy most certainly were not, no matter what function the Admiralty claimed for them. The men were at present in hospital under guard. Both had broken jaws, amongst other injuries.

Shortly after nine, a French naval officer with the rank of Captain and a civilian from the Commissariat of the Interior had arrived at Kemp's HQ with an arrest warrant for the criminal, John Rennie. The charges alleged evasion of custody while under arrest as a murder suspect and the attempted murder of two civilian officers of the Naval Security services. The warrant had been signed by an officer on the staff of General Giraud.

Kemp had refused categorically to hand over Rennie and had ordered his guards to refuse the two men admission to the building. With the departure at the moment of the Director of Police, Kemp had referred the two men to that gentleman. An undignified slanging match had then taken place on the front steps of the Provost-Marshal's HQ. It had ended with the Director of Police grinning triumphantly and the other pair retreating in high dudgeon and declaring that the matter would not end there.

Rennie neither knew nor cared about these happenings. He knew only that he was free. By the time he got back to the *Fort Daring,* bleary-eyed and unshaven, work had already begun on the transfer of naval stores from the heavily laden vessel moored alongside. It was after one in the afternoon before he threw himself down on his settee, fully clad, in the hope of catching a couple of hours' sleep.

It was not to be. The brass wall clock was showing five minutes to two when a hammering at his door woke him. He staggered through to his day room only to find that his visitor had not waited for the door to be opened. He had burst in and was standing looking around expectantly. Rennie stared, thunder-struck at the tall figure in US Army uniform.

A broad grin spread from ear to ear on the face before him.

"Don't you recognize me, John?" said the American.

"Dick Hobart!"

They stood looking at each other for a moment. Then, simultaneously, they stepped forward and seized each other in a spontaneous bear hug, faces wreathed in smiles they pummelled one another as if to confirm that each was flesh and bone and not an apparition that would suddenly vanish. They would both start to speak simultaneously and then dissolve into laughter when, after a pause to let the other speak, they would both do the same thing again.

Rennie's fatigue quickly fled. He insisted on celebration and produced whisky, filling the glasses recklessly and leaving the top off the bottle. Then they talked, the conversation leaping in all directions as they bridged the time from their last meeting. Light-headed with whisky and a profound joy at seeing Hobart again, it was some time later that Rennie cast a somber note on the occasion by telling the American of his surprise at finding Bishop in Algiers and then:

"I got a message from him last night saying he wanted to see me out at his bungalow. When I got there I found him lying on the floor, dead. I think he'd been stabbed."

"I know," said Hobart, his face no longer smiling. "I was out there this morning. I walked right into it. That's how I found out you were in Algiers."

"You were out there?" said Rennie. "At Bishop's bungalow? But why?"

"I went out to see Arlette Mercier. It was official, about the people in the same Resistance outfit as hers. The group broke up some time ago and I thought she could help track some of them down. It's just to put a few records straight."

"Put a few records straight, Dick?" queried Rennie.

Hobart smiled.

"You guessed the line of business I'm in, back in Senegal. I still can't say much about what I do, even if they've put me back into uniform."

"Did you talk to Arlette about Jean-Paul."

"Unfortunately, I couldn't. As far as she knows—and that goes for everybody else in this neck of the woods—I'm Captain Smith of the Military Records and Archives Office. No, I never saw Jean-Paul after Junot caught us on the beach. A Senegalese damn near split my head open with the butt of his gun. I woke up in a stinking cell and I was kept there for God knows how long in solitary. Then I was moved to a camp near Dakar. At the time I reckoned they'd split the three of us up but I heard all about you when I got back to the States." He looked at Rennie sheepishly. "I'm grateful to you for the way you stuck your neck out for me, John."

"It was the least I could do," said Rennie. "The three musketeers, remember? One for all and all for one."

"Yeah," said Hobart, musing. "I remember Jean-Paul, the way he put it—*mes amis, mes fréres.*" His expression suddenly became fierce. "I heard what happened to Jean-Paul only a couple of hours ago. Well, the bastards aren't going to get away with it. I'm going to get him out—and pronto."

"You may find that's easier said than done," warned Rennie.

Hobart grinned.

"I've got influence." He patted his breast pocket. "I've got a little card here with Ike's signature on it. It is a command ordering anyone to whom I show it to do exactly as I tell them and co-operate in full with any instructions which I may issue. There isn't a general—French, American or British—or a politician who isn't going to jump smartly to attention when I flash this little ticket. They'll jump through hoops if I tell 'em!"

"But they've got Jean-Paul in some sweat-hole in the middle of the Sahara."

"I know," grinned Hobart. "I'm going to present myself at the Commissariat of the Interior and pay a little call on the Chief Minister. I am going to tell him to make immediate arrangements for Jean-Paul to be taken to our Command Headquarters at Sidi Ferrouch and handed over to the US Commander."

"Do you think you'll get away with it?"

"Well," said Hobart, "maybe that isn't precisely the reason I got the authority, but I tell you what, John. If you promise not to say a word of it to Washington, I won't mention it either. What the hell, anyway. The worst they could do is shoot me."

Rennie's answering grin was joyous. He reached for the whisky bottle.

"This calls for another drink," he said.

"Hey, go easy," protested Hobart mildly. "I got work to do." But he didn't stop Rennie refilling his glass.

Later, he leaned back in one of Rennie's black leather armchairs and grinned across at his host.

"I'm getting tight as a tick," he announced. "You're gonna have to order up about ten gallons of black coffee, John, otherwise I might fall in the dock. Gee, what a day this has been!" He shook his head aimlessly. "Who'd have thought when I got up this morning just what kind of day it was gonna be. I go out to make a routine kind of a call on this man-trap that Jean-Paul got married to. I find the place crawling with people, dropping outa trees with guns in their hands. I have a nice long chat with this dish with the come-to-bed eyes and have a helluva time trying to remember I'm supposed to be a military historian. Then I go and take a look at the beach and find a guy I used to know has been knifed during the night and that a homicidal maniac called Rennie is in some cooler in Algiers and getting nailed with the rap. I high-tail it back to Algiers where this guy, Kemp, says you've been sprung . . . But he lets me read your statement and I nearly have three heart attacks reading it because it takes me straight back to dear old Senegal and another buddy of mine, a French one. I keep thinking what a hell of a bloody mess old John Rennie has got himself into, so I high-tail it down to the docks and find my old buddy is fast asleep. So, what does he do? He fills me full of whisky and get's me drunker than a fiddler's monkey. How the hell am I gonna win the war if I'm drunk, John? You tell me that. How in hell am I gonna win the war if I'm stoned clean out of my head?"

Rennie swayed a little in his chair as he considered this.

"You can talk 'em to death," he said, and chuckled stupidly. He chuckled some more. "That's it. Talk 'em to death." He focused serious eyes on Hobart. "Do you know? Do you know that you've just made the longest speech I've ever heard from you? We spent all that time looking at the walls of a jail and you never spoke more than five consecutive words at a time. You know what I think, Dick Hobart? I think you're drunk. That's what I think."

"Of course, I'm drunk. I just said I was drunk, didn't I? You're drunk, too. You were drunk before you opened the second bottle. If you hadn't been drunk you wouldn't have opened the second bottle."

"I would," argued Rennie. "I only opened the second bottle so we would get drunk. Nobody can get drunk on one bottle."

"We just did," said Hobart.

"What did we get drunk for?" asked Rennie. "I hardly ever get drunk."

Hobart grinned foolishly.

"We didn't get drunk for anything. It just happened." He lurched forward in his chair and peered at Rennie. "Oh God, no. There's two of you. I can see two of you."

Rennie looked across at his friend, smiling secretively.

"There's two of you, too. I know. I saw the picture."

"What the hell are you talking about, John. Picture?"

Rennie seemed to reach into the recesses of his mind before answering triumphantly: "I saw the picture of the other Dick Hobart, the one with the beard . . . In Morocco."

Hobart shook his head in an effort to clear his mind. He staggered through to Rennie's bathroom and Rennie heard the cold water tap running. Hobart returned, still drying his face with a towel.

"What were you saying about a picture?" he asked Rennie.

"I told you I saw it. The one taken in Morocco. I said it wasn't you. It looked nothing like you."

Hobart fished in his breast pocket and pulled out a small photographic print.

"Is that the one, John?"

Rennie looked up at him, beaming.

"That's it. The one I saw was bigger, but that's it!"

"I'll let you into a secret, John," said Hobart soberly. "That's the guy I've come to Africa to find. And I'm going to get the bastard."

Rennie studied the photograph.

"You know, I think I've seen him . . . Or somebody awfully like him. And not long ago . . ."

"Where, for God's sake? John, you've got to remember!" Hobart had grabbed Rennie by the upper arms and there was a desperate urgency in his voice.

"I don't know," said Rennie. "But it was the ears. You see the way that this one seems to stick out from his head. That's what I remember."

Hobart dropped his arms.

"Let's organize that coffee, John. Before this night's out, you're going to remember exactly where and when you saw that face."

Neither Hobart nor Rennie had any way of knowing it but, at that precise moment, the man Hobart sought was no further away than shouting distance. He was being assisted over the rail of the ship moored to the *Fort Daring* by a deck-hand. The man allowed the deck-hand to hold the case he had been carrying, while he leapt down nimbly onto the freighter's deck.

He straightened and took the case.

"Is the Captain aboard?" he asked the deck-hand in a voice that had a distinct American drawl.

Chapter Seventeen

GARRITY, the Second Steward of the *Fort Daring,* emerged from Rennie's cabin with a face like a wet November Sunday. All he had done was ask in a rather astonished voice if the Captain was absolutely sure he wanted another jug of hot coffee.

"Of course I'm bloody sure!" Rennie had roared at him. "I wouldn't have asked you to bring it if I didn't want the bloody stuff!"

No need to shout and swear at me, thought Garrity. He had already delivered three steaming brews to the Old Man's cabin and his request for confirmation of a fourth order seemed perfectly reasonable. He was the one who had to do the running up and down stairs.

The happy reunion of Rennie and Hobart had not exactly turned sour, but the euphoria of earlier in the afternoon had gone. Rennie's bombshell—that he had seen the man Hobart believed was "Emperor"—had done more to sober Hobart than the ensuing mugs of coffee. Nevertheless, he still felt slow and unsteady and he was bitterly regretting his stupidity in showing so little self-control. He didn't blame Rennie. The poor guy had had so much happen to him in the past twenty-four hours that he had done the impromptu celebrating bit like it was ten minutes to Doomsday.

"Are you sure you saw this guy?" Hobart asked for the tenth time. "Look, you've had a rough day, and a rough night. Maybe you just imagined it."

"I didn't bloody well imagine it," said Rennie testily.

Hobart sighed. "It's no good, John. We're getting nowhere. And we're beginning to shout at each other. Hell, I don't want that."

"You're the one who's been going on at me," Rennie said moodily. "How do you expect me to remember anything when you're nagging away like an old crow?"

Hobart threw up his hands.

"I know. I'm sorry. I won't say another word." He wiped perspiration from his brow with a handkerchief. "God, I feel I'm melting away. It's the whisky coming out. If a fly lands on me, it'll get alcoholic poisoning. Can't you get them fans to go any faster?"

Rennie looked up at the two laboring electric fans.

"They're just about clapped out," he commented. "Why don't you take a cold shower? Maybe it'll sober you up and put you in a sweeter temper."

"Hey, could I?"

"Sure, be my guest. You know the way? You've been running back and forward all afternoon."

It was when Hobart was in the shower and had started a tuneless rendition of "My Blue Heaven" that Rennie remembered where he had seen the man with one ear that stuck out slightly. Hobart looked up in astonishment when Rennie burst into the bathroom.

"Hey, can't a guy have any privacy around here?" he said, but Rennie was paying no attention.

"I've remembered, Dick! I've remembered! The man in the photograph is the same guy as the Navy chaplain in the bungalow next to Bishops'. That's where I saw him! He was in the shower and he came to the door with a towel wrapped round him. His hair was all wet and plastered down on his head and one ear stuck out a bit funny. His left ear!"

Hobart flung questions at Rennie as he hurriedly dried and dressed himself.

"What was his height? Write it down, John. Was he clean-shaven? He was. Put that down, too. Dark hair you said? Oh, you've got that down already. OK, any marks on his body? Think, John, think! An old scar, you say. Where, for God's sake? There! Did his towel fall off for Christ's sake? Just put lower left abdomen. Yeah, probably an appendix scar."

And so it went on. Hobart glanced at the sheet of paper on which Rennie had written down every detail he could remember about the bogus chaplain, Sullivan.

"You've done pretty well, John," he said. "For a guy who'd just found a dead body and was all shook up, you kept your eyes open pretty well."

"An old habit," said Rennie. "I walk along streets reading shop-names. I look at faces in railway carriages. But I'm hopeless at remembering names."

His light bantering tone took on a more serious note.

"Just who is this man you're looking for, Dick? I could bump into him again. Don't you think I ought to know?"

Hobart considered this.

"I reckon you've got a right." He hesitated only a moment. "He's a German agent, John. And they don't come any nastier than this one. He works for the SS."

"Could he have killed Bishop?" asked Rennie.

Hobart's eyebrows shot up. He looked at Rennie sharply.

"If he did, it opens up a lot of interesting possibilities, John. I hadn't connected Bishop's death with my mission in Algiers. But if there is a connection, it means that a trail I thought was cold is now very warm. This guy is capable of killing Bishop and the fact that he was in the vicinity makes for a high probability that he did kill him. What I have got to do is find out *why?*"

"You know Bishop was in Port Security? Anti-sabotage and all that sort of thing? Maybe he was hot on the trail of the people who've been blowing up ammunition ships around here."

"That, too, is a strong possibility. The man I'm after has a reputation for sabotage. But Bishop's job was prevention not investigation. What could he have found out that meant he had to be permanently silenced?"

"Maybe Bishop spotted our phony chaplain friend walking around the docks with a time-bomb in his hands," said Rennie.

Again Hobart looked sharply at Rennie.

"That may not be so wild as you seem to think, John," he said. "Can you think of a better way for a saboteur to get around a tightly guarded dock area than all dressed up as a Navy sky-pilot?"

Rennie had to concede that he couldn't.

"There's another thing," said Hobart. "Where do you fit in to all this, John? Whoever singled out Bishop for the knife also singled you out as he fall guy, although they took a hell of a chance in you following the script."

"What do you mean?"

"Well, what if you hadn't got that message to go out to Biship's billet? What if you'd just ignored it and decided to look Bishop up at his office in the morning? Would

Bishop have just been killed anyway? For an otherwise cunning plan, there are haphazard elements which baffle me."

"It doesn't make a lot of sense to me, either," said Rennie.

"OK," said Hobart, "let's consider another angle. Suppose it didn't matter all that much whether Bishop's death was blamed on somebody else or not. I mean, stabbings are a dime a dozen in this town. Why bother to make a smoke-screen when the blame could be put down to some passing Arab knifing Bishop for the loose change in his pocket? Why bring you in, even as an afterthought? Was it an attempt at subtlety—a way to have the whole thing open and shut in the one night? Or does somebody hate your guts enough to have seen it as a good way of getting rid of you?"

Rennie shrugged.

"Arlette Mercier?"

"Jean-Paul's wife? She hates you? Why, for God's sake? What did you ever do to her?"

"It's what I didn't do," Rennie said wryly. "Hell hath no fury like a woman scorned." He told Hobart of the night he had interrupted the Bousquet *ménage* at dinner. Hobart could scarcely contain himself as he heard Rennie out.

"Good God Almighty, John!" he exclaimed in disbelief. "You mean to tell me that she peeled to the nude and was throwing herself at you fanny-first and you said, 'Not tonight, Josephine'? Christ, you must be made out of cement!"

"That's what she seemed to think. You'd probably have done the same, Dick. All she wanted was to make me forget all about Jean-Paul and say to hell with him."

Hobart nodded.

"Maybe you're right. Maybe I would have passed her up. But maybe you don't know me all that well. I think I would probably have had my fun and *then* told her to go to hell."

"Well, it certainly didn't do much for my popularity with the lady," said Rennie. "Not that I believe she would go so far as to frame me on a murder charge. Her father, maybe—but Arlette, no. She's the kind who might get a lot of pleasure from scratching my eyes out or tearing my finger-nails out one at a time—but the other, no. Besides,

I've taken a shine to her sister. It could make life complicated. Not that there's any love lost between Geraldine and Arlette."

Hobart grinned.

"For God's sake, don't tell me any more about your love life. I don't think I could stand it. Mind you, if you're sweet on the lady, it could be useful."

"I'm not sure I like the sound of that," said Rennie.

"The father interests me," said Hobart. I'd like to know a whole lot more about him. You could pump the younger sister for me."

"Oh no," protested Rennie. "I know the old man's up to something. She told me he lives on intrigue and he's hatching something up. But if you want to find out, you ask her yourself. Or better still, go and ask the old man."

"OK, OK," Hobart gave in. Then he added: "But if she lets something slip . . ."

"No," said Rennie.

The party of naval ratings from the submarine supply vessel HMS *Maidstone* aimed their rifles in the air and fired a volley over the open grave. A bugler played the "Last Post."

Considering the fact that Commander Matthew Bishop, RN, enjoyed the friendship of few during his lifetime, the number paying their respects at his final parade was surprisingly large. In addition to the firing-party from *Maidstone* and the officers from the base, there were representatives from the RAF, the Army, all three branches of the French fighting forces and the same from the US Forces. There was also a number of civil dignitaries.

Rennie had gone with Geraldine Bousquet. During the graveside ceremony, they had stood facing another phalanx of mourners which included Admiral Bousquet, splendid in uniform, and Arlette Mercier. They had seen Geraldine but had studiously avoided affecting any kind of recognition. Later, when the proceedings came to an end and the gathering broke up, Bousquet and Arlette had walked past Rennie and Geraldine at touching distance as if the latter pair had not existed.

"Maybe it was a mistake to come here with me, Gerry," said Rennie. He had taken to abbreviating her name, saying that Geraldine would be kept for Sundays, and she had been amused. She looked up at him now, knowing there was no way of hiding the tenderness she felt for him and wondering at it and the way it had grown in the last few days from what had been a sterile hatred.

"Do not worry for me, John," she chided. "There was a time when I would have bled with shame at what has just happened, but not now. I felt nothing. No hurt. No pain. I am beyond it. All I can feel is relief that my father is making clear in public what he made perfectly clear in private—that I am no longer his daughter." She stopped and gave a nervous little laugh. "There I go again, talking about him as if he really was my father . . . when I know he isn't. I'll have to get out of the habit."

She had described to Rennie the terrible scene which had taken place with Bousquet on her return to the villa to collect some clothes. To Rennie, it had sounded like something from a highly melodramatic Victorian novel: the overbearing father demanding to know where she had spent the night, her revelation that she had helped the English sea captain escape from the estate, the fury that had followed.

He had told her she was not fit to hold the honorable name of Bousquet. She had countered that the "honor" had so far eluded her powers of observation in connection with anything he had done for the name and that she would prefer to adopt her mother's maiden name as her own.

This had provoked in Bousquet the next best thing to an apopleptic fit. Purple with rage, he had struck her and knocked her to the floor. Then he had called her mother a faithless whore—she had died when Geraldine was an infant—and said that Geraldine was just like her. Shouting like a madman, he had revealed that Geraldine was not his daughter but the offspring of one of the late Madame Bousquet's many affairs while he had been in distant parts defending the flag of the Empire.

He went on to say that he had hated Geraldine's face since his first sight of her snivelling nose. On and on he went, sparing nothing, making it all too plain why she had never known paternal love; being a constant reminder to Bousquet of his wife's adultery.

The revelation had shocked and hurt Geraldine, although the hurt was to subside long before the sun went down that day. By then, she had been dismissed from the household and told never to darken the Bousquet doorway again. By then, too, she had received the brief note from Bousquet's lawyer confirming the legal details and letting her know that she would only have title henceforth to those properties and moneys which had been bequeathed to her directly in her mother's will. The palace at Blida and the villa on the coast would hencefoward be closed to her, although arrangements would be made for personal belongings, such as clothes and jewelry, to be collected. She was to consider her position in the Delta-Afrique wine subsidiary terminated, although her directorship would continue as a result of her one-fourth ownership of the vineyards and processing plant at Blida. It was hoped that she would relinquish this interest after negotiation of a suitable capital payment towards this end.

As the result of one quarrel, it was brutal overkill. The strange thing was that it made Geraldine a happier person than at any time in her twenty-five years. For the first time in her life she was free.

The cemetery was on a high table of land far from the noise of the city. At turns in the neatly kept pathways and walks, there came unexpected vistas through gaps between the cypress trees of the sea far below. As they walked towards Geraldine's car, Rennie stole glances at the girl by his side, wondering at her serenity.

"You know, you're an amazing girl, Gerry," he said.

"Me? Why?" She smiled at him.

"As a result of doing me a good turn, you've lost just about everything you've ever known—your job, your home . . . Yet you don't seem to mind."

"I've gained much more than I've lost," she said. "I feel like a new person. I don't feel like an ugly duckling any more. I don't even belong in the duck family." She executed a gliding step with arms extended gracefully. "See, I'm a swan."

"What are you going to do with yourself?" he asked.

She made an expressive move.

"I don't know. A friend of mine has just got a job with the American Army as a driver. Maybe they'll take me on, too."

"You'd look good in uniform. Mind you, I can't say it would do my chances any good. You'll have all those Yankee colonels and generals falling over themselves to date you."

She smiled.

"I prefer English sailors to American generals."

"For someone who hated English sailors a week ago, you've come a long way, Gerry."

They had almost reached the car. She stopped, her face clouding.

"I've never really thought about the war, John. Not until now. Never *really* thought about it, that is. I've shut it out, hoping it would go away. The first time it reached into my life was when Jacques was killed. It bewildered me. The English were our friends and yet they killed Jacques. I hated the English for it, just as I would have hated the Germans or the Americans or the Italians if they had been responsible. I never thought about the reasons for wars, John—who was right or who was wrong. I only thought about what affected me, what hurt me. I was affected when the war took Jacques away from me. There were other things after that. A boy I knew from the *Lycée* was shot by the *Garde Mobile.* He was only nineteen and I had always liked him. He was nice, rather shy—but they said he was a terrorist. That affected me. People said he deserved to die, but I thought it was a crime. It just made me want to go away and hide."

Rennie put a hand on her shoulder. But she forestalled what she knew would be an attempt to change the subject.

"Let me finish, John. It's important to me that you understand how I feel now because you have a lot to do with it. I have come to see everything so differently in the last few days. I have come to realize that you can never be neutral—even in a family. You must always stand up for what you believe to be right and you must be prepared to sacrifice everthing for it. To turn a blind eye to what is wrong, to condone a wrong, is as big a crime as the wrong itself. I'm not going to hide in any more corners, John. I can be myself. As a Bousquet, I was nobody. What I felt, what I thought, how I lived, was all subordinate to the name I was known by. You once said, John, that I hated you, not for what you were but for the clothes you wore. How do you think it has been for me? I have never been loved or hated because of myself or what I am but because I was a Bousquet! But not any more. Now I am *me*."

"Finished now?" enquired Rennie, with a twinkle in his eye. She pursed her lips and put her hands on her hips, her whole attitude one of reproach.

"John, you weren't listening to me."

His answering grin was disarming.

"I was not only listening, *chérie,* I was cheering every word."

He seized her arm in his and marched her toward the car. "Come on," he said. "I've got a tricky problem to solve."

She looked at him anxiously.

"A problem?"

He fingered his chin thoughtfully, a frown on his face. "The way I see it, I have three choices. I could hide under a rug in the back like the first time I was in the car. Or I could sit in the back seat looking snooty—so you can get some practice in for driving American generals around the town. Or—" and his face broke into a wide grin—"I could sit in the front with you."

"Or I could make you walk!" she retorted, with a playful swing of her fist in his direction. But she was laughing.

They found Blom at the Coq Hardy and joined him on the terrace.

"Mademoiselle Bousquet," he greeted Geraldine. "What a pleasant surprise."

"Mademoiselle Dumont, if you please," she corrected him. "I have decided to use my mother's name."

"But of course," said Blom, and made a puzzled grimace at Rennie as he held Geraldine's seat for her to sit down. Rennie's answering signal told Blom that that was the way she wanted it and to leave it at that.

"Your American friend will be here about four," Blom said to Rennie. "He should have news for us."

Geraldine looked questioningly at Rennie.

"It's nearly four now. Perhaps I should go before this friend of yours arrives?"

"No," said Rennie. "He wants to meet you. Besides, you'll be interested in what he has to say. He'll have news of Jean-Paul."

They were interrupted by a friend of Blom's. He stood at the table, staring insolently at Geraldine. Without taking his eyes off her, he said:

"You surprise me, Gerard. I do not expect to find you swilling at the same trough as swine."

Blom was on his feet in an instant.

"Watch your ignorant tongue, Louis," he said menacingly. "And stop staring at Mademoiselle Dumont. She is a friend of mine and she does not like to be stared at."

The man pulled a face.

"Dumont, eh? Dumont? Do you think I do not know this one? Leopards change their spots more often than the Bousquets change their name. Does her daddy know she's out?"

"Buzz off, Louis! I won't tell you twice," threatened Blom.

The other man weakened before the look on Blom's face.

"I was only passing," he muttered. "I thought . . . I thought . . ."

He never got round to telling what it was he thought. He shuffled off. Blom remained standing until he was gone from sight.

"I am sorry, Mademoiselle," he apologized to Geraldine. "The next time I meet that ignorant lout, I promise you I shall make him aware of my displeasure much more forcefully."

Geraldine, who had colored deeply with embarrassment, shook her head.

"Please, Monsieur Blom, forget it. I understand. Please do not make trouble." She turned a despairing face to Rennie, who had sat, fists clenched, ready to intervene. "Now you know what it has been like all my life, John. Although, before, it hasn't often been said to my face. But that is the kind of respect the name Bousquet inspires."

The incident was forgotten with the arrival of Hobart. He arrived, breathless and beaming, scarcely able to contain his excitement.

"It's done, John," he said. "It's done. You should have seen me. I was magnificent."

He gave them a graphic description of his visit to the Commissariat of the Interior. Government officials were the same the world over, he said. There was no point in pussyfooting with them. You had to go at them face on, breathing fire and bloody thunder. You didn't say please or thank you. You had to goddamned tell them what to do. You *ordered* them. That was the only thing they understood—orders. You let the bastards see that you had *power*. And you let the bastards see that *power* was what you were going to use if they didn't get up off their butts and do as you goddamned told them.

Hobart had bulldozed his way through battalions of minions and got through to the Chief Minister. And he had treated the Chief Minister with as much finesse as all the rest. He had ordered him to prepare the necessary documents forthwith for the immediate transfer of Jean-Paul Mercier from his present place of detention at Mecharja to the custody of the US base commander at Sidi Ferrouch. The Minister would be allowed four days for the execution of the order. If Mercier was not delivered safely as instructed by noon on 4 August 1943, the consequences to the Minister—and anyone else hindering the implementation of the order—would be so dire that it caused a mild and moderate person such as Hobart great pain even to put them into words. It would be safe to say, however, that the end of the world would be a much less fearful eventuality.

Hobart had literally breathed down the Minister's neck until the necessary documents were prepared, signed and despatched. All they had to do now was wait for Jean-Paul to turn up in Sidi Ferrouch.

After calling for a celebratory drink and toasting the American's success and Jean-Paul's imminent freedom, Blom chose that moment to leave.

"I'll have to push off, too," said Rennie. "The ship we have alongside is being shifted to a quayside berth at six. I told Cole I would be back before then."

Hobart smiled blandly. He thought Rennie was making a diplomatic departure so that he would have a clear field to quiz Geraldine about Bousquet and his political games. But the reason for Rennie's departure was genuine. It did not escape him, however, that his leaving would give Hobart the opportunity he had asked for. Well, Hobart could pump her all he wanted. Rennie wanted no part of it. It surprised Rennie how much Geraldine had come to mean to him in a very short space of time. He was reluctant to face the possibility that he was falling in love with her. He was afraid, perhaps, that he would have to admit that he was—and it was too soon, the wrong moment altogether, to have to consider the consequences of such an admission. Things were fine as they were. Since the night of Bishop's death, they had drifted into an easy relationship which became more meaningful and valued with every meeting. Rennie wanted nothing to disturb the natural process of that relationship, especially not a premature attempt to define its significance.

To Hobart's chagrin, Geraldine was not particularly keen to linger at the Coq Hardy if Rennie was not to be there, but, to Hobart's relief, Rennie dissuaded her from also taking her leave. Guiltily, inasmuch as he felt he was conniving with Hobart, he clinched the argument by telling Geraldine:

"He's really quite harmless. In any case, he's just the man to fix you up with a job with the American Army." He smiled at Hobart, who was looking a little alarmed at the suggestion. "Isn't that right, Captain Smith?"

"Sure," said Hobart, with anything but certainty. "Did you say a job?"

"Geraldine will tell you all about it, old pal," said Rennie, with a broad unconcerned smile, adding: "It shouldn't be too difficult for you to see she gets fixed up. Just use some of the sheer force of that personality of yours."

"If you say so, old buddy," said Hobart weakly, but his attempt to match Rennie's smile didn't quite work.

Rennie had reached the corner of the street, and was debating whether to shorten his journey by trying to find a taxi or risk life and limb on one of the crowded street trolleys, when he heard his name shouted from behind. He turned to see Lieutenant Clifford, Bishop's exec., sitting at the wheel of a Royal Navy jeep.

"Can I give you a lift to the docks?" Clifford asked.

Rennie quickly accepted with thanks.

"I've got to stop off at the office, but only for a minute," said Clifford. "I'll take you as far as you want to go."

He commented that he had seen Rennie at the funeral earlier in the afternoon but hadn't had the chance to have a word with him. He went out of his way to let Rennie know that he knew there had been an attempt to pin Bishop's murder on him, but that it was nonsense as far as he was concerned.

"I mean, after all," said Clifford, "a knife! Old Bish was done in with a knife. It's just not the British way, is it?"

Rennie found the younger man's reasoning slightly amusing, but was glad that he was so readily given the benefit of the doubt. He was about to tell Clifford about some shipboard knifings he had seen—the Britons involved had shown no inhibitions about knives or employing them viciously—when he remembered something that had lain at the back of his mind for days.

"Tell me, Lieutenant. Does the term 'Philippeville traffic' mean anything to you?"

Clifford momentarily took his eyes off the road to glance sideways at Rennie.

"We get the sheets for Philippeville," he said, slightly puzzled. "We get them for all the ports bettween here and Bizerta."

"Sheets?" said Rennie.

"The traffic sheets. What shipping is expected. Convoy information and so on."

"Why should Commander Bishop think I would be particularly interested in the Philippeville traffic?" said Rennie.

"Search me," said Clifford. "It's classified 'Most Secret.' It's not the kind of stuff we leave lying about."

"I've got a letter from Commander Bishop," said Rennie. "He said I should look into his office and see him sometime because he had come across something in the Philippeville traffic program that would interest me."

"Do you think it could be connected with his death?" Clifford asked.

"I've no idea," Rennie replied truthfully. "If there is a connection, it certainly isn't a very obvious one. I don't even have a clue why he thought I would have any interest in ship movements at Philippeville. I'm wishing now that I had gone and seen him when I got his note. I just didn't think it was important. And he said it wasn't urgent. Now, I'm curious. I wonder what the hell it was."

"There's one way to find out," said Clifford. "Why don't you come in with me when we get to the office? You can have a quick shufti at the Philippeville traffic sheets while I'm looking out the stuff I've got to collect."

At the Port Security Offices, Rennie was introduced to the Naval Captain who, only the day before, had taken over Bishop's job. He seemed proccupied with his new responsibilities and quite glad when Clifford ushered Rennie out of his office and into the cubby-hole that was his own domain. Clifford left Rennie briefly and returned with a green folder.

Clifford extracted two typewritten sheets from the bundle of papers in the folder and handed them to Rennie.

"That's the Philippeville traffic program from July fifteenth," he said. "If old Bish said there was something to interest you on it, that's where you'll find it."

Rennie glanced down the list of shipping arrivals. He did not have far to look before he came to the information which, he knew, Bishop had wanted him to see. He drew his breath in sharply.

"Found something?" asked Clifford.

Rennie tapped the sheet in front of him.

"Yes." He read out: "Motor Vessel, *L'Esperance*, ex-Casablanca, Safi and Oran with mixed cargo. ETA Philippeville—fifteen hundred hours, thirtieth July."

"That means something to you?" The look on Clifford's face indicated that it meant nothing to him.

"It has to be the same ship," said Rennie. "A coastal schooner that used to run from Casablanca down to Dakar and Conakry. It was the one that was to pick us up when we made our break from the island where the French had us prisoner in West Africa."

Clifford shrugged.

"Why should it interest you now? I certainly don't see that having anything to do with poor old Bish getting a knife in the back."

"Frankly, neither can I," said Rennie. "It's just a loose end—a loose end from something that happened a long time ago. But I know why the Commander thought I'd be interested. The schooner skipper was a vital link in our escape plan. Bishop knew that and may even have thought that the schooner skipper was the one who shopped us to the French."

"And did he? The schooner skipper, I mean?"

"No," said Rennie. "But it would still be mighty interesting to know his side of the story. He was paid a lot of money for doing damn all. I'd like to hear what he has to say about that."

Chapter Eighteen

RENNIE swore as he typed the numeral eight instead of an apostrophe. It was the sixth error he had made in the damage survey report which he was composing for Blankinsop in London. He tore the sheet of paper from the typewriter and tossed it into the waste-paper basket to join several others.

He was carefully inserting a fresh piece of paper when there was a knock at his day room door. He looked round in surprise as Chief Officer Cole burst into the room. From the look on Cole's face, Rennie knew immediately that something was wrong. Cole breathlessly confirmed this.

"You'd better come and have a look at something we've found in number five hold. I think it's a bomb!"

Rennie delayed only long enough to grab a long heavy-duty flashlight. Cole brought him up to date on the surprise discovery as the two men quickly made their way aft.

"The Second Engineer said they were having difficulty pumping the bilges in number five, so I got the bosun and a couple of lads to have a look . . . See if there was anything clogging 'em up. This *thing* was just sitting there under some dunnage, right against the shaft tunnel."

"I hope to God they didn't move it," said Rennie.

"No. They only found it by the sheerest accident. The bosun wanted a bit of timber to poke around in the bilge. That's why young Jenkins went scrabbling around in the dunnage. He picked up a lump of wood and there was the contraption underneath."

The hold was battened down except for a couple of raised hatch boards at one corner of the coaming. The seamen who had gone down the hold had lifted these hatch boards to let a little light into its depths. Cole led the way into the mast-house and Rennie followed him down the steel rungs of the ladder which dropped sixty feet into the hold.

The light from the corner of the hatch far above was minimal. Both men switched on their flashlights as they made their way across the floor of the hold. They walked along the center of the hold, skirting the steel-plated wall of the shaft tunnel. Near the after end was a horseshoe-shaped ladder which gave port and starboard access across the top of the tunnel's casing. Between this ladder and the after-bulkhead, some spars of timber had been heaped in a loose pile. Cole pointed his torch at the heap of timber.

"There!" he said. "That box with the cotton-wool stuffing sticking out. Young Jenkins said he went to open the lid but didn't touch it after he saw wires and that gray bit of cylinder."

Rennie examined the twenty-four-inches-long container without disturbing it. He could see loops of bright green wire and one end of a gray-colored cylinder.

"Let's get out of here, Mr. Cole," said Rennie. "That may not be a bomb, but until the bomb disposal boys have a look at it, we're not going to take any chances."

Within twenty minutes of Rennie's message to Royal Navy HQ, a two-ringer and a PO from Bomb Disposal had arrived on the *Fort Daring*. Ten minutes later, they departed, taking the mysterious package with them. The speed and lack of fuss with which they carried out the operation left Rennie with a feeling of anti-climax. The arrival of the new Port Security officer, with Clifford and a team of ratings in tow, created a considerable disturbance in comparison. The ship was painstakingly searched from stem to stern but no other devices were found.

By early afternoon, the Security team had gone, leaving the *Fort Daring* silent and idle in the afternoon sun. Rennie was once more attacking his damage survey report for the owners when Hobart arrived in the company of a civilian wearing a light khaki safari jacket over dark trousers. The second man was English. Hobart introduced him as Bob Baldry.

Baldry had dark humorous eyes, a hawkish nose and a heavy, full beard. He reminded Rennie vaguely of a screen "villain" who specialized in roles such as the Sheriff of Nottingham or Pathan bandits of the Khyber Pass. In fact, Baldry, dressed for the part, had often "gone

Arab" in the course of duty and made a convincing son of Islam.

"We've come to kill one bird with two stones," Hobart announced. He nodded towards Baldry. "Bob's in the same line of business as I am. Only he works for your Government. It seems he's got to ask you something."

Rennie offered them a drink. Hobart grinned and threw up his hands.

"We're working, John," he protested. "Besides, I've got strict instructions not to let Bob get a sniff of the sauce until after sundown. And then he only gets it if he's been a good boy."

Baldry squinted at Hobart.

"You speak for yourself, sport. If Sir Francis Drake here insists on splicing the jolly old mainbrace, I, for one, am not going to be so discourteous as to refuse a noggin." He smiled at Rennie. "I'll have a large whisky, sir, with a tear-drop of soda."

Hobart shrugged good-naturedly.

"One word from me and he does what he likes."

As Rennie poured a drink for Baldry, the bearded Englishman confided to him in a loud whisper: "I'm supposed to take orders from this hick American. By God, Christopher Columbus has a lot to answer for in discovering that damned place. Why the hell couldn't the world have been square and the silly bugger sailed over the edge?"

"It's all right, John," said Hobart. "He goes on like that all the time. I'm beginning to get used to it. He's got no respect for anyone."

Baldry drained his drink in one go and gave a long sigh of satisfaction.

"You're wrong," he said to Hobart. "There is one person for whom I have undying respect, a veritable profundity of respect. Unfortunately I don't know his name, but I suspect it might be MacSporran or something of the kind . . . He is the genius, the divine intelligence who invented the golden elixir which I have just tossed with such gay abandon down the back of my throat." He held out the empty glass to Rennie. "May I have another, sir? Is it too great a favor to ask? I promise you that it shall be the last for the time being. I shall not importune you for more. But one more quick snort, sir, will reassure me that life is worth living and that civilization is worthy of my miserable efforts to save it."

Hobart looked heavenwards with affected disgust.

"It's enough to make you goddamned sick," he observed of Baldry's performance. Baldry was quick to misinterpret him deliberately, and correct him.

"Two snorts of the real stuff might make *you* sick, sport, but me, never! Indeed, wasn't it just the other day that you were tripping around like a corpse looking for its shroud, because you'd partaken too well of Scotland's holy nectar? And in the company of this hospitable mariner, no less?"

"OK," conceded Hobart. "OK. So I was a little hungover the other day. So, today I'm abstaining. I am trying to set you a good example."

"I am impervious to good examples," declared Baldry loftily, and downed the second whisky that Rennie had poured for him. He squinted fiercely at Hobart. "If you want to show me an example, sport, show me a bad example. To that I will respond. Yes, show me a bad example and I will follow you gladly to Hell."

"You'll get there soon enough," said Hobart drily. "And there's one thing for certain—the place ain't gonna be big enough for you and the Devil both!"

Baldry was not paying too much attention to Hobart. He was circling Rennie, eyeing him thoughtfully. He waved Rennie into his own armchair.

"Please be seated, hospitable mariner. Our American friend has consented that I open the bowling from the pavilion end. That is, he has agreed that I discharge my duties, as instructed by His Majesty's Government in London, first. Once my business with you is disposed of, we can talk of other things—like the little device your jolly tars found in the dark recesses of one of your holds."

"How can I help you?" asked Rennie, feeling a little overwhelmed by the way Baldry had walked into his cabin and assumed full control of the conversation and everything else.

"Tell me," said Baldry, staring hard at Rennie. "Have you got enemies in the powerful echelons of His Majesty's secret armies? Have you wronged some po-faced civil servant in the secret corridors of power? Does someone in high places dislike you?"

"I'm not sure I know what the hell you're talking about," said Rennie.

"I got a signal from London today," Baldry said evenly.

"It was more or less a reply to a report I made—a very full report for me—of the death by stabbing of one Commander Matthew Bishop and its possible perpetration by a Nazi villain who is known to our dirty trade as 'Emperor.' Thanks to a cooperative Jock major called Kemp, I included details of your skirmish with the two Apache warriors and the desire by the French Navy to have you locked up as a homicidal maniac. Well, what do you think my masters in London said to all that?"

"You tell me," said Rennie.

"They said that there was a high possibility that you *are* a homicidal maniac, that you have a history of irrational behavior as a result of brain damage . . . And that you have on three previous occasions got in the Department's hair. Hold on, I'm not finished. They also say that certain parties in Algiers have made a strong complaint through diplomatic channels to the Foreign Office, demanding your arraignment before a French court and action against the officers here in Algiers who have given you military protection against their wrath."

Rennie was about to interrupt but Baldry held up a hand.

"There's more," he said. "My illustrious masters have ordered me to investigate the possibility that you did kill this fellow, Bishop. And they say that if there is a *prima facie* case against you, I am to expedite—lovely word that—expedite your transfer to the appropriate French authority so that judicial processes, if not justice, may be seen to be in working order. In short, old chum, that I hand you over to the warlords of the French Admiralty as a sacrificial goat. The schemers of Whitehall seem to think that if we make this—er—gesture, the French Navy will give us access to certain secret Vichy documents which would, amongst other things, give us a line on the elusive 'Emperor'."

Baldry ignored the look of outrage and anger on Rennie's face and kept his hand held up to forestall interruption. There was more to come.

"London wants to soften the blow for you by having a Foreign Office legal type act as watchdog for your interests in the event of us handing you over to the French. They anticipate that our military people here and, possibly, the Americans might resist French demands for your head. In this event, I was to make it known to them that there were diplomatic obligations that demanded your sacrifice and that every step would be taken to see you got fair play from the French."

Rennie's expression was grim. The impulse to protest, about what seemed to him to be betrayal by his own and about the injustice of it, had passed. He stared at Baldry in silent bewilderment. Eventually, he said:

"Why have you told me all this. You didn't have to, did you?"

Baldry's eyes widened.

"Good Lord, no! They'd have kittens. I'm supposed to be in the Secret Service, sport. I'm supposed to act dumber than a Trappist monk and do everything I'm told whether it's bloody nonsense or not."

Rennie's puzzlement grew.

"Well, why have you told me?"

"Because I'm going to carry out my orders, sport," said Baldry with a smile. "Here and now I am going to establish what grounds the French have for putting you behind bars. Tell me, old sport, did you or did you not kill this cove, Bishop?"

"No, I didn't bloody kill him!" said Rennie.

"I believe you," said Baldry. "That's all I need to know. I'll tell them that you're pure as the driven snow and I'll advise them to tell the French complainants to get knotted. The complaint certainly didn't originate with the Free French here in Algiers. More likely some of Darlan's Navy friends."

"It's unbelievable," said Rennie. "It's as if somebody in London had it in for me."

"That's why I asked if you had enemies in high places," said Baldry.

"None that I deserve," said Rennie bitterly. "It looks like they haven't forgiven me yet for telling de Gaulle about the Island of Thieves." He looked across at Hobart. "Does Mr. Baldry know we shared a prison hut in Senegal?"

"I know the whole sordid story, sport," Baldry replied before Hobart could speak. "We've done a lot of talking about you. Otherwise, I might have been tempted to take more notice of those idiots in London. Bloody mandarins, they are! It's all a bloody game to them. They sit there moving the pieces and if one gets knocked over it's just too bad. They fish out another chess set. We're their chessmen, sport; people like Yankee Doodle and yours truly. We're fieldmen. If we make a mistake, we get a bullet in the neck. If the Whitehall mandarins make a mistake, they get passed over for promotion a couple of times—and we still get a bullet in the neck because we're on the sharp end of their mistakes!"

"So, you're not going to trade me for an in-tray of Vichy secrets?" said Rennie.

"No way!" said Baldry vehemently. "They can get some other bugger to play their Judas games. They want to trade anybody, they ought to trade that proof, Philby, back in London. It was probably his idea in the first place. I'm buggered if I know how they recruit people like that." He stopped to think about that, and then roared with laughter. "What am I saying? Hell, they recruited me. It proves they're out of their minds!"

"I just hope you don't get into any kind of trouble on my account," said Rennie.

Baldry laughed.

"Not a chance. They told me to take my orders from Yankee Doodle here until 'Emperor's' hide was nailed on the barn door. And that's what I'm doing. In any case, I don't give a monkey's. I've told them before and I'll tell them again—if they don't like the way I operate, they can kick me out on my arse."

"They might just do that," said Hobart.

Baldry gave him a sidelong glance.

"I'm not the only one with my head on the chopping-block, sport. Washington won't be clapping their hands if they find out that instead of chasing saboteurs you've been booting French backside all round the Interior Ministry trying to get a chum out of chokey." He spread his hands in an open gesture and assumed a look of ingenuous amazement. "Just what the hell did you blokes get up to in that Dakar prison camp? First, one gets put away for trying to do in the Camp Commandant, and then another gets fingered for sticking a knife in a former inmate. What the hell did they put in the tea on that damned island of yours?"

"Well, they sure were stingy on the sugar," said Hobart.

With a little difficulty, Hobart succeeded in getting Baldry to vacate the center of the stage. His call on Rennie was not social. He and Baldry had talked long into the small hours of the morning, comparing notes and discussing the fruits of their investigations so far. Hobart, in spite of his diversionary excursion to the Interior Ministry, had been far from idle. Baldry had put in a week's unremitting legwork, questioning dozens of people and patiently searching for the elusive clue that would put them on the trail of "Emperor."

There was no doubt in the minds of either man that Rennie's encounter with the bogus Amercan Navy chaplain was the one solid lead they had. And the man's proximity to the scene of Bishop's death tied that crime and "Emperor" together. And no matter how they looked at it, one key figure kept cropping up—John Rennie.

There was the Senegal connection. It repeated itself more than once.

It was in Senegal that Hobart had been taken out of circulation so that "Emperor" could steal his identity and add it to his repertoire of poses. Rennie's first link with "Emperor" was, therefore, via Hobart in Senegal. In a similar fashion, it connected Bishop with "Emperor."

The pattern in Algiers was different. Bishop, whose Senegal connection with "Emperor" was the most remote, not only encountered him but was murdered by him. Why? Had it something to do with the sabotage in Algiers harbor, which it was his job to prevent, or did the reasons go back to Senegal?

Both Hobart and Baldry favored a motive which had its roots in Senegal. Because the Senegal connection was made positive by Rennie's re-involvement. There was the clumsy attempt to hang Bishop's murder on Rennie. The attempt was only clumsy because it hadn't succeeded. What currency would Rennie's version of the story have achieved if he hadn't lived to tell it? With Bishop and Rennie both dead, there would have been nothing to suggest that "Emperor" was evenly remotely involved.

All this led Hobart and Baldry to a conclusion from which they could not escape. If Bishop had been murdered because of some deadly knowledge he had acquired in Senegal, the chances were that Rennie—whether he was aware of it or not—possessed the same knowledge, and was in very real danger. Not that he needed to be the possessor of any special knowledge to be in danger. He was the one person who could identify "Emperor"—and that fact alone put his survival at risk.

Hobart believed he knew Rennie as well as he knew

any other man. For this reason he had decided to take it on his own responsibility to take Rennie fully into his confidence. In a business where wives were not privy to their husband's secrets and sons could not confide in fathers, it was a brave enough decision for Hobart to make. Baldry helped him come to a decision. The essence of their job, Baldry said, was not—as many averred—the art of trusting to one, but the art of knowing whom to trust. We're vulnerable, he said, because if we make a bad decision, we're dead. So, we take more care than most in whom we trust. If the day comes when there's nobody left to trust, we might as well be dead—because there won't be a hell of a lot left to live for.

So it was that, as Rennie sat, his face impassive, and Baldry sipped his third helping from the bottle of Scotch, Hobart told Rennie of the hunt for "Emperor."

"You may be the only guy in North Africa who can identify him, John. So, I don't have to spell out the kind of spot that puts you in," Hobart said. "You got a gun?"

"A forty-five."

"Carry it wherever you go. Sleep with it under your pillow. And don't go ashore alone any more. I'll give you a phone number. It's an office at the St. George's Hotel. If you go ashore, ring the number from the Dock Office, day or night. You're not going to go anywhere without transport and an armed escort, courtesy of the US Army."

Rennie tried to protest but Hobart was adamant.

"I could put you under protective custody for your own sake, John," he pointed out. "Hell, I'm trying to do the friendly thing. I don't want you finishing up on a slab like Bishop."

"But all this because of one man," said Rennie. "One man! And we must have twenty thousand troops in Algiers alone."

"Don't fool yourself into thinking that 'Emperor' is on his own," put in Baldry. "He's the director, the paymaster, the chief architect—call him what you like—but don't think he's a one-man band. He'll have his own network of informers, murderers, message-boys . . . People whose morality or political philosophy is governed by only one thing—and that's the thirty pieces of silver he drops into their greedy paws. Half the Arabs who work in the docks could be on his payroll. The same goes for half the French Navy at the Admiralty, and maybe some of our own people, too. You'd be amazed at the loyalties that can be bought for a bagful of francs."

"Bob's right," said Hobart. " 'Emperor' is just the head of the octopus. He's got long tentacles and they're all over the place. He can even reach as far as the *Fort Daring.*"

"Are you trying to scare me?" asked Rennie.

"I'm stating a fact," said Hobart. "That little gadget that was found in your hold this morning . . . It didn't get there by accident. 'Emperor' put it there."

"Then it was a bomb," said Rennie quietly.

"Not a big one, but big enough to blow a hole in the bottom of this old rustbucket." Hobart allowed the glimmer of a smile to brighten his face. " 'Emperor' boobed when he left that calling-card, John. He made a mistake which could maybe cost him the ball game. That bomb would never have gone off in your hold."

"Why not?"

"It had an acoustic detonator," said Hobart. "It had been left in the right place—close to the propeller shaft—but what 'Emperor' doesn't seem to have known is that you've already had your propeller shot off. There was no way that bomb was going to work until you'd got yourself a new propeller and you started up the main engines. I reckon you couldn't have avoided finding the bomb long before then."

"Then 'Emperor' isn't such a bloody genius after all?" said Rennie.

"Oh, don't underestimate him," said Baldry. "The idea was good enough from his point of view. Where you're berthed here, you're in the right place to cause a hell of an obstruction. Assuming the bomb had gone off when you began to move, and the ship sank, you'd be near as damnit blocking the harbor entrance. Maybe he just didn't have all the information that he ought to have had. He may have known that your ship had been torpedoed, but he may not have known you left your prop at the foot of the Med. Maybe he's just a landlubber like Yankee Doodle and me and didn't understand ships enough. We didn't realize the detonator was no damned use until the naval johnnie at Bomb Disposal explained it to us. He thought it was a hell of a joke."

Rennie didn't see a lot in the saboteur's mistake to cause any hilarity.

"What worries me," he said, "is how the bomb got on

board. It must have been placed in the hold some time between the time we finished discharging cargo and this morning. That makes it any time in the past week."

"We've got our theories on that," said Hobart. "Our guess is that 'Emperor' is getting into the dock area under a legitimate cover, like posing as a ship's chaplain. He gets the hardware into the docks and he leaves it to be picked up and located on target by, maybe, a couple of Arab dock workers he's got on the payroll. The Arabs couldn't bring the stuff in because they're searched before they can put a foot in the dock gate. The guys on the gate think twice before they run a comb over a Navy preacher with a jeep full of hymn books. Although they'll damned well do it now. We've seen to that."

Although he was not unduly optimistic of results, Baldry wanted to talk to every man of the *Fort Daring*'s crew. If anyone had seen a stranger on board or witnessed the slightest action that had struck them as odd, he wanted to know about it. He also wanted details of every delivery of stores, a list of every visitor from laundry company, engineering contractor, or ship's chandler.

Baldry did not believe that "Emperor" would have dared set foot on the *Fort Daring* himself, because of the risk of being seen by Rennie, but the possibility could not be discounted. It was unlikely but it was possible that "Emperor" did not know the name of Rennie's ship—he didn't after all know that it had no propeller—so he may have risked a chance meeting. One thing "Emperor" was not short of was nerve.

Rennie brought in Cole to help Baldry set up the interviews with the crew. Baldry went off with him to press the ship's saloon into service as an interview-room.

Along with Hobart, Rennie took the opportunity to tell him of his discovery about the movements of the schooner *L'Esperance*.

"I was thinking of taking a day off and asking Blom to drive me along the coast to Philippeville. I'd like a word with that schooner skipper."

"He probably split the dough Arlette Mercier gave him with Junot," said Hobart. "He's not going to tell you anything we don't already know."

"I may be wrong. It's just a feeling I have." Somewhere in the recesses of Rennie's mind was a memory that went back to the night of the attempted escape from the Island of Thieves. It was a vague, ethereal thing, without substance or definition. Just a stirring of something remembered. Something about the schooner.

"Maybe it isn't such a bad idea," Hobart said suddenly. "You getting out of town for a day, I mean. It would take a load off my mind, if only for a day. I really think you're in danger here, John."

Rennie smiled at his friend's concern. He was touched by it but thought it unnecessary. He had even expected an argument about going to Philippeville. Hobart and Baldry had given him the impression that they wanted to keep him cooped up on the ship as the safest place for him to be. The trip along the coast, even if it were a complete waste of time, appealed to him strongly inasmuch as it afforded him an active rather than a passive role. He did not want to wait for events to overtake him. He wanted to do something even if the usefulness of his activity proved to be of little consequence.

"You're still going to get a bodyguard," Hobart insisted. "I'm not taking any chances with you. And you'll need papers. I'll organize that. Whether you like it or not, John, you're going to be looked after like you've never been looked after before."

Rennie submitted gracefully. If it made Hobart happy to organize his life for him, he would go along with it—so long as impediment was placed in the way of what he wanted to do.

Hobart brought him up to date on his subtle questioning of Geraldine about Admiral Bousquet and his activities. She had been open and frank without revealing much that Hobart did not already know. Her comment to Rennie about Bousquet "hatching something up" had been based on a flurry of late-night conferences Bousquet had had with high-ranking officers from the Admiralty and various colonial officials. Geraldine had kept herself aloof from the constant comings and goings because of her contempt for politics, but she was aware enough to know something of the factions represented amongst Bousquet's visitors. Most had aligned themselves with Giraud. Most were bitterly opposed to de Gaulle. Many were still unashamedly "Pétainists" and pro-Vichy, with varying degrees of the extent to which they had collaborated with the Germans. Some, like Bousquet, had been wooed by the Germans but had maintained a certain independence from them. Bousquet had been no more co-operative with the Germans than he had been with the Americans and the British. He often behaved and spoke like a Nazi in his home, but Geraldine scoffed at the idea that Bousquet would ever collude willingly with Nazi Germany. He despised Hitler as a peasant and Geraldine could not conceive Bousquet ever doing his bidding. There was enough Führer mentality in Bousquet, she said, to conceive a situation in which Hitler paid homage to him, but never the other way round.

"So, you don't think Bousquet has been playing godfather to 'Emperor'?" observed Rennie.

"On the face of it, no," said Hobart. "Bousquet's a political animal, a bloody unscrupulous one certainly, but there's too much of the old Republican in him for him to involve himself directly with the SS. It's just not his style."

"Then what is he up to?"

"I don't know," said Hobart, "but whatever it is, I think he hopes to gain American approval. It could be that he wants to oust de Gaulle from the FCNL and put Giraud firmly on the throne. We've already had whispers and something your girl-friend said maybe confirmed it. She was sure that a crisis of some kind would be manufactured within the next few days, while Giraud is still in the States . . . So that he can return as the conquering hero and point to the fact that he didn't engineer things, that he was chosen in his absence."

"What's your next move?" Rennie asked him. "Or is it something I shouldn't know?"

"No harm in you knowing, old friend," said Hobart. "Over the past couple of days, I've had a team from our place at Sidi Ferrouch checking with every unit within fifty miles of Algiers on missing personnel, mobile personnel or men on furlough. My theory is that 'Emperor' has a weakness for impersonating Americans and using their papers. Damnit, he impersonated me. My guess is that he moved around pretty freely, too, pretending to be that Navy Chaplain, knowing the guy was in Morocco. I think 'Emperor' has a nice safe hidey-hole from which he emerges every so often with a different identity that he knows is reasonably safe to use. Algiers is full of Americans, so what better way could he get around than in American uniform?"

"But how would he get hold of their uniforms and papers?"

"He could kill the guys who own them," said Hobart. "If it's necessary. He didn't need to kill the Navy chaplain because he knew the guy was going to be gone for a month. Anyway, you asked me what I was going to do next—I'm going to collate all the information my team has dug up. I'll be looking for floating personnel—officers who work on their own or are billeted away from their units, like Bishop was. I'm going to go into every AWOL posting and compare it with the guy's service record. If I come across one thing that doesn't make sense then I'm going to get just a little bit excited, because it could mean I'm on to something. We'll work a cross index on every name on our list—the guy's permitted mobility, regularity of absence, whether he has access to places like the dock area, known habits when he's off duty, you name it . . . If there's any pattern to the identities that 'Emperor' steals, or any clue to the way he steals them, I'm going to find it, John."

"Sooner you than me," said Rennie.

"It's what ninety-nine per cent of Intelligence work is all about, John. Sifting information. Looking for the oddity and then connecting it with another oddity. Ask Baldry. He's spent a whole week asking the same questions over and over again and comparing the answers. He's doing it right now with your crew."

"I hope he gets somewhere. I'd like to get my hands on the gent who put a bomb aboard my ship." Rennie shook his head. "I can't get over it having an acoustic detonator. That's pretty sophisticated, isn't it? Where the hell does a Jerry spy get that kind of equipment in Algiers?"

Hobart smiled wryly.

"I hate to say it, John, but that bomb was the property of His Britannic Majesty's Government, complete with manufacturing serial number. It checks with an item on that missing 'Barbary Consignment' I told you about."

Rennie made a face.

"That's what I call real cheek. Trying to hoist us with our own bloody petards."

Hobart was about to leave when Baldry returned briefly. He still had to talk to more than twenty of the *Fort Daring*'s personnel, but an item of information gleaned from one of the ship's gunners had struck him as too significant to keep to himself.

"Hey, sport," he said to Rennie, "You didn't tell me you had another ship tied up alongside for a day or so."

"We've been taking stores for the Navy in numbers one and two holds," said Rennie. "Since we're not going anywhere in the immediate future, they've made us a floating warehouse. Have you found out something?"

"Yeah, I think I have," said Baldry. "Your guys haven't come across any suspicious characters on this ship, but I'm extremely interested in a chappie who was crawling around all over this other ship, this other Fort something or other."

"The *Fort La Montee.* She's Canadian-built, same as the *Daring.* The ships are all named after forts that have figured in Canadian history."

"For God's sake, Bob, tell us about this guy," said Hobart.

"He had an American accent, sport. And he was lugging a big black case full of equipment," said Baldry. He let Hobart digest the significance of this and then looked directly at Rennie. "I got this from one of your Navy gunners. It seems he has a pal who's a gunner on the *Fort La Montee.* The pair of them were chatting on the deck of the *Fort La Montee* when this fella came aboard. He was wearing army-style dress with a stars-and-stripes patch on the shoulder, but it wasn't pukka army uniform. He belonged to some international health organization or other, but the gunner couldn't remember its name. The fellow wore a tab with letters on it."

"What did this guy want? What was he doing?" asked Hobart.

"He asked to see the Captain, but the Captain wasn't aboard. He had just gone ashore."

"If it was 'Emperor,' he maybe waited until he saw the Captain going ashore," said Hobart. "What the hell did he want?"

"He was a glorified rat-catcher," said Baldry, enjoying the revelation.

"A *what?"* Hobart was suitably astonished.

"A rat-catcher. He said he was Doctor somebody or other from this international health outfit and he was carrying out investigations into outbreaks of bubonic plague. The flea that causes the plague is carried by a particular kind of rat and he said he wanted to check out the rats on the ship. He wanted to put down some poisoned bait in various parts of the ship and he said he would look back to collect the rat remains in a day or two, probably when the ship had finished discharging its cargo."

"I'm pretty certain he didn't visit this ship," said Rennie. "Cole would have mentioned it. He has a thing about rats. He has the rat-guards on the mooring ropes almost as soon as we get a line on a bollard."

Hobart could not conceal his excitement.

The man with an American accent, a case of equipment which could carry all manner of explosive devices, a cover which would enable its possessor to poke around in the most vulnerable areas of a ship . . . It all tied in so closely with how he believed "Emperor" was working that it just couldn't be coincidence. An international health outfit? That was something else for his ferrets to check out. And time was wasting.

He left Baldry to complete his interviews on the *Fort Daring*. There was a long night's work waiting for him ashore. A fresh thought struck him, too. If "Emperor" had been poking around all over the *Fort La Montee,* wasn't it just possible he had left a calling-card there, too? The kind that goes bang. Better arrange with Port Security for a complete sabotage search of that ship as a matter of priority.

But a thorough search of that ship was to reveal nothing. Every likely nook and cranny was investigated without any sign of bomb or timing device. It would have required a superhuman effort to investigate every single item of cargo remaining in the *Fort La Montee*'s holds. Indeed, it was reasonable to assume that a saboteur could not possibly have placed any deadly merchandise *underneath* the cargo remaining to be unloaded.

It was, however, beneath the cargo—in a place where no human could reach—that a fifteen-inch-long piece of piping nestled. Part of it was packed with a highly combustible mixture and a tiny explosive cartridge. Beyond the cap of the cartridge was a striker pin which was held in a cocked position by a strong tension spring. The tension spring was held by a lead element. Since the safety clip had been removed on the device, the spring had been exerting pressure on the lead element, stretching it ever so slowly. Eventually the spring would win this long inexorable battle and the lead element would be stretched to breaking-point. The striker pin would hurl forward into the firing cap.

"Emperor" had not needed to burrow beneath the stacked rows of smoke canisters, which were the *Fort La Montee*'s cargo, in order to place the deadly device. He had simply dropped it behind the cargo battens lining the hold of the ship. And gravity had seen to it that it rolled down the inside hull and came to rest where it could not be found until the last of the cargo had been taken from the hold. What ultimately was to happen was governed entirely by the small lead element and the time required to discharge the cargo. With every passing second, the lead stretched that minute fractional distance which brought it closer to breaking-point.

Chapter Nineteen

A jeep and two GIs were waiting for Rennie at six in the morning outside the dock gate. Privates Joe Dabrowski and Milt Wheeler were an unlikely pairing. Wheeler seldom said a word and, when he did, that was invariably what it was—a word. Preferably a monosyllabic word. He was a Texan. It seemed neither to provoke him nor amuse him that Dabrowski never stopped cracking jokes about Texas.

Unlike his partner, who was lean and tall, Dabrowski was short and stubby. He was a New Yorker. And he never stopped talking. Not even when Wheeler, in rare moments of loquacity, would turn to him and say: "Joe, you talk too goddamned much." The admonition was always good-natured and always ignored. The men, veterans of the Kasserine Pass, were bosom friends.

Hobart had briefed them thoroughly on what was expected of them. He had revised his original idea that they should simply be on call for Rennie. They were to stick with him twenty-four hours a day, even to the extent of bunking on the ship.

When Rennie had told Blom of the arrangement the previous evening, the ship's agent had been crestfallen at the possibility of no longer being required to drive Rennie to Philippeville. He had set his heart on the trip from the moment Rennie had mooted it, because a large number of his old Resistance friends who had flocked to de Gaulle's colors were encamped just outside Philippeville. He had wanted to go and see them.

Rennie didn't see why the fact that the US Army was supplying free transport should deprive Blom of the trip. So, with Wheeler in the driving seat, the jeep's first stop was outside a shuttered café on the Rue D'Isly—strangely deserted and empty at that early hour—in order to pick up Blom.

Blom climbed into the back beside Rennie and, like Rennie before him, had to be treated to Dabrowski's account of Bob Hope's first words on getting off the plane at Mason Blanche earlier in the week and seeing Algiers for the first time. According to Dabrowski, the American comedian had stepped off the plane, looked around and said: "Well, whaddye know? Texas . . . with Eh-rabs!"

While Dabrowski had guffawed and gaffawed and guffawed, Blom had stretched his lips briefly to show a line of teeth, in the hope that Dabrowski would interpret the response as a fleeting smile. The look which Blom exchanged with Rennie, however, was more indicative of acute pain.

The jeep had gone little more than one hundredth of the two-hundred-mile journey before them when it was forced to a stop. Half a dozen big trucks were blocking the road as they maneuverd into a tree-lined bay just off the road. The trucks were full of French sailors in fatigue clothes and steel helmets, all carrying rifles or automatic weapons.

An officer walked across to the jeep.

"Where are you going?" he asked in French.

Wheeler looked at him stonily and made no reply.

"We're going to Philippeville," said Blom.

"That's a long drive. What business do you have in Philippeville?"

"That's no concern of yours. Are you going to hold us up all day?"

The officer glared at Blom.

"I could arrest you," he snapped. But he seemed nervous and unsure.

"You'll have the American Army on your neck if you try," said Blom.

The man wavered.

"All right. You can go through. If you're going to Philippeville, you won't be coming back for some days?"

"We'll be back tonight."

"This road will be closed tonight," said the officer.

"Will it now?" said Blom. "Why?"

The officer made no reply. He turned on his heel and walked back to the trucks.

"Let it through," he shouted.

Wheeler put the jeep into gear and edged it past the trucks. Then he put his foot down.

"What was that all about?" asked Rennie.

Blom's face was stony.

"I don't know. But I don't like it. I don't like any of it."

Wheeler drove the jeep as if he had trained at Indianapolis and had ambitions to create a new land speed record. They were in Phillippeville just after ten in the morning, having dropped Blom at the French Army camp a few miles west of the town. Wheeler cruised the jeep down the pleasant main street. It was an uncrowded place, more French than Arab in its architecture, clean-looking and bright in the morning sunlight. After Algiers, it seemed almost sleepy and resort-like—a place where life and the general pace of things were more tranquil. Yet its harbor was busy. Ships had come and gone from it since Roman times when the port was known as Cirta.

The schooner, *L'Esperance,* was moored atern of a gray three-island tramp loading ore. Wheeler drove the jeep along the quay, stopping only a few feet from the schooner's gang-plank.

"Want us to come aboard with you, Captain?" drawled Wheeler.

Rennie grinned and patted the forty-five, which he was wearing in a webbing holster on his right thigh.

"I think I've got all the protection I need right here," he said.

A black man, naked to the waist and bare-footed, a red woolen cap perched on the back of his head, was swabbing down the deck with water he was pulling from the harbor by means of a bucket on a rope.

"Qu'est-ce que vous voulez?" the man demanded sullenly.

"Je voudrais voir le Captaine, s'il vous plait," said Rennie with a polite little smile. He felt strangely excited. The feeling had grown in him along every mile of the road from Algiers, as if he were hastening towards a momentous discovery. Now, standing on the deck of the schooner, the feeling was stronger than ever. He was on the threshold of that discovery.

"Capitaine Emile!"

The black man walked aft and bawled down an open hatchway.

"Capitaine Emile!"

There was a response from below and some brief conversation. The black man indicated with a jerk of a thumb that Rennie should go below. Then he returned to his task of swabbing the deck.

Rennie picked his way down an almost perpendicular companionway. He groped his way along a dark alleyway with brown-stained wooden panelling and hand-rails on either side. A door was open at the end. Rennie knocked once on the panelling of the passage and went in. The cabin was surprisingly roomy with a double bed in an alcove. A man sat at a broad mahogany table, drinking coffee from an enamel mug. His short, wiry hair was silvery white, and he had a bushy moustache to match. His face was weathered and wrinkled, almost the same color as the mahogany table. Rennie's first thought was that he could have struck a match on the man's dried-up leather face. He had expected a shifty, sleazy individual, but the man who rose to greet him had bright, clear eyes and there was dignity in the deliberate way he squared his shoulders and faced Rennie.

Before even inquiring Rennie's name or his business, he offered Rennie a glass of Madeira wine with old-world charm and grace. Rennie declined. He introduced himself and came straight to the point. He was inquiring he said, into an agreement between the master of the motor schooner and a Madame Arlette Mercier to pick up a certain "passenger" from the Island of Thieves on 1 October 1942.

Captain Emile was plainly puzzled by Rennie's statement. He made no immediate reply. Instead, he crossed to a desk, mahogany like the table, and picked up what appeared to be a Dickensian-era ledger. It was his ship's log book. He opened it, selecting the place, and then pushed it across the table to Rennie.

Rennie read the copper-plate entry for 1 October 1942, and then turned the pages, reading the entries for both the following and preceding days. It was his turn to be puzzled.

"I don't understand," he said.

After fifteen minutes' conversation with Captain Emile, however, he was beginning to understand. And with understanding came a numbing sense of shock and horror.

Hobart was tired. He had had one hour's sleep in twenty-four, and even that had been a catnap on a couch, snatched in the face of sheer mental and physical exhaustion. He had spent the entire night in the room of the St. George's Hotel which he had set up as his operational headquarters. Over and over again, he had gone through the reports supplied to him by what he called his team of ferrets: deleting, sifting, narrowing, matching; looking for patterns and similarities, discrepancies and contradictions. Several times he had felt he was on the verge of a breakthrough. On each occasion he had had to admit to over-optimism. Unable to think straight any more, he had been forced to rest for an hour.

At nine in the morning—while Rennie and his companions had been speeding towards Philippeville—he had switched out the lights in the operations room on the realization that sunlight filled the room. The sun had come up on him unawares.

Shortly after nine, one of the three telephones in the room rang stridently. It was Baldry. He was in Cherchel.

"What the hell are you still doing in Cherchel?" Hobart roared over the phone. "I thought you said there was no trace of the guy."

Baldry had gone down there late the previous night to check out a Dr. Farancis Gardiner, an official of the United Nations Health and Medical Relief Organization and an expert on epidemic deseases. Baldry's first report was that he had drawn a blank. He could find no one who knew Gardiner. The doctor worked from a mobile van which housed both laboratory and sleeping quarters. Frequently, van and trailer would disappear for long spells as the doctor was given to making expeditions into the interior, Algiers, Oran and elsewhere. He worked entirely on his own, although he was known to the medical team at a nearby American Army hospital.

The van and trailer had not been seen for more than two weeks, and it was assumed by the medics at the hospital that Gardiner had gone off on field work somewhere.

"That's dandy," Hobart had greeted Baldry's first report in the early hours of the morning. "I was sure this guy was our rat-catcher. But how the hell do we pick up the trail of a guy who could be anywhere between here and Timbuktu. Better get your ass back here, Bob, and we'll put out a general call on that van."

But Baldry had balked at driving back to Algiers at

four o'clock in the morning. He had opted instead for a couple of hours' sleep and a hospital breakfast of fresh orange juice, flapjacks and molasses, and a huge platter of eggs and bacon. He had just been finishing breakfast when the army surgeon—whom he had roused from his bed just after 2 a.m.—stuck his head round the dining-hall door and called him out. Baldry had followed the doctor to the hospital mortuary to view a body which had just been landed from a local fishing boat.

"It was Gardiner," Baldry told Hobart over the phone.

"A positive ID?" asked Hobart.

"Yes."

"How did he die?"

"One gun-shot wound through the chest," said Baldry. "And we weren't supposed to find the body."

"What makes you so sure?"

"He was four fathoms down with iron bars tied to his legs. The Arab who fished him up thought he'd landed Moby Dick. He wants a new net or compensation, by the way. They had to cut the net to get the body out."

Hobart put down the phone. It was probably too late, of course, but a general alarm would have to be put out for anyone purporting to be Dr. Francis Gardiner. He gave instructions to Ferris, the Intelligence Sergeant who was in charge of Communications for the operations room.

"I want that information out right away, Sergeant," he said. "I want every SP unit between Bone and Oran looking for that guy, every guard post, every check-point, every dock gate. I want it out, too, to the British Provost-Marshal and British Field Security. I want so many eyes looking for that guy that he won't be able to pop out from a crack in the road without being seen!"

Hobart looked at his watch. It was 9:23.

He turned again to the reports of interviews with members of the Algiers Resistance Group, code-named "Alpha." There was something nagging at his mind about one of Baldry's interviews with one of the group. Something somebody had said about another member. It had seemed trivial at a first and even second reading, but Hobart was convinced that it had king-sized significance, if only he had the brains to realize why this should be so.

He began at the top and began to read his way once more through Baldry's reports.

Twenty minutes later, he stopped at a sheet which outlined a conversation between one Jean Perotto and Baldry. And there was the phrase which had rung some kind of bell. Perotto, a Socialist politically, had left the "Alpha" group for another because of an alleged practice of class distinction by its hierarchy. Claiming that another member of the group had been given privileged treatment not shown to him, Perotto had commented: *"Of course, I didn't have the benefit of an expensive European education."*

With a mounting feeling of excitement, Hobart got up and crossed to the heavy strong-box which sat on one corner of the room. In a room full of sensitive documents, it was here that the most secret were securely locked. He opened the strong-box and extracted the copy-documents provided by the British SIS from their files. There was the dossier on the members of "Alpha." Hobart put it to one side. Then, from another folder, he took the profile of "Emperor" compiled by BSC for Kerslaw: the file on Franz Dorf.

Hobart's finger ran along the line that gave details of Dorf's education. He had been educated at the Kurt Klein International School, Geneva, Switzerland.

Hobart reached for the telephone. He gave a name and address to the operator, with instructions to find the telephone number and try it for him. The operator rang back to Hobart within a minute.

"You're through now, sir," he said to Hobart.

Hobart took a deep breath and told Geraldine Dumont, otherwise Bousquet, that he was sorry to disturb her but he had a question that he wanted to ask her. She told him she didn't mind. Hobart asked the question and held his breath as he waited for the reply.

There was a pause, and then Geraldine said:

"The Kurt Klein School in Geneva. Why do you want to know?"

"Just curiosity," said Hobart, and hung up. He let his head fall forward on his arched hands and let his breath out in a long-drawn sigh. He had made the breakthrough. He had found the link which completed the chain. It seemed so simple now that he felt the truth must have been staring him in the face for a long time. He had slipped up by not looking for Franz Dorf's North African connection right from the start—the schoolmate from that fancy European college for the sons and daughters of rich colonials.

If events had moved slowly before, they now began to move at breakneck speed. Hobart had scarcely time to consider the significance of his discovery when the telephone shrilled to tell of a new and startling development.

Sergeant Ferris handed the receiver across to Hobart. "It's from British Army Security at the docks—the East Gate. Seems one of their people has been shot."

Hobart listened to the voice on the other end, asking only an occasional question. Finally, he said: "I'm on my way," and put down the phone. The tiredness of an hour before had completely gone. He spoke to Sergeant Ferris as he buckled on his gun belt.

"Look after the shop, Sergeant. If Baldry phones in for me, tell him I'll be down at the docks. I think we've just gotten lucky. We've winged an 'Emperor'."

Sergeant Logan Balharry of the Hampshire Regiment was not in any way delighted to draw two weeks' guard detail at Algiers docks. The Battalion was leaving North Africa shortly and, while most of the men were spending the waiting time leading the life of Reilly at a cushy transit camp just outside the city, his platoon were playing gate policemen amid the heat and squalor of the docks. It was just his bloody luck!

He had just waved through a French Navy jeep after checking the papers of the driver, when he was called to the guard-house telephone.

"East Gate, Guard Commander speaking," Balharry said into the phone.

He listened while the Navy PO from the Post Security Office read out to him the details of a wanted person who might be masquerading as a Dr. Francis Gardiner, an American employed by the United Nations Health and Medical Relief Organization.

Balharry let him get so far, then he was interrupting furiously.

"He's just gone through the gate!" he shouted and left the earpiece dangling on its cord, gurgling unanswered questions from the man at the other end. Balharry was calling out the guard as he ran. Detailing two men to close the gate and let no one in or out, he sent parties of four men to right and left round the nearest cargo sheds with orders to detain a man in US-type uniform, who was driving a French Navy jeep.

Four other men were instructed to follow him and he set off at a trot down the road facing the gate, towards the quays crowded with ships. It was along this road that the jeep had driven.

Balharry drew up with surprise when he realized that the jeep was only fifty yards away. It had pulled in behind a cargo shed and was sitting there with engine running while its driver consulted what seemed to be a map.

Balharry motioned his men to halt and cover the jeep. He walked on alone, not hurrying but alert, his service revolver in his hand.

"Dr. Francis Gardiner," he called out to the man in the jeep.

The man turned, surprise leaping to his eyes as he saw the four soldiers some distance away with their rifles held at the port.

"Is something up?" the man in the jeep asked. He had an American accent.

"You'll have to come with us, sir," said Balharry. "We have orders to detain you."

"There must be some mistake," said the man. "I'm a doctor."

"I'm sorry, sir. I have my orders." Balharry allowed himself to relax as he approached the driver's side of the jeep. He realized his error as the driver's hand, which had been hidden from sight, was suddenly raised. It held a heavy automatic pistol. Balharry had only time to register surprise, his eyes wide, when the automatic exploded twice at close range. The Sergeant was flung backwards, his face masked in blood and pieces of brain tissue erupting from a gap in the back of his head.

In almost the same instant, the jeep was surging off down the narrow lane between the sheds. It all happened so quickly that the four soldiers had no time to recover and fire at the man who had killed their sergeant. The jeep was careering between stacks of machine crates and reached the next intersection of roads between the sheds almost simultaneously with the party of four guards, whom Balharry had sent off to the right from the dock gate. They leaped for their lives as the jeep veered sharp left and hurtled in the direction of the quays.

One soldier, whose reactions were quicker than his

mates', brought his rifle up and fired from the shoulder. There was a screech of brakes and the jeep ploughed into a mountain of small wooden crates stacked high near the open doors of a corrugated iron cargo shed. When the pursuing soldiers reached the jeep, its driver was nowhere to be seen—but the seat and door of the jeep were wet with his blood.

Franz Dorf, alias "Emperor," gritted his teeth against the pain in his shoulder, as he ran between the banks of smoke canisters stacked in the cargo shed. Through open doors at the far end of the shed, he could see the gray hull of a ship berthed against the quay.

Something was happening there. People were running in all directions. He reached the end of the shed and peered cautiously out. Arab dock workers were shouting at the pitch of their voices and seemed to be running in all directions. Dorf ventured out on to the quay holding his shoulder stiffly. He began to walk briskly along the quay in the crowd but did a quick about-turn when he spied four soldiers with rifles emerge cautiously from behind the cargo shed, peering about them. He realized, too, that if he continued in his fresh direction he was sure to run into the group who had wounded him. He found himself at the foot of the ship's gangway, buffeted by more Arab workers hurrying from the ship.

It was his only option. He fought his way up the gangway against the tide of humanity streaming down. Just in time. He reached the deck of the ship as two groups of searching soldiers converged on each other through the shouting Arabs. On the deck, men were also running, here, there and everywhere. No one seemed to take any notice of him. The bridge seemed to be deserted. He climbed the ladder to the Captain's deck without challenge, then from there to the flying-bridge. The wheelhouse was empty and tempted him but he went higher still, painfully up the vertical ladder to the monkey-island. He crouched there, gasping breath and cursing himself for being too ambitious. It was too exposed up here. He eyed the ladder against armor coating which led into a gun-nest. He could see the barrel of the Oerlikon pointing skyward. Well, why not? If it came to the last ditch, if this was where it all ended, then that Oerlikon would be something. He wouldn't go down alone.

He climbed into the gun-pit and slumped to the bottom

of its stepped timber interior. He lay there in the shadow of the gun's shield-plates. The pain was trembling from his shoulder in waves, making him faint. He wavered on the brink of consciousness. He could smell smoke. It rose in acrid clouds from beyond the forward wall of the gun-pit.

His head dropped forward as consciousness left him.

Below, on the fore-deck of the *Fort La Montee*, desperate efforts were being made to fight the fire which had mysteriously broken out in one of the fore-holds.

Already, word of the blaze had been flashed to the Port Commandant. Yet another desperate crisis faced him. The congestion in the harbor was almost beyond description. Vessels were moored side by side like sardines against those at the quayside berths. The *Fort La Montee* herself was hemmed in by three other ships.

The Port Commandant was heartened by the news that only 120 tons of cargo remained in the blazing ship. Hopes rose that the fire could be put out quickly with not too much in the holds to burn and allow the fire to spread. These hopes were dashed in almost the same instant as they were born with the revelation that the cargo remaining comprised over ninety tons of smoke bombs and twenty-five tons of Amatol.

The smoke bombs represented a fire potential that didn't bear thinking about, but the news of the Amatol was enough to fill the heart with terror. If the fire reached that, the consequence would be more than catastrophic—especially if it occurred among other ships loaded with petrol and high explosives and surrounded by cargo sheds filled with the same. A quarter hundredweight of Amatol was enough to blow a ten-thousand-ton ship clean out of the water. It was the stuff that torpedoes and depth charges were made of. What would happen if twenty-five tons of Amatol were to blow in one confined space defied imagination. As a detonator for the ordnance packed into the harbor, it had the potential to devastate the entire city of Algiers.

Rennie scarcely spoke. He sat tight-lipped in the back of the jeep looking straight ahead. He was still trying to come to terms with what he had learned from Captain Emile. His mind kept returning to the horror of that floodlit beach on the Island of Thieves: hearing again the agonized cry from Jean-Paul as Junot had thrust down with the bayonet.

Blom, who had not been too happy at having his reunion with his friends cut short, had tried to get him to tell why he was now in such an all-fired hurry to get back to Algiers, but Rennie wouldn't talk about it.

"I don't know the whole truth yet," Rennie had said. "There's only one person can tell me that now. Only one person can tell me *why*. All I know at the moment is what isn't true—and that's nearly more than my mind can take in."

"Two heads are better than one," Blom had replied.

But Rennie had refused to be drawn. It was not because he was deliberately trying to be secretive. It was because talk and speculation no longer interested Rennie. All he wanted now were answers, not more questions. And he knew who could provide those answers. This alone filled his mind. The coming confrontation. Nothing and no one was going to stop him from cutting his way once and for all through the elaborate web of vicious lies that had enmeshed him for so long. It was personal too. Others might in their own way elicit the same truths for which he sought, but he was past waiting for what others might do.

Rennie looked at his watch. It was now almost noon and there was a hell of a long way to go.

The fire-fighters on the *Fort La Montee* had been given until noon to fulfil their belief that the fire in the foreholds could be put out. At about five minutes to midday they had to admit defeat. The blaze had far too fierce a grip.

The very nature of the main cargo, smoke generators, made it impossible to get anywhere near the seat of the fire. Men with breathing apparatus had tried valiantly to penetrate the dense and poisonous clouds, but had been compelled to work completely blind and had become disorientated. The battle had swung briefly the way of the fire-fighters during the first hour and hopes had risen high enough then to inspire the belief that the fire would be out by midday. Foam and gallons of water poured into the holds had given the impression that the fire was dying down and that things would be controllable once a bank of smoke bombs, which had ignited spontaneously, ceased to belch out their noxious clouds.

These hopes had vanished with a fresh eruption of smoke and flame and the realization that the blaze had not started on the top of the cargo and was spreading down but had begun at the bottom and was working its way up.

At noon, the order was given to tow the blazing ship from the harbor. In the meantime, the fight to put the fire out would be maintained and would continue throughout the ship-moving operation.

The ships berthed outside the *Fort La Montee* had set about raising steam on the main engines from the first moment of the alarm. But the start of their evacuation had not waited for this process to be completed. Tugs had been summoned and the slow and laborious task of maneuvering the ships had been begun before eleven.

Hobart had arrived at the docks in time to see the body of Sergeant Logan Balharry stretchered into an ambulance. He requested and got more squads of soldiers to join in the manhunt for Franz Dorf. As they arrived, he briefed them from the back of his jeep and deployed them systematically to cover every inch of the ten or more square miles within the dock perimeter.

The fire on the *Fort La Montee* created complications and confrontations. It was pointed out to Hobart in no uncertain terms that catching a wounded killer was of no consequence whatsoever when the entire city of Algiers was threatened with imminent destruction.

It was not a point which Hobart could contest. Consequently, in those areas where Hobart's manhunt impeded or got in the way of those efforts concentrated on saving the port, it was the hunters who had to back down.

Hobart acknowledged the necessity which made it so, although it stoked the burning frustration in him caused by "Emperor" 's inexplicable vanishing act. The dock area was sealed off completely and there was no way that Franz Dorf could have got out. In any case, he had run towards the wharves. That meant he was still somewhere within a narrow peninsula of cargo sheds and warehouses topped by the half dozen berths where the *Fort La Montee* had been moored.

This rectangle of less than a square mile had been cordoned off very quickly and, although the rest of the docks had not been neglected by the searchers, it was here that Hobart concentrated the main search. Fifty men, spread out in a line, began to beat through every warehouse and shed, every nook and cranny, between the dock gate and the wharf.

Hobart himself drove his jeep to the quayside to await their arrival. It was here that Baldry found him. He was watching the seamen on the *Fort La Montee* get their bow rope to the after-deck of a French tug, while smoke belched from the hold behind them and firefighters on the wharf sent arches of water into the ship.

"They've got their work cut out there, sport," said Baldry. "How did it start?"

"They seem to think a smoke bomb in the cargo went off on its own," said Hobart. "But there's no way of telling."

"It wasn't 'Emperor' then? That's the ship we had searched, isnt it?"

"She was searched from top to bottom but that doesn't mean a thing. We know 'Emperor' got aboard. She may have been the target all along, not John Rennie's ship. She's carrying twenty-five tons of Amatol."

"Holy Christ!" exclaimed Baldry. "How close is that fire to the stuff?"

"How thick is one bulkhead?" said Hobart quietly.

Baldry stared at him goggle-eyed.

"You mean . . . She could go up at any minute!"

"If she does, we won't feel a thing. We'll be fried right here. You know what Amatol is?"

"I just know it goes off with a ruddy great bang," said Baldry.

"So does TNT," said Hobart. "Amatol's a mixture of TNT and ammonium nitrate. The ammonium nitrate provides what you might call the fireball ingredient. That ship out there could make Vesuvius look like a damp match."

Baldry gazed silently at the *Fort La Montee*. He could see officers on the bridge and hear orders shouted. The men were calm, nothing excited nor agitated about their deliberate movements. So were the seamen on the fo'c'sle-head and at the stern, methodically handling ropes as if it were a normal departure. The only sign of anything approaching frenzy was shown by the men manipulating hoses and darting here and there in the vicinity of the smoking hold but, if it was frenzy they showed, it was not born of fear or panic. It was the frenzy of intense physical activity directed with discipline and haste.

The bravery of the men on the ship stunned Baldry. Nor was it lost on Hobart. They all knew, those men on that ship, precisely what was at stake. They knew that at any second they could be incinerated where they stood; that every movement, every word, every breath, could be their last. Yet whatever inward fear they may have felt, they showed none. It was as if all had decided that, if their last moments were upon them, then they would be borne with supreme dignity.

Hobart glanced at the cargo sheds impatiently. The searching soldiers were taking a hell of a long time to flush out Franz Dorf. He looked at his watch, momentarily allowing himself to be hypnotized by the regular, inexorable jump of the second-hand as it made a complete sweep of the dial. It was now ten minutes after one o'clock.

Where the hell was Franz Dorf? Where?

Time and place had ceased to have meaning for Franz Dorf. He could feel hot sunlight on his outstretched right leg but, because his face was in shadow, he could not connect the burning warmth he felt in the region of his knee with the agent causing it. Thinking about the warmth of his leg momentarily distracted him from the dull ache of his shoulder. Every now and then, however, pain would lance across his body from his shoulder. It was like a red-hot knife being drawn across his chest.

In those moments, he would close his eyes and will his body to shut out that pain. And it worked. He had to divorce his mind from his body. He would concentrate all his thoughts on a beautiful flower-filled garden. He could remember the detail of the garden perfectly from when he was a small boy in the Lebanon.

At first, his mind would be able to see the garden and feel the pain in the shoulder, then—as he concentrated all his thoughts on the peace and serenity of the garden—its utter tranquillity took over and he felt no pain. In this way, Dorf's dreaming became his reality. The occasional waft of smoke in his nostrils, the distant shouts and sounds of movement were intruding dreams which he tried to shut out.

Chapter Twenty

A road-block had been created by standing empty oil drums across the road. It was manned by French sailors wearing fatigue clothing and steel helmets. It was the same lot who had halted the jeep early in the morning. Wheeler stopped the jeep twenty yards short of the barricade.

"These guys look like they mean business," he said over his shoulder to Rennie. "Maybe we should bust our way through and the hell with it."

It was a different officer from that of the morning who approached. This one spoke English.

"What is your destination?" he asked.

"American Army Headquarters," said Wheeler.

"Who are your passengers?" He nodded towards Blom and Rennie in the back.

"What's this all about?" asked Wheeler.

"It is a French matter," said the officer. "If none of you is French, we shall not delay you long."

"We're all on American Army business," said Wheeler. "And we're in a hurry. It would be an obligement if you just asked your guys to move them tin cans aside and we'll be on our way."

The officer ignored Wheeler and circled the jeep, stopping opposite Blom.

"May I see your identification?"

Blom hesitated. Then, with an apprehensive look at Rennie, he handed over his papers.

"Gerard Blom," read out the officer. "One moment, please." Still holding Blom's papers, he walked over to the side of the road to where a French sailor was operating a field radio. The officer spoke to the radio-man. He remained beside him as the man spoke into the telephone attachment but nodded to a group of sailors, who fanned out in front of the oil drums and covered the jeep with their rifles.

"I don't like the look of this," said Rennie.

"Neither do I, " said Blom. "It looks like the Navy are taking over Algiers. If it's the old Vichy crowd, I could be in trouble. They'll have me on their black-list down at the Admiralty."

"Keep that engine running," Rennie muttered to Wheeler. "We may have to make a break for it after all."

"Just you say the word, Captain," replied Wheeler. "Then get down low as you can. Them hombres could start shooting."

Below the road and to the right was the Bay of Algiers. Ahead was the city itself. The bay was full of ships at anchor and, from their high vantage-point on the road, the occupants of the jeep could see the forest of masts in the harbor and the white ribbon of breakwater where the *Fort Daring* was moored. Rennie noticed, but the fact scarcely registered with him, that a Fort ship with smoke billowing from it, was moving out through the harbor entrance. He looked again and it struck him that the ship was in some kind of trouble. The smoke was coming from the fore-deck. The after part of the ship was partly obscured by a destroyer on her quarter and several tugs in attendance were jetting water from cannon hoses at the smoking fore part of the ship.

The French officer was still standing beside the sailor with the radio telephone, in no hurry to let the jeep through. Rennie glanced impatiently at his watch. It was twenty minutes to four.

In that instant, a huge pillar of fire shot skywards from the port entrance. Feathering gray-black smoke at its fringes and peak, it soared beyond five thousand feet in seconds and it was still rising. Moments later, came the sound—a cataclysmic rolling boom which seemed to fill the entire visible concave of blue sky with a noise so great that the firmament shuddered. A gust of wind like the breath of hell swept over land and sea, sending quaking tremors to the foundations of buildings in its way, hurling glass window panes before it, bending trees double in its path, whipping placid blue water into rushing waves.

The four faces in the jeep stared at the spectacle, spellbound.

"Holy Mother of God!" said Dabrowski.

The French sailors manning the barrier turned to gape

at what had happened at the harbor. They ran to the side of the road, pointing in wonder and making excited comments. Even the officer had rushed over to the verge on the seaward side to get a better view. It was Rennie who recovered first inside the jeep and noticed that the barrier had been temporarily abandoned.

He thumped Wheeler on the shoulder. "Now!" he shouted in his ear. "Now!"

Tires spinning, the jeep shot forward, scattering the empty oil drums in all directions. The sailors made no move, their attention suspended between the drama at the harbor and the jeep's surprise take-off. The vehicle was fifty yards distant before anyone moved. By then, it was too late. Wheeler kept his foot down and flung his charge in a screaming skid at a broad bend in the road, accelerating fiercely into a long straight that hid the barrier and the French sailors from view. They were through.

Franz Dorf was too weak to move. He was fully conscious now. Blood was still oozing from his wound. There was a pool of it on the boarding of the gun-pit where he lay. His shirt was saturated and sticky. He looked stupidly at his right hand. It was crimson from blood that had run down his arm and dripped from the tips of his fingers.

He tried to move but couldn't. He had no strength. He looked up at the barrel of the Oerlikon pointing at the sky. The sky seemed to be full of scurrying clouds, but it was smoke billowing up from the burning hold and across the bridge.

His helplessness dismayed him. The thought that struck him was that he would bleed to death, here above the top bridge of an enemy merchantman. How long does it take to bleed to death? Dorf had a vivid vision of a painting he had seen in a gallery in Rome—of Christ in his crucified agony. It had repelled him. He had been unable to look at it. He had imagined himself on that cross.

Now the nightmare feeling came back to him. That's how his own dying would be. Pain-racked. Stretching over hours. He saw before him only a long agony . . . Minutes that seemed like years, hours like eons, day stretching into night, a night without end.

In fact, Franz Dorf had less than five seconds to live.

As the tugs labored to pull the *Fort La Montee* clear of the harbor entrance and the main channel, the stricken ship was less than half an hour away from seaway where she could be abandoned and her officers and crew of fifty men escape. But it was not to be. The fifty had known for close on four hours that their end could come at any moment. Clear of the entrance, they must have known, too, that their brave action had saved the port and possibly the city: a triumph, but the price was to be exacted.

Not a person on the *Fort La Montee* was to escape, not one body to be found.

From a distance Rennie had seen the pillaring explosion which had occurred when, finally, the flames had reached the Amatol. At close quarters, the horror was mind-searing.

The entire fore part of the merchant ship erupted, wrenched away from the rear half of the vessel—two thousand tons of metal borne upward in a blast of volcanic force. The whole of the bow section was folded up and back so that it fell across the stern, the mangled fore-deck lying across the top of the funnel.

A vast expanding balloon of flame, five hundred feet across and growing, flowered out from the exploding merchantman. It enveloped the entire fore part of the attending destroyer, HMS *Arrow,* instantly killing more than thirty of the crew and all but two of the officers. More than eighty others were grievously injured.

The blast from the *Fort La Montee* blew *Arrow's* fo'c'sle-head apart. A whirlwind of liquid fire roared through every exposed tube and crevice of the destroyer like a racing tide. It reached into the mess decks, flooded through the galley flat and a boiler-room, licked fiery darting tongues to every corner of the bridge and pom-pom deck and curled from beam to beam abaft the after-tubes.

The great mainmast of the *Fort La Montee* fell across *Arrow*'s after-steering-position. Steel plates and beams from the merchantman rained down on *Arrow*'s upper deck. The *Fort La Montee's* forward winch and her twelve-pounder gun from the bows dropped out of the sky through *Arrow*'s deck. Fire rolled over the destroyer's ammunition lockers on the pom-pom deck. Pom-pom and Oerlikon shells began to explode in every direction.

The tugs attending the merchantman had no way of escaping the horrendous blast. One, abreast the *Fort La Montee*'s foredeck vanished. Another, further out, had her superstructure blown clean away, leaving nothing above deck level and giving her the appearance of an abandoned coal barge.

Pieces of the *Fort La Montee* showered down from the ten-thousand-feet-high cloud of smoke and fire which hid the sun. A seaman, hosing the decks of his ship nearly two miles away, was sliced in two by a lump of falling steel. Scarcely a window in the city was left unbroken. To the citizens in the streets, the noise sounded like the end of the world. It was heard clearly enough in Oran, two hundred miles away, for house-holders to run outside to investigate.

On the quay, which had been vacated less than four hours before by the *Fort La Montee.* Hobart and Baldry stared at each other, tense and white-faced, and then ran into the cargo shed to escape the rain of metal falling from the skies. Their thoughts ran parallel. They wondered if the explosion had occurred before or after the merchant ship had got far enough out to be abandoned.

The sweep through the cargo sheds had revealed no trace of Franz Dorf. Now, the search had been extended to the ships berthed at the quay. It would be an hour or so yet before a fresh start would be made to the search with a pair of hunting dogs. Their starting-point was to be the abandoned jeep with the bloodstains on the seat and door.

Darkness was falling when Hobart, unsatisfied with the first attempt by the dogs, ordered them to be taken back to the starting-point and the exercise repeated. It had precisely the same result as the first run. The dogs trailed through the cargo shed, emerging at the empty wharf. They went a short distance along the wharf, stopped, turned, and then came back along their original track. Then they ran back and forward along the same fifty yards of wharf, obviously baffled. Repeatedly they returned to the spot where the *Fort La Montee*'s gangway had been and barked at the dark, unresponsive waters of the dock.

By then, the truth was beginning to dawn on Hobart and Baldry, but neither man was willing to accept the possibility that Dorf had boarded the *Fort La Montee.*

Hobart ordered the handlers to take the dogs back once more to the starting-point for a third attempt. This time, they were convinced.

Once into Algiers after getting past the road-block, Wheeler—on Rennie's instructions—drove straight to the St. George's Hotel. There, Rennie was disappointed to learn that both Hobart and Baldry were at the docks. As they were expected back soon, he decided to wait.

Wheeler and Dabrowski, assured by Rennie that he would stay put, went off in search of food. Blom, now without any identification papers, also went off. He looked a very worried man. He was deeply disturbed about French sailors putting up road-blocks, and he was not going to rest until he knew the reason. He reckoned that some of his Resistance friends at the Coq Hardy would know what was going on. He would come back if he got any news.

Rennie was like a cat on a hot griddle. He fumed and fretted at the non-return of Hobart. He decided that if the American hadn't returned by 7:30, he would go ahead with what he had to do without him.

Just after seven, Blom re-appeared in a highly agitated state. With him was a French army lieutenant, a Paul Giacobbi, who—it turned out—was on leave from the unit Blom had visited that morning in Philippeville.

The two newcomers drew Rennie to one side of the open reception area, where Rennie had been patrolling impatiently. Two white-helmeted American soldiers at the foot of the stairway eyed their conference with interest.

"It is bad news," said Blom. "Some Army and Navy brass-hats are planning a putsch. There is open talk of de Gaulle being arrested and put on trial as a traitor . . . And half the National Liberation Committee as well. If they get away with it, it will be the Vichy days all over again."

"What are our people doing? The British and Americans?"

Rennie was perplexed. His sympathies were with Blom one hundred per cent, but there was little he could do to help. He was as powerless as they were.

"The British and the Americans won't lift a finger," Giacobbi answered. "Some of our people have already spoken to the American envoy. He says the Allies have no power to interfere in what is a French political matter."

"Is Bousquet at the back of this?" Rennie asked.

"He could be," said Blom. "A lot of his cronies certainly are. Some sort of declaration is going to be made at midnight. It'll all be out in the open then. We've got to do something before then."

"I'm just a ship's captain, and a foreigner. I'd help if I could—but what can I do?"

"You have a powerful radio on your ship, John," said Blom. "Paul, here, is a Communications Officer. If we could get a message to the Colonel of his regiment at Philippeville, he and his men will not stand by and allow de Gaulle to be taken."

Rennie frowned.

"Civil war? It could come to that, couldn't it? And if I pass the message on to Philippeville, I would be the one who lit the fuse. That's a big responsibility."

"You've had a taste of the Vichyists, John," said Blom passionately. "Can you turn your back on us and let it happen all over again? De Gaulle has no troops here in Algiers to defend him. You've got to help."

Rennie considered this. He hated fence-sitters—and he wasn't about to become one.

"All right," he said. "I'll see that the message goes out. But it would take an hour to get down to the ship and send it from there. Why can't we use the transmitter upstairs? I know there's one because I've met the man in charge of it, a Sergeant Ferris."

Rennie wasn't permitted to go up to see Ferris. Ferris however, came down to see Rennie. He knew all about Rennie but they had met only once, and briefly, introduced by Hobart. Ferris was doubtful when he heard Rennie's proposition about transmitting the message to the Free French unit in Philippeville.

"It's more than my job's worth," he protested. "Uncle Sam's very touchy about meddling in French politics. I could wind up on the wrong end of a court-martial."

Rennie was not to be defeated.

"How about passing a message from a British shipmaster to a major in the British Army?" he asked Ferris. "Would you risk that?"

Ferris looked thoughtful.

"I pass messages for Mr. Baldry all the time," he said. "He's British."

"Then you could do the same for me."

"Who's this British major you talked about?"

"Major Sopwith. He's a tank warfare instructor. I met him for the first time in my life about eight or nine hours ago, when I collected Mr. Blom here from the Free French camp at Philippeville. Major Sopwith is on loan to the French, helping with their training. He is a very close friend of Lieutenant Giacobbi's commanding officer."

Both Blom and Giacobbi were grinning broadly at the way Rennie was proposing a way round Ferris' objections to handling a purely French transmission. Ferris was not slow on the uptake. The beginnings of a smile lightened his face and he nodded his head up and down in appreciation of Rennie's outflanking maneuver.

"I like it," he said. "I like it."

It took Rennie less than five minutes to pencil the text of the message, aided by Blom and Giacobbi.

Ferris looked questioningly at Giacobbi.

"You're sure your base won't be closed down? I mean, if it's just a training camp . . ."

"We're fully operational," said Giacobbi. "There's a twenty-four-hour listening watch. There has to be. We've been making arms drops to the Resistance in Corsica and have put in a dozen of our boys with radios in the last month. They never know when they're going to be able to transmit, so we've got a round-the-clock listening watch. I'll give you the call-sign."

When Ferris had gone, Blom, in an extravagant show of emotion and with his sad face wreached in smiles, hugged Rennie.

"Thank you, my friend. You are one of us now. But now we must leave you. The Resistance is not quite dead in Algiers. The spirit of November Eighth still lives. We must go now to mobilize what strength we have. The Vichyists and the Giraudists will not get it all their own way."

Next, Giacobbi stood formally to attention and shook Rennie's hand with a simultaneous bow of the head. Then they were gone.

Rennie was still standing gazing thoughtfully at the

arched doorway through which they had disappeared when Wheeler and Dabrowski returned.

"We've been thinking we should maybe get you back to your ship," said Dabrowski. "Things are happening in the old town tonight."

The two Americans revealed that the city was rapidly taking on the appearance of a ghost town. All British and American servicemen had been confined to barracks and the city declared off limits. The French Army had declared an eight o'clock curfew and warned all civilians to be off the streets by then.

"They say it's on account of Communists blowing up that ship at the docks today," said Dabrowski. "You reckon the Frenchies are starting another revolution, Captain?"

"I doubt that very much," said Rennie. "How would you boys like to go on another trip?"

"You mean tonight?" drawled Wheeler.

"I mean right now," said Rennie. "Along the coast. But in the Oran direction this time." He paused. "There's only one snag. There could be more French road-blocks. It would help if I could look more . . . more American."

Rennie explained that he wasn't too popular with the French because of something that had happened and that if he could give the impression of being an American, it might be a whole lot easier getting past barricades manned by French sailors.

A gleam came into Dabrowski's eye.

"If you and Milt could just wait outside in the jeep, sir, I got me an idea," he said.

Rennie hesitated.

"Don't ask questions, sir," said Wheeler. "Just do as Joe says. If he says he has an idea, just never ask no questions."

They waited in the jeep for nearly fifteen minutes. Dabrowski arrived whistling his own improvisation of the "Jersey Bounce" and trying to look innocent. He carried a bundle under his arm. He climbed into the jeep and suggested they drive quickly to somewhere less conspicuous.

Wheeler drove down a quiet back-street and stopped. Dabrowski unfolded the bundle on his knee and handed Rennie an American military helmet. It was a dark olive color and highly polished. The bundle was a military jacket which had been folded inside out.

"Jesus Christ!" exclaimed Wheeler, staring at the helmet which had two small stars emblazoned on the front. "This belongs to a two-star general!"

"So does the jacket," said Dabrowski unconcernedly. "And this, too." He fished a tie from his pocket and handed it to Rennie. "Try 'em for size, Captain."

Grinning at the absurdity of it, Rennie donned the borrowed uniform. He was wearing American-made light khakis with a sheen finish, so the jacket and tie were complementary. Diffidently, he tried on the helmet. It wasn't too bad a fit.

"Christ, Joe, we'll be twenty years in the stockade," Wheeler was saying. "Where in hell did you get them?"

"It was easy," crowed Dabrowski. "The General was in the shower and I just walks into his bedroom. "Who's that?" he shouts out. 'Laundry detail, sir,' I reply. 'Why the hell weren't you here this morning?' he roars out. 'Our truck broke down,' I reply. 'Well, better late than never,' says he. 'You'll find my shirts on the floor of the closet.' So I opens the closet and there's this whole lot of uniforms and the helmet sitting on the shelf. So I help myself. 'Sorry to disturb you, sir,' I call out. Like I say, it was easy. I think I was superb."

As Rennie had suspected, a French Navy road-block had been set up on the west highway out of the city. He had carefully instructed Wheeler what to say. Rennie himself—trying not to feel faintly ridiculous in the scuttle helmet and acutely aware that he was rather young for the part—sat stonily in the back, affecting total disinterest.

"The General has an urgent appointment with Admiral Bousquet," Wheeler told the young lieutenant who presented himself at the side of the jeep. The officer peered inside the jeep. Rennie rewarded him with a look that bestowed on the young man the status of a maggot. Then he deliberately looked the other way.

The officer drew himself to attention and gave a smart salute. The jeep was waved through.

They were stopped again by men guarding the entry to the side-road from the highway.

"What is the General's name?" Wheeler was asked.

"Hickock," said Wheeler blandly. It was the first name

that came into his head. They should really have thought about a name.

"From here on in, you're Wild Bill, Captain," Wheeler muttered over his shoulder as the guard walked over to the field telephone on the wooden pillar. The guard spoke for a moment into the telephone and then returned to the jeep.

"The Admiral is not expecting any American general, and he doesn't know one called Hickock."

Wheeler was prepared for this.

"The General has an important message for the Admiral from the American Envoy in Algiers. He has to deliver it in person."

The guard had a further conversation on the telephone. This time, when he returned to the jeep, it was to tell Wheeler that he could drive straight to the villa. He would not be stopped again.

They drove past more guards at the gate to the driveway. Indeed, the number of personnel packing weapons of various kinds drew the comment from Dabrowski that the place was more heavily guarded than Fort Knox.

"I just hope we can talk our way out as easy as we talked our way in," was Wheeler's observation.

A radio truck and several other vehicles were drawn up in the stable-yard. A Chasseurs captain emerged from the shadows and came to meet the jeep.

Wheeler jumped out smartly and held the door open for Rennie to alight. The Chasseurs captain saluted.

"Jay-nay-ral 'Eecock?" he ventured. Rennie guessed that English wasn't his strong point.

"Follow me, boys," he muttered to Wheeler and Dabrowski. He threw a sloppy salute at the Chasseurs captain and walked straight past him, leaving him open-mouthed with surprise. The two Americans fell in behind Rennie, who made straight for the stone-flagged path leading to the front of the house.

"Mais . . . Jay-nay-ral . . . ?" The Chasseurs captain made a half-hearted protest and ran a few steps after them. Dabrowski turned and faced him, barring his way.

"It's OK, Buster. The General's been here before. He knows the way."

The Chasseurs captain eyed the way Dabrowski was cradling his short-barrelled automatic rifle and decided that further remonstration was pointless. He had been told to admit the American general and conduct him to the terrace-room but, if he chose to ignore the courtesies, that was his business. The Americans were strangely uncouth people.

The terrace window was closed. Rennie posted Wheeler and Dabrowski at each end of the window and told them to let no one in. Then he opened the window and walked into the room.

Chapter Twenty-one

HOBART read the letter a second time, then passed it to Baldry.

"The fool!" he snorted. "The goddamned fool!"

He whirled on the Corporal seated behind the reception desk.

"When did you get that note?" he demanded angrily.

"About an hour ago, sir. The English guy just asked me to give it to you the moment you came in and to tell you that he couldn't wait any longer. Did I do something wrong, sir?"

"You could have goddamned stopped him!" Hobart shouted, then realized he was being unjust. He lowered his voice. "No, you couldn't. I'm sorry. I'm upset, that's all You weren't to know."

Baldry handed the sheet of paper back to Hobart.

"I agree with your assessment, sport. Our honest mariner friend is out of his bloody mind."

Hobart turned to the Corporal again.

"Did the English guy have a couple of GIs with him?"

The Corporal pondered.

"There may have been two, sir. I can't rightly recall. There definitely was one. Yeah, they went out together. The English guy and a GI."

"At least that's something," said Hobart.

"He could spoil everything," said Baldry. "You realize that, don't you? Our mariner friend could go and spoil everything. Apart from the fact that he could wind up very dead, he could tip off Dorf's rat-pack . . . Send the whole bloody lot scurrying for their holes in the ground. What do you think made the man go off at half-cock like that?"

"Anger," said Hobart quietly. "The anger of a righteous man. He'd be no damned good in our business, Bob. He's too damned straight. He has been used and abused, and without any idea why. Now, he thinks he knows who started all the using and abusing and he's burning up inside. He's not going to rest now until he has *reasons*. He's got to know the *why*. It's personal with him. The goddamned fool isn't worried about getting killed, because getting killed isn't important to him if there's a reason. That's all he wants—*reasons*. That's all he worries about—*reasons*. He's had his head kicked in . . . A coupla guys used him for target practice when he had only two bare hands to defend himself . . . He has been double-crossed blind by friend and enemy alike . . . And damned little of it has made any sense to him. Now, he's madder than a bull elephant with the toothache, and seeing things just about as straight! That's why he went charging off."

"Well, that answers me pretty comprehensively," said Baldry with a tight smile. "But what do we do now? Call out the Marines? Send for the Seventh Cavalry?"

The look which Hobart threw at Baldry was venomous.

"We sure as hell aren't going to sit around here thinking up smarty-pants cracks like that anyway!" he snarled.

Baldry raised his hands and waved them soothingly.

"Sorry, sport. Sorry. No offense intended. No need to lose the jolly old duster with me."

"Well, I just lost it!" snapped Hobart. "And just for the record, there's something else you'd better know. John Rennie's not the only one who's riled up about this thing! Right now, I'm mad as a raised she-bear—and John ain't the only one who's taking it personal. It's personal with me, too! So help me, if anything happens to that crazy Limey sonofabitch . . . !"

Baldry got the impression in that moment that, whatever happened, Hobart wasn't going to be on the side that lost the war.

In the long room at the Bousquet villa, John Rennie had the feeling of arriving at the critical point in a personal war, which—until that moment—he had been fighting with a blindfold over his eyes. He would not have entirely agreed that anger was the prime motivation in him in that instant. Certainly, there was a strong element of anger—but it was contained and refrigerated, not open for inspection. It was not boiling over, blinding his reason.

His anger had cooled during the long day. The excess had worked itself off on the sharp edge of his impatience, and finally evaporated as soon as he had committed himself to the precipitate and possibly unwise course of coming to the Bousquet villa.

He removed the ridiculous scuttle helmet as he entered the room and faced the three people staring at him from the far end. Bousquet was sitting at the table with some papers in front of him. Arlette stood behind one shoulder. A man in the uniform of a colonel in the French Army stood at Bousquet's other shoulder.

Bousquet and Arlette recognized Rennie almost simultaneously. Their faces registered disbelief and then quite different reactions. Arlette's tinkling laughter was a response of astonished delight. Her father's recognition was marked by a deepening scowl. It was he who spoke.

"I don't know what kind of stupid trick this is, but it could not have been more ill-timed," he said angrily. "It's one you will pay for."

Bousquet glanced towards the door and would have called out if Rennie had not anticipated his intention and warned: "No, Admiral." The softly uttered warning was no deterrent. The appearance in Rennie's right hand of a forty-five caliber pistol was.

Rennie waved the pistol casually.

"I haven't been introduced to your friend," he said.

"He is Colonel Baraud," said Bousquet gruffly. "You may not have made his acquaintance but, by tomorrow, he will be the new Minister for the Interior. It will probably give him some pleasure to accommodate you in one of his many prisons."

"A Vichyist, is he?" asked Rennie. "I've had Vichy hospitality before. And what post will you be holding in the new Government, Admiral? The one you and your friends are foisting on the people, whether they like it or not?"

"Who is this man? He is not American," Baraud put in tersely.

Bousquet smiled coldly.

"Niether is he a general. He is an Englishman. A very troublesome Englishman."

"Correction, Admiral. Troubled, not troubleseome.

I have been very troubled. That's why I've come here to-night. I want the answers to some questions that have been troubling me." Rennie smiled. "But, first, bring me up to date on all the fun and games. I'd like to know why there are road-blocks all round Algiers and if there is any truth in the rumors I've heard about de Gaulle?"

"This farce has gone on long enough," said Arlette. "Get the guard in, Father. He will not shoot."

Rennie pointed the gun straight at her.

"Wouldn't I, sweetheart? Don't tempt me!" His words were honed to an edge with threat.

"Let's humor him, my dear," said Bousquet. "He's patently mad and there's no harm in him knowing what he'll have a long time to regret."

He gestured with a limp hand towards Rennie.

"Please be a good fellow and point that thing away from us. I give you my word we shall not be interrupted. Perhaps we might even persuade you to give up this nonsense."

Rennie folded his arms. Although the gun no longer pointed down the table, his eyes remained fixed on the trio at the far end.

"You have my undivided attention, Admiral," he said. "Perhaps we can all be seated?"

Baraud and Arlette sat down on either side of Bousquet. They both looked apprehensive. Bousquet in comparison, was calm. He seemed even to be enjoying himself. Rennie sat down opposite them. He placed the revolver on the table near his right hand.

"You mentioned de Gaulle," said Bousquet, smiling. "What rumors did you hear?"

"That he was to be arrested."

"He has to be stopped, I grant you," said Bousquet. "But 'arrested'? It is such a strong term. It suggests trial and punishment." He considered his own words. "Well, perhaps it will come to that. He has got too big for his boots." He smiled again. "De Gaulle has been placed under restraint. By that, I mean that the Villa des Oliviers has been surrounded by seven hundred volunteers, mainly true French sailors from the battleship *Richelieu* . . . Men who declined the invitation to sail their ship to the United States and serve the purposes of America and Britain. They have chosen instead to serve France."

"As you serve France, Admiral?" suggested Rennie.

The smile left Bousquet's face.

"Yes, Englishman," he snapped. "As I serve France. And will serve France until my dying breath." He beat his first on the table and glared fiercely at Rennie. "My countrymen in Algeria have seen fit to do me the honor of inviting me to serve as the first President of the Governing Council for all French External Territories. At midnight tonight, a declaration will be made dissolving the so-called French Committee of National Liberation and announcing the formation of the new Council, with me at its head. De Gaulle will be no part of it. Nor will the Bolsheviks and Anarchists and ten-a-penny Radicals who support him. Our movement has the support of the Navy and the Army and great numbers of the people. We will restore to the Overseas Territories the pride that was once that of France. And we will renew and bind the ties which hold us to our Motherland, so that she can again be free and supreme among the nations."

"You won't be opting out of the war then?" asked Rennie.

"Our involvement in any armed struggle will be dependent on the attitudes of the American and British Governments, but mainly the American Government. If Roosevelt gives us the dollars and the materials to re-equip our forces, and if he recognizes us as equal and capable of governing our own affairs, he will not find us lacking in friendship."

"And Giraud?" prompted Rennie.

"Giraud will be offered the command of the Army," said Bousquet. "He will be only too happy to accept."

"And you think the Americans and the British will go along with this?"

Bousquet regarded Rennie scornfully.

"The Americans have said time and again that they do not wish to interfere with our internal politics. They will not intervene. The British do not count."

It was plain that Bousquet was tiring of humoring Rennie.

"You do not count either, Englishman," he went on. "You would be wise now to surrender your gun. This silly cross-examination has gone on long enough."

"It hasn't started yet." said Rennie. "Im not all that interested in politics, especially the kind you play. I'm more interested in games like 'Happy Families'—yours for instance—or 'Truth and Consequences'."

"I have no idea what you are talking about."

"Happy families, Admiral—like you and your darling daughter there. Your right hand, is she? Runs Delta-Afrique for you. Plays hostess for your chummy little house-parties. She has a lot of hidden talents, does Arlette. But some of them could cause you a little embarrassment when people get to hear of them. What are people going to say when they find that their great new president is the father of a vicious scheming murderess? Not that she always does the dirty work herself. She prefers others to do the actual killing. Don't you, Arlette?"

Arlette Mercier was glaring hate at him, her beautiful face white with fury.

"You're insane!" she spat.

"No, sweetheart—not me. But you could be. That's what I want to find out. That's what I can't understand. Why you did these terrible things. With all you had going for you, it just didn't make sense. It still doesn't make sense."

"Father, are you going to stop this madman, or must I?" Her voice was shrill. She pushed her chair back and stood up. Rennie's hand leapt to the gun. The look in his eyes did the rest. She subsided again into the chair.

"It's truth and consequence time, Arlette," Rennie said softly. "I want to know why you did those things. Why?"

"What exactly are you accusing my daughter of?" asked Bousquet.

"Murder," said Rennie. "Cold calculated bloody murder."

"You're mad," said Bousquet.

"So everybody keeps telling me. But I took a risk coming here, Admiral. The last time I came out this way, I only got away with my life by the skin of my teeth. I wasn't meant to, was I, Arlette? But then, your little schemes have a habit of going wrong when you leave the dirty work to others. Bishop was the exception. Nice of you to go to his funeral, Arlette. I'm sure he would have appreciated that. It shows a touching respect on the murderer's part, attending the victim's funeral."

"It was you who killed him!" she flared.

"Lies, Arlette. Lies." Rennie's voice was so calm that

even Bousquet now looked at his daughter anxiously, doubt in his mind where before there had been none.

"I want to know about Jean-Paul," Rennie went on. "Why did you want him killed? Was it because he stood up for what the believed in? Was it because you just no longer wanted him and saw an opportunity to get rid of him for good? Why? And to go to such elaborate lengths. Wouldn't it have been easier just to leave him to stew, forget him? Why go to the trouble of getting him killed when he was out of the way anyway?"

"Just what the devil are you talking about?" demanded Bousquet.

"Oh, you were in it, too, Admiral," said Rennie. "An accessory before the fact. But I don't suppose you have any idea how she traded on your name and used you. And would you have cared all that much if Jean-Paul had been killed? I doubt it. You probably thought that when she went to Dakar, it was simply to plead with Jean-Paul to recant and go along with the diabolical Vichy propaganda exercise. But that wasn't the story she told me. No, she was all loving wife and a real Vichy-hater, a member of the Algerian Resistance and a true-blue heroine. She had come to Dakar to help Jean-Paul escape—and she'd laid it all on. He had to get down to the beach at a certain time and, lo and behold, a schooner would come along and whisk him off to the Gambian shore to freedom. Did you know about that part, Admiral? This was the story she told me. I heard it all from her sweet pearly lying lips—and I believed her. *I believed every word.* That was *madness* for you! I believed her when she told me how she had found the schooner in Dakar and paid a small fortune to the skipper. But that was all fiction, like the rest of it . . ."

"This is preposterous," interrupted Bousquet. "I'll listen to no more."

"Oh, yes you will," snapped Rennie. "You're going to hear it all. Haven't you noticed how quiet she has gone? She's scared, Admiral. She's scared because I'm telling the truth. Well, there are others. There was an American
the truth. Well, there are others. There was an American
as well as me, somebody she didn't even know about. But it was because of us her plans all went wrong. She was very insistent that when Jean-Paul made the escape, he went alone. That was what she cooked up with that hero

of France, Major Junot. That was the deal. Jean-Paul was to get to the beach alone, just as Junot did one of his sea patrols. There would be a challenge when Jean-Paul was spotted on the beach and then, bang! Junot's soldiers would open fire. End of Jean-Paul. Shot while trying to escape. But it didn't work with Jean-Paul any more than it worked when she tried it a second time, on me. And you know why it didn't work? Because of the American and me. Jean-Paul talked us into escaping with him. He wouldn't go without us. And that's what threw Junot. That's why he chickened out on the deal he'd made with your darling daughter."

"It's lies! Lies!" screamed Arlette.

"Do you think I'm making this all up, Admiral?" went on Rennie. "Can you think of any reason why I should even try? One of Junot's Senegalese goons nearly kicked me to death on that beach, Admiral. I've had nightmares about that a hundred times since. I could hear Junot ranting and raving like a madman. That was when he bayoneted Jean-Paul. I couldn't understand what was making him so mad, why he was raving on so much about Arlette . . . But I know now. He wanted to kill Jean-Paul. He really wanted to. But he balked at killing an American and an Englishman as well. That wasn't on the contract. That was where he thought Arlette fouled things up. That was why he was so mad at *her*. He was ready to kill a Frenchman as an obligement for a night in her bed, but he wasn't going to risk diplomatic incidents and God knows what by killing an American. As you said, Admiral, the British don't count—but killing an American . . . That would have been trouble. Big trouble . . ."

Bousquet was visibly shaken.

"Can you prove any of this?"

"The American lived to tell the tale. He knows the full story now. So did Jean-Paul. You can ask him. He's not far away. The Americans obtained his release. There are others who can testify . . ."

"Who?"

"I mentioned a schooner. Someone must have told Arlette that it called at the Island of Thieves every first of the month. She used the schooner's existence so that she could spin a plausible story to us. It wasn't likely that anyone was going to ask questions afterwards. All that mattered was Jean-Paul should be lured outside the wire to a place where Junot would have a legitimate reason for shooting him. Unfortunately for your daughter, Admiral, four people were told about that schooner and the part it was supposed to play. Arlette told me. I told Jean-Paul, the American, and the late Commander Bishop."

Rennie looked straight at Arlette.

"Did Bishop mention to you that the schooner, *L'Esperance,* was due in Philippeville this week and that he intended to tell me about it, Arlette?"

She remained silent, staring at him sullenly.

"That's why he had to be killed, wasn't it?" Rennie continued. "It must have been a shock to find out he'd even heard of the schooner. But Bishop knowing about it was no real threat to you. The real danger was in me finding out that it was just along the coast and maybe doing a little checking. You had to stop Bishop telling me about the schooner and you had to stop me raking up the truth about what happened on the Island of Thieves, so you worked out a neat little plan to get rid of both Bishop and me at one go. He was to be bumped off and I was to get the blame—only I wasn't going to be allowed to live long enough to say otherwise."

Still, she made no reply.

"What you can't have known," Rennie went on, "was that Bishop wrote me a letter. He didn't mention the schooner in it. Poor Bishop. He didn't think it terribly important at all. But he did mention Phillippeville. I didn't think it was important either . . . Until today! I went to Philippeville today, Arlette. I spoke with the captain of the schooner. He had never heard of you, Arlette; never seen you in his life, never had anyone approach him about an escape from the Isle of Thieves. His ship didn't even call at the island last October. It was laid up in Dakar with engine trouble. The captain showed me his log-book."

There was a look of hunted desperation in the way she stared back at him now. Her lower lip gave an involuntary tremble but, still, she did not speak.

"Do you remember that day back on the island?" Rennie asked softly. "Do you remember bathing the cut on my face and all the things you said to me? You were so precise about the instructions I had to pass on to Jean-Paul: the sailing time of the schooner, when he had to swim out to the buoy . . . You had thought of everything . . . And all of it lies! Lies from beginning to end. Elaborate lies! You didn't want Jean-Paul to escape. You wanted him dead. But why did you have to go such lengths? Why, when it would have been so much easier just to have stayed away, to have left him to rot?"

There was a long, painful silence. Baraud seemed mystified but interested in the exchanges that had taken place. Bousquet suddenly looked sick and old.

"Why?" said Rennie into the silence. It was almost a cry. "Why did you do it?"

She looked at him definatly.

"I was obeying orders," she cried. "That's why! Can you understand that? I was obeying orders!"

A choked sound came from her father. He looked at her beseechingly, his eyes searching her face, seeking forlornly for a sign that he had not heard her correctly.

"Orders?" he whispered. "Orders?"

She turned on him.

"Why do you look accusingly at me?" she flamed. "Look what you have gained. Look what you are going to lose if you desert me now. I have given you French Africa on a plate. Do you think it was your efforts? Do you think it was because of you that they are giving you a country to rule? Do you think that?"

Now Bousquet could not believe his ears. His face seemed to be falling apart, muscles quivering as if he had lost all control over them.

"What are you saying?" His voice trembled and shook.

"I'm saying that you owe everything to me. I'm the one who did it all. Do you think that Sanson and Carpentier and Colliard and de Fresnes would have supported you if it hadn't been for me sharing their bed and telling them what to do? Even Baraud here. Ask him!"

Baraud was looking distinctly uncomfortable now. There was no need for Bousquet to ask him if what she said was true. He slumped back in his chair, his face haggard.

"Orders," he kept repeating, staring at Arlette. *"Whose orders?"*

She looked at him contemptuously.

"You old fool. I get my orders from Berlin. I've been working for Germany since I was seventeen years old."

The words seemed to cut Bousquet like the lashes of a whip. He turned his crumpled face to Baraud.

"You . . . You knew this?" he whispered.

"I swear I knew nothing of this," said Baraud.

Even Rennie was shaken by her revelation. He had suspected some kind of relationship between her and Hobart's quarry, the man known as "Emperor," but certainly not an involvement with the Germans which must have started before the war. Rennie could also feel a stunning sense of surprise in the fact that his dogged pursuit of the underlying reasons for all that had happened had forced the truth out of her. He had done so with the aid of one or two solid facts and a great deal of educated guesswork laced with threat. He had somehow expected her to go down lying, denying everything and pleading innocence to the last. Her sudden abandonment of any mask or cloak of the real persona rather took his breath away. Not only had he neglected to think as far ahead as the situation in which he now found himself but, having arrived at it, he had no idea what to do next.

It was almost as if Arlette Mercier sensed the uncertainty that her confession had provoked in him. It certainly had the effect of purging her of fear of what Rennie might do. Boldness returned.

"Pull yourself together, father," she ordered. "Now that you know my secret, it doesn't have to make any difference. Colonel Baraud won't be saying anything about it, if he knows what's good for him, and the Englishman isn't going to get very far with the knowledge. They said he only had two men with him. What good are three men against the numbers we have? How do they think they're going to get out of here?"

"It's impossible now," said Bousquet. "How can I go on, knowing that my daughter has betrayed me? And France."

"Just the same as before," she snapped, "only I shall be in command. You will do what I tell you instead of me having to persuade you what you must do and then convince you that you thought of it all on your own. It was me who made your dream of power come true, father. It was me who worked it out. It was me who schemed and cajoled and organized to make you the strongest man in France and the Empire. Without me, you would still be sleeping in the sun dreaming the impossible dream and hoping for miracles. Well, I've made your miracle for you. You're not going to back out now! In three hours' time you have a broadcast to make, and you are going to make it!"

"I gave you everything you ever wanted," wept Bousquet. "How can you repay me like this?"

She stared at him with icy contempt.

"Because you are a man and you think like all men. Because you have no idea what women feel and think. It was all right for Jacques. You had great plans for him—the Navy, then a glittering career. But what did you have in mind for me? Marriage to some carefully chosen senior civil servant and a life of keeping house and bearing children I didn't want. Well, the English put paid to your plans for Jacques—but I had decided the way I wanted to go long before that. You sent me to school in Switzerland to make a lady of me . . . Well, they did that! But they preached a different gospel from you. They didn't train women to become ornaments and chattels for men. They preached a new freedom for women—a freedom where women could head great business corporations or fight in the front line like soldiers. I wanted to be part of that revolution. I wanted to run risks, to take chances, to fight the old order. And I was given the chance."

"You betrayed your country?" said Bousquet, anger fighting through his weariness and disillusion. "And you betrayed me!"

"You taught me how," she replied bitterly. "You stole and robbed and cheated, and all for the love of your country. Ha! If that is patriotism, the jails should be full of patriots."

Rennie felt that he had been reduced to a spectator. He was no longer a protagonist. The real battle was between father and daughter. Yet curiosity made him intervene.

"Why did you marry Jean-Paul?" he asked. "Was it just to steal him from your sister?"

She looked at him, startled by the question. Then she laughed.

"Do you think I wanted to marry that ass?" She gave another scornful laugh. "Geraldine would have been welcome to him, Captain Rennie. The trouble with Jean-Paul was that he had old-fashioned ideas about love and marriage. The only way I could get into his bed and into his life was by marrying the fool. He worked in the Cipher Department at the Admiralty at the time, and my employers very much wanted copies of all his keys without him ever knowing about it. I couldn't bribe or seduce his secrets out of him, so I had to marry him and steal them. Now you know why his stupidity at Dakar gave me a heaven-sent chance to become his widow. I'm just sorry that that fool, Junot, bungled it."

She left her place beside her father and walked round the foot of the table, stopping only a few paces from Rennie, to face him.

"Well, Captain Rennie? What do you do now that you know the whole sordid story? Kill me? Do you have the guts to kill a woman? An unarmed woman? Have you ever killed before? You're going to have to use that gun, you know, if you are going to get out of here alive. Not that you would get very far."

"You might as well stop pretending, Arlette," said Rennie calmly. "The show's over for you. You're not going to play it on the road again. It's too late. Your father isn't going to play ball with you. You've destroyed him. Maybe he could have gone on dancing like a puppet with you pulling the strings if he hadn't known there were any strings and you were the one who made him dance. But he knows now. And if he had any self-respect, it's gone now. Nothing you do or say will ever bring it back. Just take a look at him. Look at his face. He's finished."

The calm certainty with which Rennie spoke made her hesitate. The initiative that she had grasped slipped a little away from her. His confidence was unnerving.

She glanced nervously at her father, long enough to confirm that what Rennie said about him was not ill-founded. Then she moved. Desperation and fear supplied the impetus. She flung herself across the table, her outstretched hand reaching for the revolver in front of Rennie. He made no move to stop her.

Holding it out in front of her with both hands, she circled the table. "Get back against the wall," she ordered Baraud, who did as he was told. Rennie did not move from his seat.

"Put it down, Arlette. It's too late . . ." She cut him off in mid-sentence.

"You prepare to die!" she hurled at him. "You don't

have long." She pointed the gun at Rennie, then brought it round to face her father. "Tell him first that he was wrong, father. Tell him that you're not finished . . . That you are going to do as I tell you. Tell him!"

"It's no good, Arlette. He's right. I am finished." Bousquet looked despairingly at her, his eyes bleak with hopelessness.

"I'll kill you, too," she screamed. "I'll kill all three of you if I must."

"Then do it," said her father, staring lifelessly at the barrel of the gun which she held inches from his face. His eyes closed as he saw the gleam of decision in hers and the whiteness of her finger as it tightened on the trigger. Baraud, too, read the intent in her as she stood profile-on to him, her arms extended.

He snatched the spear from the wall beside him—one of several such trophies adorning the walls—and flung it from a range of no more than six feet. There was a loud click as the firing pin of the heavy revolver echoed metallically in the empty chamber towards which it was projected. Arlette registered dumb surprise and only had time to turn to face the threat she sensed from her right when the spear struck her just below the left breast, the long two-inch-wide blade sliced into her flesh, throwing out a squirt of blood on impact. The spear sank to the shaft and oozed a bubbling red in a small circle at the point where it stopped. She fell back, wheezing more blood from her lungs as she gasped for breath.

Baraud stood back, horror on his face, not quite comprehending why the shot he had expected to hear had not rung out. Bousquet, too, expecting death and waiting for the explosion that would have signaled it, opened his eyes wide in horror.

Rennie had moved but now stood, frozen, hands on the table, his chair fallen sideways behind him. He had tried to tell her. He had tried but she had cut him off in mid-sentence. It was a chance he had deliberately taken. Foolish, perhaps, but calculated nonetheless. He had not loaded the gun.

The Chasseurs captain crossed the stable-yard from the radio truck. There was not enough light for him to make out the time on the clock in the red-tiled tower above the stable. He looked at his watch. The luminous hands pointed at eleven o'clock. Still one hour to go. What was going to happen? He was nervous now that the Americans had intervened. He had gone along with the venture to install Bousquet as the President of the Overseas Territories in the belief that the Americans would stay out of it. The Captain was already wishing that *he* had stayed out of it. Something was very far wrong.

His first intimation that something was amiss had come just after he had heard that Bousquet's daughter was dead, just before ten. The American jeep had roared into the yard at the head of what seemed to be a flying column: a fleet of light trucks with Browning machine-guns mounted behind the driver and manned by grim-faced American soldiers. He had learned a short time later that the American force was two Companies strong. The guards at the highway and drive entrance had not tried to stop them, just stood aside and let them pass. They hadn't expected the Americans any more than he had, of course.

Their leader, in spite of the fact that he personally had seen three majors, was a wild-eyed captain in the first jeep. The Captain had been accompanied by a civilian with a beard. They had stormed into the house and had been closeted with Bousquet and Baraud ever since. American infantrymen had taken up stations all round the villa. They were an extremely business-like lot. Or they looked it. The Chasseurs captain guessed, although he could not be sure, that they were from the special training camp at Sidi Ferrouch. He had heard a lot about the supersoldiers the camp was supposed to produce. Some kind of elite strike-force.

The Captain entered the villa from the yard door and made his way through to the front of the house. He knocked and then entered the long terrace-room. Half a dozen faces turned from the table to inspect his.

"What do you want?" asked Bousquet. His face was chalk-white. He looked a hundred years old.

"Another radio message from the Admiralty, sir. They say that the Gaullist units from Philippeville, the ones who over-ran our positions east of the city, are grouping in the Bois de Boulogne for an attack on the groups we have encircling the Villa des Oliviers. The Admiralty have intercepted signals from the forward Gaullist units to others still on the way from Philippeville. It is estimated that they must have at least a regiment committed. Admiral

Durand says this is greatly in excess of any opposition forces expected to be encountered by his men. If it comes to a battle, he is not optimistic about our chances. He says however, that the Gaullists are waiting for the broadcast at midnight and are unlikely to attack before then. It will be some hours yet before the main force reaches Algiers."

Bousquet thanked the Chasseurs captain and asked him to wait outside. Those in the room were not to learn until some days later that the intercepted radio messages were part of a calculated bluff by Blom's friends in the Free French units which had raced at breakneck speed to Algiers and swept past the eastern road-blocks. There were no reinforcements on the way from Philippeville. Every man who could travel was in the "advance force." There was no other. The signals had been a deliberate ruse to give the Vichyists an exaggerated picture of the oppositions's strength.

In the terrace-room, Hobart faced Bousquet and used the news brought by the Chasseurs captain to give weight to the arguments he had been putting to the Admiral.

"You have the chance, sir, to stop a civil war and save hundreds, if not thousands, of French lives. You must take it. We can still get you to the radio station in time. Tell the people that you are rejecting the invitation to take power, that they must pin their hope on the FCNL. Call the dogs off de Gaulle. Admiral Durand is obviously having second thoughts. Tell his men to go back to their barracks."

"Very well," said Bousquet heavily. "Perhaps, if it saves French lives, it will make my last service to France be seen as one of honor."

Within minutes, the cavalcade of military vehicles was on its way from the Bousquet villa to the city. Hobart rode with a silent Bousquet. Rennie travelled with Baldry in the back of the jeep driven by Wheeler, who had Dabrowski at his side.

They detached from the procession inside the city limits, so that Rennie could be dropped at Geraldine's apartment. He had much to tell her and they could listen to the broadcast together.

From a darkened apartment in a high block opposite the radio building, a man watched the cavalcade arrive. He saw Bousquet step into the patch of light at the entrance of the radio station, followed by an American in uniform. The man gave a small sigh, and switched on the radio standing on a table.

At just three minutes after midnight, the chords of the "Marseillaise" vibrated over the radio waves. Then Admiral Bousquet was introduced by an announcer.

His voice was grave and shook with emotion.

He had been done a great honor, he said. A group of distinguished and honored sons of France had invited him to become the President of a Council which was being formed to govern all the overseas territories of France. Their intentions were good, he said, because they envisaged a new era in which France was again eminent among the nations of the world, no longer a vassal to a foreign power, no longer racked by bitter internal conflicts, but an independent France, subservient to none.

Then Bousquet dropped his bombshell. He was not accepting the invitation to preside over overseas France, because all Frenchmen were not united behind the vision which others had had. To accept would have meant bloodier and more bitter conflicts between Frenchmen and he, for one, was not going to preside over new and greater agonies for France.

He called on those who had committed themselves to his support to return to their homes, their ships and their barracks and not to bear arms against their brothers.

It was a powerful performance, full of clichés but moving nonetheless. He ended by urging all Frenchmen to put their minds and strength behind the FCNL and work for its greater harmony and success. Long live the Empire, he declared. Long live France.

In her apartment overlooking the commercial center, Geraldine wept in Rennie's arms. For the first time in her life, the father who had rejected her had moved her to feelings of reluctant respect. Defending the tears which had sprung to her eyes, she said the speech had all the elements of a death-bed repentance and that, if God could forgive, so could she, who was so much less than godly.

In the high apartment, opposite the radio building, the lone watcher turned off his radio as the "Marseillaise" rang out again. He crossed to the open window and picked up the English-made deer rifle which he had left leaning against the wall. It was a beautifully balanced weapon.

The man knelt on the cushion he had previously placed on the floor below the sill of the open window and cradled the rifle against his shoulder. He squinted through the telescopic sight and brought the rifle to bear on the entrance to the radio building. Then he settled to wait.

He did not have long to wait.

Less than ten minutes had passed when activity around the entrance signalled the emergence of Bousquet, still followed by the American officer.

The man at the window corrected his aim until the cross of the telescopic sight centered on Bousquet's chest. He took a half breath, held it, and fired. He saw Bousquet fall back and sprawl on the steps.

Hobart, close to Bousquet, had moved out of light into shadow, intending to speak to the officer in charge of the strike-force from Sidi Ferrouch. The Americans had provided Bousquet's escort. Hobart had squinted up at the building opposite at the precise moment the marksman had fired. He saw the muzzle flash as the trigger was pulled.

Leaving others to see to Bousquet, Hobart was running across the street while the shot still echoed. He shouted orders as he ran, calling to the American soldiers already spilling from their vehicles.

"I want that man alive," he shouted as he sent men racing to cover the apartment block from the rear and others to enter from the front. A strange urgency gripped Hobart. It was more than the trained reflex reactions to sudden emergency. It went deeper, an almost animal instinctiveness which had nothing to do with reason.

He was ninety-nine per cent sure that Franz Dorf was dead. But from early evening, ever since he had called off the manhunt, Hobart had been waiting for something to happen. It was just a feeling, nothing rational, perhaps aroused by the slimmest doubt over Dorf's death. If he had tried to describe the feeling—and nothing would have induced him to do so—he would have said that he expected Dorf still to strike back from beyond the grave. And, in a sense, he had.

Dorf had planned the assassination of Bousquet.

Epilogue

August 1944

In a little over half an hour it would be light. The ferocious naval bombardment of a moment before had ceased. The convoy had now passed through the cordon of French, British and American warships which had been pounding thousands of shells into the German battery emplacements along the French Riviera coast. Now it was up to the merchant ships and their landing-craft. All that remained was the final twelve-mile run-in to the landing beaches.

Cole came out of the wheelhouse of the *Fort Daring* and found Rennie hunched against the rail of the flying-bridge. He was peering into the darkness ahead, waiting for the first glimpse of the landmass that was France.

"This is the dodgy bit, isn't it?" said Cole.

"You saw the sealed orders?" asked Rennie.

Cole smiled ruefully.

"That's what I meant by dodgy. They're pretty uncompromising, aren't they?" He quoted from the opened orders which Rennie had left out on the chartroom table for him to read. " 'Transports will proceed to anchorage positions regardless of fire from enemy batteries.' Do you see where we have to go?"

"I saw," said Rennie. There had been a mimeographed sketch of the Gulf of St. Tropez with its half-mile-wide neck. On either side of the neck had been marked the positions of the German sixteen-inch batteries. The *Fort Daring* and the other ships were to pass between the batteries into the Gulf and anchor four hundred years offshore.

"Trust the Navy to lie twenty miles off while we're elected to go ding-a-ling through the gates of Hell," said Cole bitterly.

Rennie smiled.

"The Navy have done their work," he said. "With luck, those big German guns will be nothing but scrap-metal by now. You'd better get the Third Mate up on the bridge now, Mr. Cole. Then you'd better rouse out the Chippy and the Bosun and stand by the anchor."

"Aye aye, sir," said Cole. He went off, leaving Rennie alone again to his silent communion with the night.

More than a year had passed since the events in Algiers. For Rennie, the time had flashed by. There had been so much that was good.

He thought now about that amazing reunion party in Geraldine's tiny apartment: Hobart, once more the silent man, now that the immediate action was over and there was no need to organize and order; and Jean-Paul, lean but astonishingly fit in spite of his maltreatment, weeping with heart-felt emotion and embracing them all. *Mes amis, mes frères.*

Baldry had been there, too. And Blom, elated still that his old comrades in the Algerian Resistance had rallied from Philippeville and bluffed the leaders of the coup into believing their force was ten times greater than it actually was.

Crucial to the successful winding up of the "Emperor" and "Barbary Consignment" affairs had been the speedy capture of Bousquet's assassin, a French Army deserter called Pascal Ros. Although it had not saved him from a firing squad. Ros had talked his head off. A man, whom Hobart's investigators were able to identify beyond doubt as Dorf, had paid Ros 20,000 francs to assassinate Bousquet within minutes of his acceptance of a new Presidency and his abolition of the FCNL.

It was an act which Dorf had probably not confided to his partner-agent, Arlette Mercier, on the order of his SD masters in Berlin. The crime was to have been used as the excuse for a wave of wholesale repression against the Gaullists in North Africa. It would have created a situation, too, wherein a Vichy hardliner would have succeeded Bousquet as President. Indeed, it was revealed much later that the Vichyists in the Bousquet plot had received prior assurances from both Vichy and the Nazi hierarchy that support of Bousquet would be a stepping-stone to the kind of paramilitary dictatorship which they wanted to establish in Algeria. They went into it knowing that Bousquet's leadership was likely to be numbered in days if not hours.

The German and Vichy plotters, of whom Franz Dorf was the chief executive, made several miscalculations. They did not foresee that Dorf would be killed. Nor did they anticipate that Bousquet would do a last-minute about-face. The consequence of the latter was that his assassination boomeranged in the faces of the Vichyists. It caused many Frenchmen in Algeria, particularly those in the armed forces, to question their allegiance hitherto to the ultra-conservative Vichy elements—and they flocked to join de Gaulle.

From information provided by Pascal Ros, Hobart and Baldry were able to backtrack on Franz Dorf. They were able to locate the house from which he operated and, by maintaining a watch on it, were able to identify and pick off one by one the network of informers, collaborators and saboteur accomplices he had built up.

Hobart and Baldry had stayed on in Algiers long enough to back-trace the careers of both Dorf and Arlette Mercier as well as they could. They were able to tell Rennie some, if not all, of the story.

Arlette had, in fact, been recruited before Dorf by an ardent Nazi who was a teacher at the Klein School in Geneva. Unlike Dorf she had never worked for the Abwehr, who seldom recruited female agents, but had been exclusively in the employ of the SS. Her first step along the path to complete indoctrination had been into her teacher's bed. In exchange for her virginity, she had been given a bell-book-and-chapter sell of the Great New Order—and she had lapped it up.

When the teacher reported back to blackshirt headquarters that he had an enthusiastic novice in the shape of a French Admiral's daughter, Heydrich himself had ordered the most careful nurturing of this prize convert. She had proved only too willing to co-operate. A consummate actress, rather than a political idealist, she leapt at the chance to lead a dangerous double life . . . because she was always on stage. She was born to deceive and she did it well.

Hobart and Baldry unearthed indications, but not proof, that one of her first assignments might have been the seduction of a young French naval officer, Henri Aubert, and extraction of secrets about the French *Surcouf*, the world's largest submarine. Aubert was subsequently arrested, tried by court-martial and executed by firing-squad. The German agent responsible for his subversion was never found.

Arlette provided a continuous stream of intelligence from Algiers after the outbreak of war. She did not come into her own, however, until Dorf arrived in Africa to seek out Allied escape lines which were routed through Marseilles, Algeria and Morocco. Arlette's job was to identify the clandestine groups operating these escape lines and then introduce Dorf to them in the guise of an escaped RAF pilot or Polish Army officer.

It was a peculairity of Dorf's that he insisted always on using the idenity of an actual person rather than a fictitious one. It was one he maintained to the end. In the house he used in Algiers were found clothes, uniforms, papers and credentials for twenty-three different men, some still alive but most of them dead.

The stealing of the "Barbary Consignment" had been a joint triump for Arlette and Dorf. Arlette, in a reversal of her usual role, had penetrated the Resistance group, "Alpha," with the full intention of blowing the whistle on its members. Dorf, however, had persuaded her that there were advantages to be gained from leaving the "Alpha" group at large, with her as an "insider." This was borne out when she heard whispers of a large arms consignment for "Alpha" and some unspecified Allied military operation with which it was connected.

Arlette failed to secure any details of "Operation Torch"—the North African landings—because she was not on the exclusively male operational wing of the Resistance group. Her job was to feed information to the group from mixing with the Vichy brass and, occasionally to act as courier to other Resistance groups. The material she fed to the Resistance as intelligence was sifted by Dorf, who supplied her with sufficient of the genuine article to make a considerable impression on the group's leaders. Her value to the Resistance shot up accordingly.

She gleaned just enough about the "Barbary Consignment" for Dorf to enable him to hijack the truck containing the explosives and eliminate the American agent, Ritchie.

Jean-Paul's one-man rebellion came as an acute embarrassment to Arlette. The Vichy Secret Police, unaware of her German connections or her partnership with Dorf, began to suspect that she might be tarred with the same brush as her husband. The "Alpha" group became worried by the interest the Secret Police began to take in her activities.

Berlin insisted that, on no account, was Arlette's SD connection to be revealed to Vichy. Consequently Arlette and Dorf had to find their own solution to the situation. The plan they evolved was one of callous simplicity.

Arlette was to meet the threat from Vichy's Gestapo network head-on by proving to them where her loyalties lay. She would "turn" her husband and persuade him to co-operate with the Vichy propaganda machine or she would arrange for his elimination. Vichy's Gestapo were suitably impressed. It was the kind of deal they understood. Arlette Mercier went up in their estimation because, wherever her affections resided, they certainly weren't with her traitor husband. Any reservations they may have had about Jean-Paul's subsequent survival were superseded by other considerations when the Allied armies landed in North Africa.

On Berlin's orders, both Dorf and Arlette were instructed to keep low profiles while investigating ways of undermining the political stability of North Africa and creating as many problems as they could for the Allied forces. They were also to exploit in every way they could differences between the British and Americans.

As Vichy influence in North Africa waned, from February 1943 onwards, Dorf and Arlette laid plans for midsummer mischief. They were to work towards political upheaval on the one hand and accompany his initiative with acts of terrorism and sabotage to aid it. Dorf was quick to realize how Admiral Bousquet could be used as a key figure, especially with Arlette's great influence over her father. And from June on, Dorf had no doubt about the main target of his activities—General Charles de Gaulle.

The Americans distrusted de Gaulle. The Colonial mandarins of French North Africa hated him. The British could not control him. Yet it was through him that the fiercest and most passionate French enmity to Nazi Germany was channelled.

The plan to elevate Bousquet, therefore, had to have built into it the instruments for the political annihilation of de Gaulle. Acts of sabotage and terrorism were to be placed at the door of the Communists, Radicals and Socialists whom Vichy had suppressed but to whom de Gaulle had appealed for support in his passion for national unity and a suspension of party political rivalry.

Dorf was not content to let de Gaulle's propaganda machine frighten the complacency of the French opposed to him. He stirred them into activity with threats against their lives and property and made sure that authorship of these threats was accredited to Gaullist factions. Bousquet, for one, became utterly convinced that de Gaulle wanted him dead.

Looking back, it awed Rennie to think of the baffling complexity of issues into which he had stumbled like an innocent babe. The waters that had been stirred by the events of that summer would go on rippling with consequences for years. Some divisions would be patched over but would never heal.

Hobarts and Baldry's mission had ended with the discovery in a Delta-Afrique warehouse of the bulk of the "Barbary Consignment," cleverly concealed in what was believed to be casks of maturing wine. But even Hobart and Baldry had only unmasked a few of the Vichy and pro-Nazi activists in Algiers: those involved in Dorf's operations.

Hundreds of others, not immediately implicated—in the Army, in the Navy, in senior positions of Colonial administration—continued to foster and actively aid the aims of Nazidom.

There were to be more plots of military and political nature to eliminate de Gaulle during 1943. Vichy intelligence was to be so effective in Algiers right into 1944 that Vichy Radio was regularly to give news of local events—and such things as top-secret visits by Churchill and others—two days before Radio Algiers broke the news or Allied Military Headquarters issued the relevant communiqué.

The twenty-fourth of August 1943 was perhaps the most politically significant day for French North Africa. That was the day Britain formally recognized the French Committee of National Liberation as the body responsible for the administration of those French overseas territories acknowledging its authority. The British declaration noted with sympathy the desire of the FCNL to ensure the administration and defense of all French interests.

The United States followed suit, but with less enthusiasm. The State Department, while welcoming the establishment of the FCNL and confirming their intention to co-operate with all patriotic Frenchmen, emphasized that their statement did not constitute recognition of a Government of France or the French Empire.

For John Rennie, a much more significant day than 24 August came exactly four months later—on Christmas Eve. For that was the day he married Geraldine Dumont in a simple civil ceremony. Beside them as best man, and wearing the uniform of *France Combattante,* was Jean-Paul Mercier. He had celebrated his release from imprisonment by joining the Free French Army. At the wedding, he had on his sleeve the chevrons of Sergeant, having just completed three months' training in Tunisia and been posted to a Motorized Scout Reconnaissance Unit awaiting embarkation to Italy.

Thus it was that Rennie was often to look back on 1943 as a year packed with significant historical dates —but with one outstanding: 24 December. The day, he would recall, when the most important Anglo-French Alliance of all time was signed. His and Geraldine's.

"It's different from all the others," he would tell Geraldine softly, "because all the others have been political expedients. Ours has the ingredient that nations and empires haven't yet learned to write into their treaties—real honest-to-God love." And, if Rennie was sure of anything, he was sure that he and Geraldine had found the kind of love that lasts forever.

Such a certainty had stayed with him in the first weeks of separation from Geraldine when, finally, the *Fort Daring* had been restored to full operational seaworthiness. It shone in the letters they wrote daily which were delivered according to the vagaries of the wartime mail. It was still strong in Rennie as he stood on the bridge of his ship in the pre-dawn of a new August day, minutes from the beaches of St. Tropez.

Eight months was no length of time at all, he knew, on which to base boasts of a marriage's durability or the eternal nature of the love its components enjoyed. Yet Rennie was sure of what it was he had found with Geraldine. One doesn't discover a diamond and verify it as a diamond and then begin to think that time or wear will dim its beauty or diminish its worth. It will last forever.

Rennie was distracted from his reveries by shipboard signs of activity amongst the soldiers who were the *Fort Daring*'s passengers. In Taranto, they had taken on board five hundred French and American troops: battle-hardened men who were to become the spear-head of General Patton's drive from the south of France towards Germany and Austria. Now, within hours, these men would be on French soil and beginning the great push north from the shores of the Mediterranean. Those who had tried to get some sleep through the thunder of the naval bombardment were now emerging from below decks as H-Hour approached.

Rennie had scanned the faces of the French troops as they had filed aboard in Taranto, hoping to see, miraculously, the face of Jean-Paul among them. But he was not there. The French commander of the troops, however, knew of Jean-Paul's unit and said that almost certainly he was on one of the other ships of the convoy.

Rennie thought of Jean-Paul now, imagining his feelings at what would be his first sight of the homeland after four long years.

"Land ahead," droned a voice from the fo'c'sle-head of the *Fort Daring,* wrenching Rennie back to the immediate responsibilities of his command.

"Aye aye," he acknowledged the lookout's call. And there it was—the dark shape that was the pine-forested range of hills above St. Tropez. France!

The Third Mate emerged from the wheelhouse. He was nervy but trying to appear cheerfully nonchalant. He illustrated this in his desire to chirrup inconsequentially to his Captain.

"The Frenchies aren't half excited, sir," he chattered. He pointed to one French officer who was perched only a few feet below them on the cab of a big army truck which was wired securely to the deck beside number two hatch. The man was staring at the land ahead and sobbing audibly. He kept brushing the tears from his face with a large handkerchief.

"Look at him," said the Third Mate. "He's crying."

"Do you find it strange, Third Mate? Does it amuse you?"

The young ship's officer turned, eyes wide, at the whiplash rebuke embodied in Rennie's tone of voice.

"No, sir," he mumbled. "I'm sorry, sir." He cursed himself for forgetting that the Old Man's wife was French.

"They're weeping with joy," Rennie said, turning to look thoughtfully at the land that was France. He thought of Jean-Paul. "Can't you understand?"